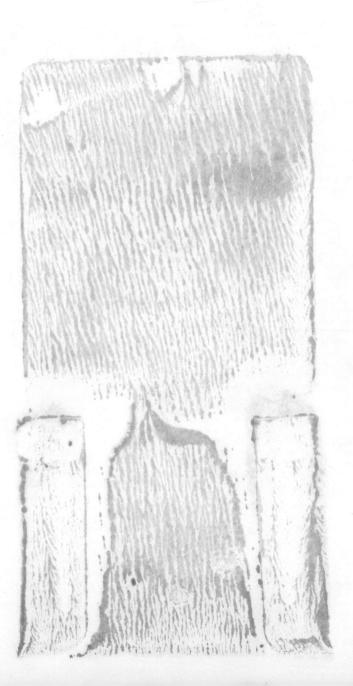

First Principles of Atomic Physics

First Principles of

ATOMIC PHYSICS

by **RICHARD F. HUMPHREYS**
PRESIDENT
THE COOPER UNION FOR THE
ADVANCEMENT OF SCIENCE AND ART

and

ROBERT BERINGER
PROFESSOR OF PHYSICS
YALE UNIVERSITY

HARPER & ROW, PUBLISHERS
NEW YORK, EVANSTON, AND LONDON

FIRST PRINCIPLES OF ATOMIC PHYSICS

F-Q

CONTENTS

v

Part Three: Atomic and Nuclear Phenomena

Appendix

This text is designed for use in an introductory physics course for the student of the humanities or the social sciences. Its essential task is to present the physicist's modern view of the natural world in the limited time which the general student can devote to such study and without using all of the physicist's analytical equipment.

For the science student the introductory course merely sets the stage for more intensive study, but for the general student one must design a terminal course which carries the student to some overall picture which he can incorporate into his general knowledge. One attack on this problem has been the survey course; another is the historical or philosophical approach to science. We do not accept either of these as wholly valid, since they do not use the scientist's methods in treating physical phenomena. There is a vast difference between teaching science and teaching *about* science. In this text we have chosen to teach science, and acknowledge the limitations imposed by a single nonprofessional course by selecting carefully from the whole body of physics a portion which can be constructed logically and with some degree of termination.

In pursuit of this aim we have made no attempt to be comprehensive. Instead, one field of thought—the physicist's concept of the atomic world—is developed with the aid of only that part of macrophysics whose understanding is required in atomic physics. Indeed, most of the material of the conventional physics course is omitted, while much is included which is not normally found in elementary books. It is believed that an integrated view of physics can thus be presented more successfully than in an abbreviated version of the usual introductory course. The plan is thus diametrically opposite to that of the nontechnical survey or general science course.

The school training and the aptitudes of the general student pose a number of difficult problems to the college physics teacher. One of these is the use of mathematics, which must be kept to a minimum, for few students possess outstanding mathematical training. Yet one must not present a course without mathematics, since this would seriously distort the physicist's methods and sterilize the logic of physics. We have tried to meet this problem by employing only algebra and geometry in derivations and proofs and by including even the more obvious steps which are "easily shown." Where a logical construction demands it, the mathematical treatment is more rigorous than that of the usual introductory text, and, in particular, there are fewer results set down without proof. A real attempt has been made to carry through the mathematical reasoning that leads from general principles to experiment and application.

A glance at the contents of the book will show its "vertical" plan of attack, the extent of this plan, and the scope of its omissions. In brief, the subjects treated are particle dynamics, electrodynamics, and atomic and nuclear phenomena. Particle dynamics is based on Newton's laws of motion. Rigid body dynamics, fluid dynamics, and machines are almost completely omitted; on the other hand, the conservation laws are treated rather fully. The next section introduces the atomic hypothesis and applies dynamics to atomism by way of the kinetic theory of gases. In electrodynamics the view is again essentially atomic. Circuit theory and electrical machinery are minimized. The atomic physics section treats atomic phenomena and their interpretation on classical and quantum mechanical grounds. Particular reference is also made to light propagation and the ether paradox, and some development in special relativity is carried out. In the final section nuclear phenomena are considered. Emphasis is laid on the role of the Einstein mass-energy equation in nuclear reactions; the last chapter describes neutron physics and nuclear fission.

A course including the material of this text may cover either one or two semesters, depending on the frequency of meeting and the extent of outside reading and problem assignments. It is now being taught to freshmen at Yale for the eighth time as a one-semester course meeting for three lecture-demonstration sessions and one discussion plus laboratory session per week. Both student-performed and demonstration experiments are employed, arranged to correspond with the lecture material as closely as possible. Classes, discussion section, and laboratory are conducted by the same instructor and limited to thirty students. Their response as well as that of the instructors participating has been largely encouraging, and we feel that the present approach to the problem of making science meaningful to the liberal arts student has been shown to be feasible.

A course plan as specific and different as this one naturally raises a number of controversial questions among its instructors. Many such questions have been met, thoroughly thrashed over, and resolved with the assistance of the several instructors who have taught this course with us. To these instructors the authors express their considerable indebtedness, as well as to the many students who have been patient and coöperative in the development of a new course. It is our sincere hope that other instructors and other students will find this approach to physics sound and profitable.

R. F. H.
R. B.

February 1950

PART ONE

The Dynamics of Particles

CHAPTER 1

The Nature of Physics

1.1 The Study of Science

The history of science relates the accumulation of a large body of knowledge of the natural world, just as cultural history includes the factual records of human institutions. The growth of scientific knowledge unfolds day by day in historical sequence. Each discovery and development has its chronological place and owes much of its significance, if not its existence, to those discoveries which preceded it. In this historical growth there are periods of great activity in which new discoveries are announced and exploited, and there are periods of relatively calm reflection and organization of the new gains. In this sense science is a cumulative effort by man toward the goal of understanding nature.

There is, however, another way to view the body of scientific knowledge. Just as in cultural history, there is a philosophical or logical facet to science which lies outside the sequence of discovery of the facts. Each new discovery contributes to the history but also to the whole of a logical structure which comprises our integrated knowledge of nature. Indeed, this structure is frequently called science, the daily activity of the scientists and the historical aspects of their discoveries being ignored. It is this continual effort of logical construction that forms the backbone of the much-mentioned "scientific method." It is not the aim of this text to demonstrate *the* scientific method, for there are many methods employed in furthering our knowledge of nature. There is no set of rules which can or have been followed in the development of scientific knowledge. There is, however, a mental attitude which science assumes—a logical, stepwise procedure devoid of preconceived opinion, which insists on carefully made observations and the verification of hypotheses. It is the intention of this book to illustrate the power of scientific thought when derived from accurate experimentation in one field of science, the physics of the atom and its internal structure. It is hoped to induce in the reader a respect for and some facility in systematic reasoning.

It is not maintained that scientific thinking is the only means man should employ in developing his philosophy of living—it is extremely doubtful, for instance, if the methods of science would have improved Shakespeare's dramas. Science itself cannot wholly rely on logical reasoning, and we shall see in the course of our study of atomic structure that intuition plays a highly significant role in science—the progress of physics is marked with many examples of clever guessing. However, these outbursts of intuition are successful largely because they emanate from minds disciplined by logical thinking. Logical reasoning is an important and fruitful part of the training of an intelligent mind, and it is the conviction of this proposition that governs the material presented in these pages. If in the process of studying this method the student learns some factual material of the world around him, then he has reaped an additional dividend for his efforts.

Traditionally the study of physics is divided into mechanics, heat, sound, electricity and magnetism, and light. These compartments, which at the beginning of this century were almost airtight, are now leaking rather badly among themselves and are drawing much sustenance from the new and vigorous upstarts of atomic and nuclear physics. We are led, therefore, in our wish to present an idea of modern physical thought, not to a recompartmentalization of the subject, but rather to a search for a unifying idea to build on. What such a method loses in completeness through the inadequacy of our present knowledge it gains in vigor and in at least an assumed grandeur, and it avoids, in part, the piecemeal treatment of the older compartmentalized study. In such an approach, it would seem that the modern notions of the atomic and particle nature of matter are perhaps the most widespread and unifying ideas in modern science, and that an approach through particle concepts is the most fruitful, not only for exploring the results of new research, but also more especially for illustrating the logical construction of physics.

This atomic and particle idea in physics is not particularly new, but its present form took shape around the turn of the present century and its modern growth dates from that time. It has been one of the most successful concepts ever introduced into physics and it dominates most modern physical thought. It is definite and yet constructed with great subtlety, since none of the modern particles can be reached by direct sensory perception. Their properties are arrived at by many diverse experiments, and each particle possesses many deduced properties. An electron is a mechanical, an electrical, and an optical entity of great complexity, and yet identical in every respect to the billions of billions of other electrons in every gram of matter in the whole universe.

In choosing particle physics as our study we do not slight the more important aspects of the well-understood and basic studies of mechanics, electricity, and light, but require their results and methods in understanding the atom and fundamental particles associated with it. It was the familiar laws of these studies which led to the invention and description of the modern physical particles, and it is these particles which in turn bring a real understanding of the composition of matter, the nature and behavior of electricity and heat, the origin of light, and other traditional studies in physics.

1.2 The Essentials of Scientific Procedure

Although there is no fixed discipline in scientific work, no recipe book by which one follows instructions to the letter, there are certain basic principles of procedure in the study of the natural world. These can be identified, at least roughly, under the following headings:

> Observation
> Measurement
> Experiment
> Correlations and laws
> Theories

It is not meant to imply that the scientist uses this as a check list to measure the progress of his research, for he is usually too engrossed with one small stage of this development to be concerned immediately with its other stages. However, in this text we are concerning ourselves with the logical methods encountered in atomic physics, and it will be well to understand and keep in mind these guideposts of scientific procedure.

Before elaborating these essentials of scientific procedure it might be wise to suggest the realms in which they do not apply. There are certain requirements necessary to the scientist in his study of the world, and it is the nature of these requirements to exclude certain questions as being outside of the realm of science. It is required that scientific phenomena arise in the objective world and that they be susceptible to observation and measurement by the scientist. It must be recognized that with this restriction a considerable portion of human experience falls outside the region of scientific activity as it exists today. Certain subjective (personal) experiences will almost surely remain outside, but it is quite possible that the future will see a loosening of such self-imposed limitations, and the growth of science will extend into new regions of experience. This has happened in the past, as for example, in the case of psychology, and it is not advisable to advocate a static philosophy for science.

1.3   Observation

The natural sciences are, as the name implies, concerned with the phenomena of nature. The observation of such phenomena is common to all men and makes up what is called objective experience. Although the demarcation of the objective world from the subjective world may be a problem in pure philosophy, it seldom presents any complication to the scientist. We are generally agreed that our senses convey to us the working of this world and will term such information *observables*. It is these observables which are of interest in natural science. Neither the ultimate nature of existence nor the ultimate reason for existence is of concern. Science is limited to the description of nature through observables, and questions which cannot be reduced to something accessible to observation are beyond its limits, no matter how interesting or profound they may be.

By our definition an observable is any happening which is conveyed to us by our senses. It may be directly accessible to sense perception or may require an instrument or detecting device as an intermediate agent. In modern natural science the latter is more prevalent, and the great refinements in instruments have broadened by many times the range of scientific observations. A modern telescope enables us to see or to photograph myriads of stars too faint for direct visual observation. However, we make no primary distinction between these observations and those of unaided vision. The interposition of an instrument does not affect the reality of the observation.

When science was young and before the day of instruments and apparatus, the observables were seen and felt and heard directly. The motions of bodies, the pattern of the stars, and the positions of terrestrial objects intrigued the scientific spirit in men and led them to catalog their experience and to generalize from this experience. In this process of cataloging and generalizing it must have become evident even in the earliest times that there are relations between sets of observables.

1.4   Measurement

Perhaps the simplest correlations in nature are qualitative relations between observables. Water by itself flows toward the center of the earth; most bodies released from the hand will fall; the sun rises and sets daily; radio interference and sunspot activity are related. Such relations between several observables are widely known and accepted and are often too trite to be considered a part of science. More advanced scientific efforts go beyond the mere listing of trends and qualitative statements of natural behavior. There is applied to observation the process of measurement, the assignment of a number to the observable which tells its size or magnitude.

The nature of measurement is probably well known to the reader. One selects a standard or unit of measurement which is used as a sort of divisor in ascertaining the number of times it is contained in the observable. Thus in length measurement one selects a foot rule or meter stick as a standard and expresses distances between points as lengths in feet or meters. The operation which yields the measurement is the dividing of the distance into these standard units. It is frequently asked whether the number arrived at is really the length or merely our description of some more profound properties. The physicist's answer is that the concept of length is so inextricably tied up with the process of its measurement that it has no physical meaning aside from the operations which determine it. That is, the definition of length in the physical world and of all other measurable observables is simply a description of the processes employed in finding the appropriate measurement number. Of course, when the measuring operations are generally understood and agreed upon by all observers they may be omitted from discussion, just as the definitions of all words in a sentence need not be contained in footnotes.

The process of measurement is seen to have two aspects: the selection of a unit or standard for the particular observation contemplated, and the determination by some physical procedure of a number which is the number of times that the unit is contained in the observable. The number itself without a unit appended is clearly without significance as a report of observation; it is just a symbol used in counting. Hence, in science and in commerce great pains are taken to assure that the standard of measurement is truly standard, unchanging with time and the same in all laboratories and market places. One important function of the National Bureau of Standards in this country is to provide such standards.

Since the measurement of each kind of observable may require a different unit, there are in physics a great number of such units, and it might be thought that the cataloging of these would be a major and unending task. Fortunately, however, the exact relationships which link various observables will also link the units of these observables. It is possible in physics to select a few quantities which we can designate as *fundamental observables* and arbitrarily to assign to them a set of units. From these few units we can build all other units needed for other observables. The set of units which one gets thereby is a close-knit system in which all but a few units are secondary or *derived units* and for which no primary physical standard need be provided.

There is a considerable degree of arbitrariness in the selection of funda-

mental units or even of the observables themselves which we should designate
as fundamental. The choice used in physics rests on a combination of historical, philosophical, and expedient grounds. The choice is this: *The fundamental observables shall be length, mass, and time.*

Having chosen the three fundamental observables we must next establish
the units of measurement for each of the three. Quite evidently we can measure
length in inches, feet, miles, centimeters, etc. We shall choose a set of units
related to the standards of measurement in the *metric system.* These standards
and units were designed by a group of scientists beginning at the time of
the French Revolution. In our version of the metric system the units of the
fundamental observables are:

Length—centimeter (cm)
Mass —gram (gm)
Time —second (sec)

This is often referred to as the centimeter-gram-second or cgs system of units.
One of its advantages lies in the decimal relationships between the fundamental units and other units of the same observable. These relationships are
indicated by prefixes:

mega	1,000,000	(10^6)
kilo	1,000	(10^3)
deci	1/10	(10^{-1})
centi	1/100	(10^{-2})
milli	1/1,000	(10^{-3})
micro	1/1,000,000	(10^{-6})

Thus a kilogram (kg) is 1000 gm, a microgram is a millionth of a gram, a
millisecond is a thousandth of a second, etc. These units have obvious relations to the cgs units; this certainly cannot be said of the units of the British
system used in this country where the pound is 16 oz and the mile 5280 ft.
Though the cgs system will be used throughout this text, the following approximate relation may help to associate metric units with the better-known
British units:

One inch   = 2.54 centimeters
One mile   = 1.61 kilometers
One pound = 454 grams
2.20 pounds = 1 kilogram
1.10 quarts = 1000 cm³ = 1 liter

It is essential to provide physical standards for the cgs units. There is a
platinum-iridium bar in a constant-temperature vault at Sèvres, France. The

distance between two scratches made on this bar defines the standard meter, and as the name indicates the centimeter is just one-hundredth of this length. Likewise there is in the same vault a cylinder of similar material whose mass is by agreement 1000 gm (a kilogram). The second is defined as 1/86,400 of a mean solar day. (The mean solar day is the average over a year of the time required for the earth to complete a single revolution on its axis.) In the United States a similar meter bar and kilogram cylinder are deposited at the National Bureau of Standards, and they have been accurately compared with those in France.

There remains finally to determine what we shall mean by the cgs units of quantities other than mass, length, and time. The answer has already been indicated: The relationships which link the observables link their units. Thus, velocity is a quantity defined as the ratio of the displacement (distance moved) to the time for this displacement. Or

$$\text{Velocity} = \frac{\text{Displacement}}{\text{Time}}$$

The cgs unit of velocity is obtained by assigning cgs units to the observables by which it is defined, namely, length and time. Hence it must be a centimeter per second (cm/sec). Similarly, the cgs unit of volume must be the cubic centimeter (cm^3), of area (cm^2), etc.

The great advantage offered by adhering to the cgs system of units lies in their ability to breed other cgs units. (True, this advantage exists in certain other systems of units also.) Regardless of what mathematical manipulations are performed, or to what extent observables are scrambled, if numerical magnitudes are retained in cgs units, then cgs units will survive to the end. Their use is a form of insurance guaranteeing the correct unit for any quantity involved in the most complicated relationships of observables. This will be demonstrated frequently in subsequent work in this book.

1.5 Experiment

Thus far we have not described any process for the collection of observables and measurements except to imply that the observation of the physical world is common among men. Without any act on man's part many natural phenomena are displayed for observation, and certainly these are intriguing and useful to science. However, in physics and in many other sciences most observations are collected in a more sophisticated manner and one which simplifies the construction of the logical framework of the science. The method of collecting data is called the *experiment* or the experimental method, and much popular credit is given to it as a tool in scientific research. In essence the method is very simple. A physical system or mechanism is isolated from all extraneous influences both known and suspected. One then varies at will one or more observables of the system and measures any processes set off in the procedure. The power of the method is that the processes set off are demonstrated to be related to those observables which are varied by the experimenter and thus suggest that some physical relation must be involved. Further, the mathematical form of this relation can be empirically discovered by systematically varying the conditions of the experiment and noting the result. It is, when properly done, a convincing and sure method for uncovering the working of nature. For example we might wish to know the relation between the pressure of a gas and its volume. To isolate the gas it must be enclosed in a container whose volume can be measured; to eliminate extraneous influences we must be certain that the container does not leak, that the gas will not react chemically with the container material, that the temperature of the gas remains constant, that the molecular structure of the gas does not change during the experiment, etc. Presumably we should then be able to learn the relation between the pressure and volume of a gas by systematically varying the pressure and noting the corresponding volumes (Boyle's law).

There are, however, a few restraining words needed, lest the reader think that by twisting all available handles in nature and at the same time keeping his eyes open that he can open new realms of research. First of all, an experiment must be done well to be useful. It is necessary to establish the causal relation between the influences and the results. This is a matter of technique, both in design of the physical system—the apparatus—and in its employment. One must be careful and painstaking and a bit skeptical. One runs "control" experiments and tries to repeat observations and suspects and checks all known extraneous influences at each stage. This matter of technique takes time and many false starts and confusions for its development.

A more serious problem in employing experiments lies in the difficult matter of deciding what experiment to perform, since most, if not nearly all, experiments are useless or trivial in supplying new fundamental knowledge. Here we leave the safe confines of logical reasoning and demand an insight or intuition of nature which seems well developed in some men and in some ages and largely lacking in others. Like other forms of artistry, experiment in the hands of a man of genius may take the form of a deep insight into established knowledge or may employ leaps of imagination to arrive at the invention of new concepts and technique. Understandably, we have nothing to reveal in this matter.

It is frequently stated that the birth of the experimental method came with the Renaissance and with such great men as Galileo. It is hard to imagine that this is strictly true. Outstanding exceptions exist in the recorded histories of earlier civilizations. True, there was a great awakening in science with the Renaissance, motivated by works of experimental genius, but this was not the invention of a method but rather its successful exploitation in the choice of experiments. Man experimented, occasionally with rather refined technique, from the times of our earliest records. What he did not do was to seize upon experiments which aimed directly at the core of the problem, experiments such as those of Galileo which disclosed the fundamental processes in the motion of bodies and began the uninterrupted progress which leads to modern physics.

Although the experiment is an essential ingredient in physics, by itself it offers limited progress in the overall task of constructing the logical framework of the science. The interpretation of an experiment and the coordination of the results of groups of experiments are just as essential. We shall now look into this aspect of scientific reasoning.

1.6 Correlations and Physical Laws

The organization of the vast body of natural experience has reached a high degree of formalism in physics. This formalism is the language and method of mathematics, and the rigor of this discipline is exploited in the correlation of observations. The supreme glory of mathematics lies in its unambiguous relating of conclusions to premises in logical sequence. Of all logical methods it is the most precise. In its use in physics, mathematical symbols are attached to various observables, and the relationships among these are expressed in mathematical form. These relationships are combined with others by mathematical rules, and an attempt is made to reduce the whole to a simple, comprehensive form.

The simplest way in which mathematics is used in physics is in the formulation of *physical laws*. These laws are quantitative statements of the relations between the several observables of a certain physical system. That is, they are relations between sets of measurements. In enunciating a physical law the measurements must be defined as well as the statement of the law itself, and in general something must be said about the nature of the physical system and any limitations on the validity of the law. For example, in the case of bodies falling to the earth, the time t elapsed from the release of the body and distance s fallen in that time are found to be related by an algebraic equation:

$$s = \text{Constant} \times t^2$$

for a very large class of falling objects. True, hydrogen-filled balloons do not obey this formula, and indeed refined measurements on all objects show it to be only approximate. It is almost exactly obeyed for bodies falling in a vacuum and is a fair enough approximation for all heavy and compact objects if the elapsed time is not too long. These are the kinds of statements which prescribe the limitations of a physical law. They are usually inexact, employing such words as "approximate" and "almost" as concessions to the limited precision with which we can describe nature. In one form or another approximations are always present in physics; the exact relations of mathematics contain physical quantities measured only to a limited precision.

Some physical laws are arrived at solely by seeking and finding numerical relationships between sets of observables. Once a law is found an attempt is made to find its region of validity. Some condition kept constant in the earlier experiments is now varied and its effect is noted. It may be found possible to include this in the law as well, by representing the measurement by a symbol and inserting it into the formula. Then the several variable conditions are changed by greater and greater amounts until the law breaks down. Further modifications are then attempted in order to buttress the law. This procedure of modifying the law for an expanded region of validity is continued until it is possible to characterize a physical system of considerable generality. If the results are sufficiently general and useful, they will claim the attention of workers and students and probably be ennobled with a proper name, such as Boyle's law for the behavior of confined gases.

This empirical procedure in finding and formulating physical laws is the method used in advancing much of science. It ends with a sort of catalog of formulas and directions as to where and when they may be used. It lacks the unifying principles of present day physics, which employs other means as well in exploring nature and choosing experiments. Nevertheless, this empirical method is continually turning up new and useful information in the hands of an energetic and intuitive experimenter.

1.7 Physical Theory

The other aspect to physical research and to the use of mathematics in physics is known as theory. The nature of this method is not as easily described as that of the experiment. Both the methods and the results of theory are more abstract in that they are less closely associated with the observables which they are designed to correlate.

It must be understood that theories in physics are not simply a distilled essence of formulas and laws deduced empirically. Rather, they are attempts to explain these laws with a set of abstract principles which are presumed to be fundamental in nature, but frequently not directly accessible to observation.

Sometimes the theorist employs an analysis of the results of many experiments, finding in them some unifying, common principle. Sometimes he proposes principles by analogy or sheer invention, and the theory is complete before any but the most meager observations are assembled. Sometimes a theory may grow from existing theories and is more in the nature of an application to new circumstances than of new principles.

The formulation of a theory begins with a set of axioms or assumptions which are somehow suggested to the theorist as being basic and fundamental in nature. These principles may concern observables, but often they are statements about manufactured concepts and are only later correlated with observation. Frequently these assumptions are in the form of equations. In the next step the assumptions are combined and expanded and developed by mathematical methods until some relation between possible observables is found. This may be a known law, but now revealed in a new light, or it may be a new and untested relation in the form of a prediction. It is the prediction of new and subsequently verified relations which marks a successful theory. Important theories embrace whole regions of the science, deriving many observed relations from a simple set of premises. Newton's dynamics which starts with three simple premises—three "laws of motion"—can be developed to include all ordinary dynamical processes. The behavior of all moving and stationary bodies, their positions, paths, speed, and all dynamical observables assignable to them are related by Newton's theory. The power and scope of such a theory is impossible to appreciate except by a detailed study of its application, but it is immediately clear that its premises and methods must be very close to the roots of natural behavior.

This poses the interesting question of the basic relations between nature and theory. Whereas the results of theory may be well verified by experiment, the basic *meaning* of theory and its place in nature is largely open to debate. The great usefulness of mathematics in manipulating abstract concepts and turning out physical laws leads some people to conclude that nature operates in basically mathematical ways. Or at least, some aver, nature itself must have a logical structure, since mathematics, a logical method, is applicable to the description of nature. On the other hand, mathematics is often invented from natural anaologies, or at least by mathematicians who live in the world and feel its impact in even the most abstract studies. Thus, it is not so strange that mathematical methods are applicable to nature. The basic logic of mathematics is so conditioned by our notion of truth and in turn by nature's influence on us that the harmony of nature and mathematics is perhaps to be expected. Any detailed treatment of these views is beyond our needs here, and we raise the questions only to point to the challenge which modern physical theories offer to the philosopher. As theory becomes increasingly abstract and embracive, the basis on which this admittedly successful procedure rests is apparently becoming no clearer. To the physicist, the usefulness and power of theory in its own right is quite enough.

We have spoken of physical theories in the plural since there is no one theory in modern physics. This does not mean that uncertainty exists as to which theory to apply to a set of circumstances, but rather that different aspects of nature require theories that often have little in common. There is no one theory of matter, but a theory of its mechanical behavior, another of its electrical behavior, a third of its optical properties, and so on. The reader may be aware that the electromagnetic theory of Maxwell linked many of the electrical, optical, and mechanical theories of earlier investigators. Einstein's relativity theory synthesized certain aspects of both electricity and gravitation into a unified whole. The modern quantum theory has succeeded in correlating the electrical properties of matter with the emission and absorption of light. As physics progresses, new and more embracive theories are proposed to supersede the old, but we are yet far from a universal theory. A very thorny problem of the last few decades has been the attempted construction of a unified field theory—one which related all the gravitational, electrical, and dynamical properties of matter. In a more restricted realm there remains to discover a theory which explains the behavior and constitution of the atomic nuclei whose technical potentialities are now being exploited in nuclear fission. All these and many less grand projects keep the theorist's docket well stocked with future work, and the future holds promise of much new progress in theory.

PROBLEMS

(The first problems are designed to review the handling of powers of 10.)

1. Express as a power of ten the following: (a) 1000 meters in centimeters; (b) 200 micrograms in grams; (c) 10 kilocycles in cycles; (d) 0.01 mm in centimeters.

2. Find the area in square centimeters of the following: (a) a square 5 meters on the side; (b) a circle of 0.01 mm radius; (c) a rectangle 10 km by 100 meters.

3. Find the volume in cubic centimeters of the following: (a) a cube one meter on the side; (b) a sphere ($V = \frac{4}{3} \pi r^3$) of 2 mm radius; (c) a sphere of 3 meters radius.

4. Find: (a) $\sqrt{10^4}$; (b) $\sqrt{10^{-6}}$; (c) $\sqrt{10^7}$; (d) $\dfrac{10^3 \times 10^{-6}}{10^4}$; ($e$) $9.1 \times 10^{-28} \times (3 \times 10^{10})^2$.

5. Calculate your weight in kilograms and your height in meters.

6. The distance from New Haven to New York City is 75 miles. Express this in kilometers.

Suggested Reading

DAMPIER, SIR WILLIAM, "A History of Science," New York, The Macmillan Co., 1946.
> Chapter X treats the philosophical and mathematical aspects of science.

JOAD, C. E. M., "Philosophical Aspects of Modern Science," London, George Allen and Unwin Ltd., 1943.
> Chapters 8–11 on conceptions of reality. Criticizes the scientist's interpretations and philosophy.

LINDSAY, R. B., and MARGENAU, H., "Foundations of Physics," New York, John Wiley & Sons, 1936.
> Chapter I gives a careful treatment of the logical structure of physics.

MOULTON, F. R., and SCHIFFERES, J. J., "The Autobiography of Science," New York, Doubleday Doran and Co., 1945.
> Excerpts from Roger Bacon's concepts of experimental science.

SHAPLEY, H., WRIGHT, H., RAPPORT, S., "Readings in the Physical Sciences," New York, Appleton-Century-Crofts, Inc., 1948.
> Page 401 gives an account of the scientific method in chemistry.

CHAPTER 2

Some Mathematics of Physics

2.1 Mathematics in Physics

The use of mathematics in physics has been mentioned in connection with the measurement of observables, the formulation of physical laws, and the construction of theories. Our discussions were only by way of illustration and contained no details of the application of mathematics to physics or the forms of mathematics required in physics. Of course, both of these subjects involve the study of physical theories and a full understanding of physical measurements; and it is not our immediate purpose to summarize these diverse fields. Rather, we wish to show and develop by example some of the more elementary mathematical notions current in almost all our physical ideas.

Mathematics of itself is a science of great breadth and diversity. Some of the elementary branches are presumably familiar to the student; but most of mathematics, including much that is useful to physics, is probably not known. We shall assume only a knowledge of arithmetic, elementary algebra, and plane geometry in our studies and will use these in carrying out the developments and proofs in what follows. Our lack of higher-powered mathematical tools will sometimes force us to forego certain considerations in the theories and to treat others in somewhat roundabout and over-simple fashions. It is a truism that for the physicist the more complex branches of mathematics perform the hardest jobs in the easiest ways. Nevertheless, to the physicist mathematics is primarily a tool, not an end in itself; and the physical aspects of our study will claim first attention.

2.2 Scalar Quantities

Perhaps the most elementary use of mathematics in physics is in the assignment of numbers in the measurement of observables. These numbers, which express the number of unit quantities contained in a given observable, are exactly the familiar numbers used in counting. They are added, multiplied, divided, and subjected to all the other arithmetic operations familiar to the reader.

When the nature of all the physical observables is explored, one finds that many of them can be completely described by a measurement which assigns a certain number together with a suitable unit of measurement. That is, many quantities possess only the property of *magnitude* or size. Such quantities as mass, length, area, and interval of time are completely specified in this manner. An observable requiring only magnitude (and a unit) for complete specification is called a *scalar*. Scalars are the simplest physical quantities from the point of view of mathematics. The measurement numbers of scalars—which we shall contract to the term scalars—follow all the usual laws of arithmetic, with certain restrictions on the compounding of scalars having different kinds of units. These restrictions are rather obvious; one cannot add or subtract scalars of differing units just as one does not add apples and oranges in grade-school arithmetic. Scalars with the same unit may be added or subtracted. Multiplication and division may be performed with scalars of differing units. The elementary algebra learned by the student is more completely called scalar algebra; hence, he is already familiar with the mathematics of scalars. There exist, however, observables in physics for which scalar algebra is not adequate, and one class of these must now be considered.

2.3 Vectors

Of the observables of greater complexity than scalars the simplest are *vectors*; a vector is a quantity which possesses a definite *direction* in space in addition to its *magnitude*. The complete description of a vector requires a measurement number, a unit, and a specification of a direction in relation to some reference body in space. For example, the velocity of a particle moving in a horizontal plane is such a quantity. Its magnitude (often called its speed) is the time rate at which distance is being traversed; and its direction is the direction of motion of the particle, which might be specified as the compass point toward which it is moving. Another common vector is displacement, the amount and direction by which a particle is moved in going from one point in space to another, i.e., a vector having length and direction. A vector quantity must always have both magnitude and direction. The magnitude of a vector is more completely termed its scalar magnitude to emphasize that it contains no suggestion of direction.

In describing scalars we require a number and a unit. In describing vectors a third property, direction, must be included. Direction may be indicated in a number of ways, but perhaps the simplest is to make a picture of the vector. One draws an arrow of length proportional to the magnitude of the vector and points it in the direction of the vector. The specification of the direction may be referred to a set of ordinary rectangular axes x and y, the directions of the compass, or other convenient means of indicating direction. Such a picture is shown in Fig. 2.1, representing an airplane flying east on a horizontal course at a speed of 300 mi/hr. The arrow end of the vector, called the *terminus,* points in the direction of the motion. The other end of the vector is called the *origin.* The length of the arrow is three units of length as referred to the 100-mi/hr scale unit shown in the figure. Notice that only the length and direction of the arrow are fixed; it may be drawn anywhere on the sheet of paper with equal justification, and can be moved parallel to itself without altering its value. All airplane velocities of 300 mi/hr to the east are represented by the same vector (if the curvature of the earth is not considered). It is very convenient to move vectors from place to place on a plane in discussing vector addition. The symbol for a vector is a

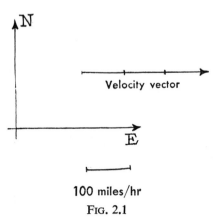

Velocity vector

100 miles/hr

FIG. 2.1

letter in bold-face type, e.g., **A** or **v.** As a symbol of the magnitude of a vector **A** we will use *A,* that is, the letter in italics.

Vectors, like scalars, are subjected to certain mathematical rules for their manipulation. However, because of their direction properties, the algebra of vectors is more complex than scalar algebra. We will concern ourselves with only two processes; the multiplication of vectors by scalars, and the addition of vectors with vectors. It is not possible to add vectors and scalars because they are unlike quantities. There are rules for the multiplication of vectors by vectors, but since we do not need to perform this operation in the text, it will not be necessary to discuss it.

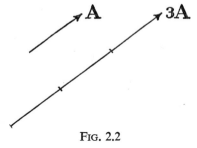

FIG. 2.2

2.4   Vector Algebra

The simplest mathematical operation in vector algebra is the multiplication of a vector by a positive number. This is illustrated in Fig. 2.2 where the vector **A** is multiplied by the number 3. The result is a new vector 3**A** whose direction is that of **A** and whose magnitude is 3*A.* When a vector is multiplied by a negative number or negative scalar the result is the same except that the *direction* of the vector is *reversed*. This suggests the meaning of a negative vector as one of equivalent magnitude but reversed direction. That is, $-\mathbf{A}$ is the negative of $\mathbf{A}$ since $-\mathbf{A} = (-1)\mathbf{A}$.

The second operation we shall need to understand is *vector addition*. Vectors of like kind may be added to each other by a rule which we will illustrate by an example. Suppose two displacement vectors $\mathbf{A}$ and $\mathbf{B}$, lying in the same plane, are added; that is, compounded to give a total displacement. This sum, resulting from adding vectors, is termed the *re-sultant* vector. Since each displacement is just the transfer of a particle by a

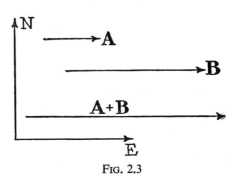

FIG. 2.3

certain distance in a certain direction, it is clear that the resultant displacement must give the cumulative effect of two such transfers. If both $\mathbf{A}$ and $\mathbf{B}$ point east, the situation is as shown in Fig. 2.3, and the resultant vector $\mathbf{A} + \mathbf{B}$ is of magnitude $A + B$ and also points east. Thus for the addition of parallel vectors, the resultant vector points in the direction of the original vectors, and its magnitude is the sum of the individual magnitudes.

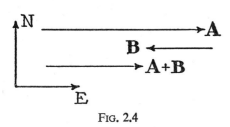

FIG. 2.4

If one of these parallel vectors is negative, as in Fig. 2.4, the resultant is less than $\mathbf{A}$ since its magnitude is $A + (-B) = A - B$. If one of the two vectors is exactly the negative of the other, the resultant is zero, just as in scalar arithmetic.

It is not necessary to restrict vector addition to parallel vectors, for, in general, any set of similar vectors may be summed regardless of their directions in space. Consider, for example, two non-parallel vectors (Fig. 2.5). If they are

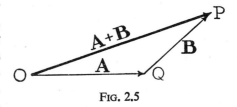

FIG. 2.5

displacements, the resultant must give a displacement which is the cumulative effect of the individual displacements. That is, the resultant displacement takes the displaced particle from its original position to a final position; and this latter must be the same as if the two original displacements were carried out one after the other. By simple geometry this means that the resultant vector is the third side of a triangle whose other two sides are the vectors being added. In the construction of Fig. 2.5 the displacement O to P is the same when produced by vector $\mathbf{A} + \mathbf{B}$ as when carried out by $\mathbf{A}$ and $\mathbf{B}$ individually by going through the intermediate point Q. Hence, the resultant $\mathbf{A} + \mathbf{B}$ is found by completing the triangle according to the following rule:

The resultant of two vectors lies along the third side of a triangle formed by placing the origin of the second vector at the terminus of the first. The origin of the resultant vector is at the origin of the first vector, and the terminus of the resultant is at the terminus of the second vector.

This convention for the origins and termini is obvious if one thinks of the meaning of the cumulative effect of two vector displacements.

In the formation of a resultant the order in which the vectors are added is immaterial. This is clear from the geometry of Fig. 2.6 where vectors

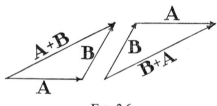

FIG. 2.6

$\mathbf{A}$ and $\mathbf{B}$ are added in the order $\mathbf{A}$ first and $\mathbf{B}$ second to form $\mathbf{A} + \mathbf{B}$, and in the order $\mathbf{B}$ first and $\mathbf{A}$ second to form $\mathbf{B} + \mathbf{A}$. The vectors $\mathbf{A} + \mathbf{B}$ and $\mathbf{B} + \mathbf{A}$ are equal; the order in which the vectors are taken is immaterial in forming the sum. (This is called the commutative law of vector addition.) Of course, ordinary numbers obey this law in arithmetic addition; that is, $5 + 8$ is the same sum as $8 + 5$.

The extension of vector addition to more than two vectors lying in a common plane is illustrated in Fig. 2.7 for the addition of $\mathbf{A}$, $\mathbf{B}$, $\mathbf{C}$, $\mathbf{D}$ in that order. We see that the intermediate resultants $\mathbf{A} + \mathbf{B}$ and $\mathbf{A} + \mathbf{B} + \mathbf{C}$ are unnecessary and that the construction may be simplified by drawing $\mathbf{A} + \mathbf{B} + \mathbf{C} + \mathbf{D}$ directly from the origin of $\mathbf{A}$ to the terminus of $\mathbf{D}$. That is, in adding more than two coplanar vectors the resultant is the closing side of a polygon whose other sides are the original vectors, with the origin

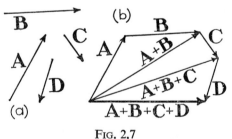

FIG. 2.7

of each at the terminus of the preceding vector in the sum. It is easily verified geometrically in the case of Fig. 2.7 that the commutative law holds; i.e., that the resultant is independent of the order of addition.

Example of Vector Addition.   As an illustration of vector addition, consider an airplane flying north on a horizontal course with a speed of 150 mi/hr in a crosswind of 40 mi/hr from the east. The resultant of these two velocities is the velocity of the airplane relative to the ground. Figure 2.8 shows the construction of this resultant **v**. The direction of the resultant may be specified by measuring angle θ with a protractor, and the magnitude of **v** is obtained by measuring its length to scale.* In Fig. 2.8, $v = 155$ mi/hr, and $\theta = 15°$.

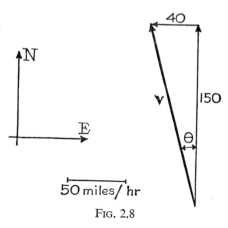

FIG. 2.8

It has been assumed that the vectors treated above lie in the same plane. However, this restriction is not essential. In the case of adding two vectors it is clear that they are always coplanar if one is moved parallel to itself until the two intersect, since two intersecting lines uniquely determine a plane. The resultant, therefore, lies in the plane so chosen and is found by a triangle construction in that plane. In the case of more than two vectors there is, in general, no common plane for all the vectors. However, the construction of the resultant may be accomplished by the method of Fig. 2.7 where first the plane of **A** and **B** is chosen and **A** + **B** is drawn in that plane. Then the plane common to **A** + **B** and **C** is chosen and **A** + **B** + **C** drawn in that plane. Finally, the plane of **A** + **B** + **C** and **D** is chosen and the final resultant **A** + **B** + **C** + **D** is drawn in that plane. Or one can construct a warped polygon in space using the vectors **A, B, C, D** and **A** + **B** + **C** + **D**.

2.5   Rectangular Components of a Vector

It is useful to decompose a vector into two other vectors which are *perpendicular* to each other and whose vector sum is the original vector. These two vectors are called the *rectangular components* of the original vector. Usually, there are certain preferred directions along which the components

---

* The use of trigonometry is evident to the reader trained in that branch of mathematics. $\tan \theta = 40/150$, from which $\theta = 14°55'$. $\sin \theta = 40/v$ from which $v = 155.4$ mi/hr.

are desired. These are frequently a set of x and y axes such as indicated in Fig. 2.9, where the x and y components of the velocity vector **v** are shown. Quite evidently the Pythagorean theorem is applicable to the magnitudes v,

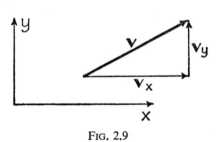

FIG. 2.9

v_x, and v_y: in any right triangle the square of the hypotenuse is equal to the sum of the squares of the remaining two sides. Thus in Fig. 2.9,

$$v^2 = v_x^2 + v_y^2 \qquad [2.1]$$

For example, the velocity of the airplane discussed in the preceding section has rectangular components of 150 mi/hr north and 40 mi/hr east. Its magnitude (its speed) is given by

$$v^2 = (150)^2 + (40)^2 = 24{,}100$$
$$v = 155.4 \text{ mi/hr}$$

Its direction may be found by the use of a protractor or, better, by using the trigonometric relation ($\tan \theta = 40/100$).

Thus the construction of the components of a vector, given a set of axes for the components, is simply a matter of forming a vector triangle such that the components add to give the original vector. For rectangular components, as in Fig. 2.9, this triangle is formed by the intersection of a line drawn from the origin of **v** parallel to the x axis with a line from the terminus of **v** drawn parallel to the y axis. The identifications of the origins and termini of the components are performed by the triangle rule which assures that the sum of the components is just the original vector.

In three dimensions the construction of rectangular components follows the method shown in Fig. 2.10 which shows the x, y, z components of the vector **v**. v_y is parallel to the y axis having a length determined by the line $\overline{PA}$ which is drawn

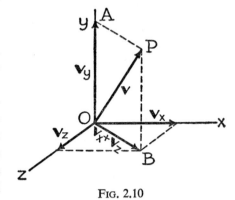

FIG. 2.10

parallel to the x-z plane. This fixes the triangle OBP and the component $v_x + v_z$. Drawing the components v_x and v_z in x-z plane completes the con-

struction. We now apply the Pythagorean theorem twice to relate the magnitude of **v** to its components. From the figure we see that

$$v^2 = v_y^2 + \overline{OB}^2$$

But

$$\overline{OB}^2 = v_x^2 + v_z^2$$

So

$$v^2 = v_x^2 + v_y^2 + v_z^2 \qquad\qquad [\,2.2\,]$$

Quite evidently there are three angles which determine the vector's direction
(one with each of the coordinate axes). These are found in the usual way.

PROBLEMS

1. What is the length of the hypotenuse of a right triangle whose sides are 30 cm
and 40 cm?

2. Draw to scale the following vectors and find their resultant: (*1*) 20 cm northeast;
(*2*) 50 cm south; (*3*) 30 cm northwest; (*4*) 20 cm north.

3. Repeat Problem 2, adding them in the following orders: (*a*) 1 + 3 + 4 + 2 and
(*b*) 4 + 3 + 1 + 2.

4. A displacement vector 50 cm long makes an angle of 45° with the horizontal.
What are its horizontal and vertical components?   *Ans.*   35.4 cm each.

5. The horizontal component makes an angle of 45° with its vector and has a magnitude of 8 cm. What is the magnitude of the vector itself?   *Ans.*   11.3 cm.

6. Two forces, one of 4×10^{-12} dynes and one of 0.03×10^{-10} dynes, act on a
particle. The angle between the forces is 90°. Find the magnitude of the resultant
force.

7. A displacement vector in three-dimensional space has the following components: 12 cm along x, 4 cm along y, and 7 cm along z. Find the magnitude of the
vector.   *Ans.*   14.5 cm.

CHAPTER 3

Particle Dynamics—Accelerated Motion

3.1 The Science of Dynamics

The understanding of the motions of material bodies was one of the first important achievements in the science of physics. *Dynamics*, as the science of such motions is called, provided a method of approach and a body of knowledge which have been of continuing use in our further understanding of nature. In particular, the names of Galileo and Newton are associated with these early researches, for it was they who first conceived of the important observables in the motions of bodies and the laws which relate them. Until recently, with the advent of relativity and quantum theories, there were no truly fundamental changes in these basic ideas, and the intervening years brought chiefly the application and coordination of the principles of dynamics. Even today, Newton's ideas in dynamics are used exclusively in most of science and technology. The alterations demanded by the relativity and quantum theories are necessary only in special circumstances where very high velocities and very small particles are being considered.

The science of dynamics is a good starting point for our study of matter and atomic physics. Its early perfection and wide application to motions directly observable in the world gave a group of concepts which are used in all the other branches of physics. That is not to say that all the problems in nature can be solved by Newton's dynamics, but rather that the concepts and results of dynamics have been incorporated as a part of our understanding of the more modern and abstract parts of physics. A very great part of all physical inquiry is concerned with material bodies, and even where other aspects of nature are predominant there is a need for the science of the motions of material bodies. This is no less true in atomic physics where the electrical nature of the atomic particles and the peculiar properties due to their smallness are of primary importance.

3.2   Particles

The simplest part of dynamics treats the motions of the so-called particles—bodies of such small size or great remoteness from each other that their internal constitution and internal motions may be neglected. We are concerned only with the motion of the body as a whole and neglect deformations in the body such as stretching or twisting, and internal motions of the body such as rotation about an internal axis. Effectively we are considering the particles as points possessing the properties of material bodies and studying the motions of these points, their speeds, and the paths along which they move.

In many respects the description of atomic processes employs such particles so that this particle dynamics is sufficient for the present study. For many purposes we can treat atoms and molecules as almost ideal particles; they have great rigidity, and their internal motions are of secondary importance in atomic dynamics.

3.3   Space and Motion

The idea of motion in dynamics concerns the body which moves and a space in which to move. We must assume that both the body and the space are intuitive concepts, for it is probably impossible to analyze them in more elementary terms. They are, in fact, inseparably related since the notion of physical space is founded on reference points which are actually observable bodies, and the notion of a body presumes a portion of space occupied. The quantitative description of space involves distances or lengths, and these lengths are given meaning only in terms of the process of length measurement in which bodies, the measuring sticks, are used. Space also has form, right and left, up and down, flat or curved; and we must also take these properties as being defined by common experience.

In ordinary dynamics three observables in space, or *space variables* as they are called, are of fundamental importance. These are *displacement, velocity,* and *acceleration.* They are all vectors. Displacement, as we have stated earlier, is a vector which describes the transport of a body from one point in space to another; its magnitude is the length or distance moved, and its direction is the direction in which the movement proceeds. It is drawn as a vector arrow connecting the initial and final points of the motion, with its terminus at the final point. Its units are those of length, i.e., centimeters, feet, and miles, the first being the cgs unit. As with all vectors, its specification requires a set of fixed axes or bodies of reference, a so-called *reference system.* Frequently the observer is at rest in the reference system being used, in which case it is called the observer's reference system. Thus, the laboratory room in which a body is dropped forms the reference system for the falling motion, since we are interested in this motion relative to the floor, ceiling, or walls of the room. Were the motion referred to a new reference system, say that of a moving elevator cage, the results might be quite different. In ordinary dynamics it is generally assumed that the dimensions of a rigid body are independent of the reference system in which they are measured. This belief has been markedly changed by the theory of relativity, but for our immediate purposes it is quite adequate.

Velocity is defined as the ratio of displacement to the time required for this displacement. Since it is a vector divided by a scalar, velocity must be a vector pointing in the direction of the displacement. Its magnitude is called *speed*. If we use the symbol s for displacement and *t* for time, then in symbols the definition of velocity is

$$\mathbf{v} = \frac{\mathbf{s}}{t}$$

and its cgs unit is centimeters per second (cm/sec). As with displacement, one must specify a reference system in any measurement of velocity. In fact, it is seen that both the magnitude and direction of a velocity vector are dependent on the reference system. For example, a man seated in a train is at rest in that reference system, while in the reference system of an observer along the track he may be moving at 60 mi/hr.

3.4 Uniform, Instantaneous, and Average Velocities

The measurement of velocity is accomplished in the following way. One picks two points along the path of a moving body, which are a known distance apart and fixed with respect to the observer. One then measures the time interval required for the body to go from one point to the other. The speed or magnitude of the velocity is:

$$\text{Magnitude of velocity} = \frac{\text{Distance between reference points}}{\text{Time required to traverse distance}}$$

The direction of the velocity is the relative direction of the second point with respect to the first. If the body's motion is *straight* and of *constant speed*, this procedure is adequate and unambiguous, and no restrictions as to distance between the two points or the time interval involved are necessary. Such a velocity is said to be *uniform*.

The two requirements for a uniform velocity, namely, constant direction and constant speed, suggest two ways in which velocity may vary. The dis-

cussion of the effect of variation of direction will be delayed until later
(§3.7). Let us here consider a particle moving in a straight line but with a
changing speed, as for example a marble rolling down an inclined trough. It
is evident that no single vector will represent the velocity at all times, because
the length of that vector must be steadily changing. To apply the procedure
for measuring velocity we must pick the two points along the path of the
moving particle sufficiently close together so that the change in speed between
them is negligible; for the short
time interval required to cover the
distance between these two points
the velocity is considered constant.
To improve the precision of our
measurement we would choose the
points still closer together, the cor-

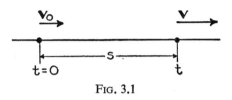

FIG. 3.1

responding time being still shorter; when the two points were only an infinitesimal distance apart then we would be measuring effectively the velocity
at one point and at the instant at which the particle passed that point. This
velocity is termed the *instantaneous velocity* of the particle and is designated
by the same symbol used for uniform velocity, v. To write a defining equation
for instantaneous velocity we shall employ the symbol Δ (delta) to mean "a
small change of"; thus Δs is a small change of distance, Δt a small time interval. (Note that Δ is *not* a multiplying factor, but simply an abbreviation of
words.) Then instantaneous velocity is defined as.

$$v = \frac{\Delta s}{\Delta t}$$

It is clear that if the velocity is uniform the instantaneous velocity has every-
where this uniform value. Quite obviously, if the velocity is not uniform, it will
be difficult if not impossible to measure instantaneous velocities, for we have
no means of measuring infinitesimal distances or times. However, as we shall
see, such velocities can be calculated under certain conditions if we know
certain other space variables of the moving particle.

If the motion of the particle is *not* uniform (Fig. 3.1) a measurement of the
total displacement and the total time required for that displacement will give
us only an *average velocity*. Our general definition of velocity, namely, $v = s/t$, gives us only an average value of v, unless we know from other information
that the velocity is uniform. It is customary to represent average quantities by
placing a bar over the symbol for the quantity. Thus

$$\bar{v} = \frac{s}{t}$$

The situation can be summed up as follows: If the motion is non-uniform the instantaneous velocity, $v = \Delta s/\Delta t$, changes as the particle progresses, and it will have an average velocity, $\bar{v} = s/t$, which in general will be different from the instantaneous velocity. If the motion is uniform the instantaneous velocity is the same throughout and equal to the average velocity; we then speak only of a uniform or constant velocity, v.

3.5   Accelerated Motion

In dynamics the way in which the velocity of a body changes is a very important quantity. Changes in the velocity of the body are described by its *acceleration*. This is defined as the change in velocity divided by the time required for this change. Suppose at the instant we start observing, that is at $t = 0$, the particle has an instantaneous velocity v_0 (Fig. 3.1), and at some instant t seconds later it has an instantaneous velocity of v. Then in symbols the definition of acceleration is:

$$a = \frac{v - v_0}{t}$$

Since acceleration is a vector divided by a scalar, then it itself must be a vector pointing in the direction in which the velocity is *increasing*. The cgs unit of acceleration is found from those of velocity and time; it is thus centimeters per second, per second: (cm/sec)/sec or cm/sec². Note that velocity is the time rate of change of distance, whereas acceleration is the time rate of change of velocity. Just as with velocity, acceleration may be uniform or it may vary. (This suggests continued definitions—one for the time rate of change of acceleration, then one for the time rate of change of that quantity, etc; fortunately there is little need in physics for these additional definitions.) If acceleration varies, then we must define an instantaneous acceleration in the same way as we defined an instantaneous velocity. However, in this book we shall be concerned largely with uniform accelerations (at least uniform in magnitude) and will not consider the problems of variation of acceleration in detail.

It should be noted carefully that acceleration says nothing about the velocity at any instant, only the *change* of velocity with time. Thus our rolling marble may have an acceleration of 100 cm/sec², and this means that whatever velocity it has, that velocity is increasing 100 cm/sec every second. It might at some instant have a velocity of 50 cm/sec, in which case it has a velocity of 150 cm/sec a second later; or at the instant we view it, its velocity might be only 10 cm/sec and hence 110 cm/sec a second later; in either case its acceleration is the same.

3.6   Uniform Acceleration

In a large number of motions in dynamics the acceleration is *uniform* or constant in magnitude and direction. This is true in the simple case of bodies falling from rest to the earth when the resisting effort of the atmosphere is neglected. It is true in other problems where the motion itself is along a curved path of some complexity. These are called constant force problems, and we will investigate some of them in a later chapter. For the present we will derive the relations between the displacement, velocity, acceleration, and time in the case of *linear* (straight line) motion under a *uniform* acceleration.

Suppose that a particle moves with a uniform acceleration. Clearly since the particle moves in a straight line, its displacement, velocity, and acceleration vectors all point in the same direction (Fig. 3.1). Hence, we will drop our vector notation and deal only with scalar magnitudes. As before, let us assume that the particle has an instantaneous initial velocity, v_0, at the instant we start counting time, $t = 0$; t seconds later it has an instantaneous velocity, v, which is different from v_0 since the particle is being accelerated. We can determine v from the definition of acceleration

$$a = \frac{v - v_0}{t}$$

$$v = v_0 + at \qquad\qquad [\,3.1\,]$$

From the definition of average velocity we may write

$$\bar{v} = \frac{s}{t} \quad \text{ or } \quad s = \bar{v}t$$

Since the velocity is changing *uniformly*, the average velocity, s/t, will be equal to the arithmetic average of the initial and final velocities

$$\bar{v} = \frac{v_0 + v}{2}$$

or using Eq. 3.1

$$\bar{v} = \tfrac{1}{2}(v_0 + v_0 + at) = v_0 + \tfrac{1}{2}at$$

Hence

$$s = \bar{v}t = (v_0 + \tfrac{1}{2}at)\, t$$

or

$$s = v_0 t + \tfrac{1}{2}at^2 \qquad\qquad [\,3.2\,]$$

Equation 3.1 is independent of s, Eq. 3.2 is independent of v; it is convenient to obtain a relation that is independent of t. It is necessary to eliminate t from Eqs. 3.1 and 3.2.

From Eq. 3.1

$$t = \frac{v - v_0}{a}$$

From Eq. 3.2

$$s = t \left(v_0 + \tfrac{1}{2}at\right)$$

Substituting,

$$s = \left(\frac{v - v_0}{a}\right)\left(v_0 + \frac{a}{2}\frac{v - v_0}{a}\right)$$

$$s = \left(\frac{v - v_0}{a}\right)\left(\frac{v_0 + v}{2}\right)$$

and

$$2as = v^2 - v_0^2$$

or

$$v^2 = v_0^2 + 2as \qquad\qquad [\,3.3\,]$$

Equations 3.1, 3.2, and 3.3 completely describe the space variables of a particle subject to uniform acceleration. The procedure we have used to obtain them is called a *derivation* and is quite common in physics. Derivations serve the purpose of drawing together and summarizing with mathematical conciseness assumptions we have made, aided by definitions upon which we have agreed. Their great usefulness lies in the new viewpoint which they may present, conclusions which they often make clear and evident, and the economy of effort they afford in making quantitative calculations.

The derivation of the equations of linear accelerated motion which we have just completed is the first of several we shall encounter in this book. Since it illustrates the general procedure let us review the steps taken.

Definitions used: acceleration; average velocity (2 forms)

Assumptions made: Motion is linear; acceleration is uniform; initial velocity and acceleration known; and either displacement or time or final velocity is known.

Result of derivations:

$$v = v_0 + at \qquad\qquad [\,3.1\,]$$
$$s = v_0 t + \tfrac{1}{2}at^2 \qquad\qquad [\,3.2\,]$$
$$v^2 = v_0^2 + 2as \qquad\qquad [\,3.3\,]$$

Of course, if we cared to simplify our calculations we should be clever and start counting time just as the particle starts moving from rest; then $v_0 = 0$, and the equations take the simpler form:

$$v = at \qquad [3.4]$$
$$(v_0 = 0); \quad s = \tfrac{1}{2}at^2 \qquad [3.5]$$
$$v^2 = 2as \qquad [3.6]$$

As already suggested, one advantage gained from this derivation is the conclusions which we can now make about uniformly accelerated motion which were by no means obvious before. Equation 3.4 states that the velocity increases in proportion to the time; Eq. 3.5 says that displacement, however, increases with the *square* of time, that is, a particle will travel four times as far in two seconds as it did in the first second, nine times in three, 16 in four seconds, etc.; and finally Eq. 3.6 shows the instantaneous velocity varies with the square root of displacement, i.e., at the end of 4 cm it will have twice the velocity it had at the end of the first centimeter, after 9 cm it will have three times the velocity, etc. It is certainly undesirable and unnecessary to learn these as an elaborate set of details concerning accelerated motion; the derived equations contain in three lines the equivalent of several pages of description. And they allow us to make quantitative calculations.

Example 1. Suppose a particle is constrained to move in a straight line and has an acceleration of 100 cm/sec². How far has it gone after 3 sec if it started at rest?

GIVEN: $a = 100$ cm/sec²; $v_0 = 0$; $t = 3$ sec
$s = ?$

Solution: Eq. 3.2: $s = v_0 t + \tfrac{1}{2}at^2$
$$= 0 + \tfrac{1}{2} \times 100 \times 3^2 = 450 \text{ cm} \qquad Ans.$$

What is its velocity after three seconds?

GIVEN: $v = ?$
Solution: Eq. 3.1: $v = v_0 + at$
$$= 0 + 100 \times 3 = 300 \text{ cm/sec} \qquad Ans.$$

What is its velocity after traversing 800 cm?

GIVEN: $v = ?$ if $s = 800$ cm
Solution: Eq. 3.3: $v^2 = v_0^2 + 2as$
$$= 0 + 2 \times 100 \times 800$$
$$v = \sqrt{100 \times 1600} = 10 \times 40 = 400 \text{ cm/sec} \qquad Ans.$$

What time was required to traverse 800 cm?

GIVEN: $t = ?$ if $s = 800$ cm
Solution: Eq. 3.2: $s = v_0 t + \tfrac{1}{2}at^2$
$$800 = 0 + \tfrac{1}{2} \times 100 \times t^2$$
$$t^2 = 16$$
$$t = 4 \text{ sec} \qquad Ans.$$

Example 2. Let us reverse the situation in the above example. Suppose at the instant we start counting time the particle has a velocity of 200 cm/sec and it is being *decelerated* (negatively accelerated) at 100 cm/sec². How long will it require to come to rest?

GIVEN: $v_0 = 200$ cm/sec; $a = -100$ cm/sec²; $v = 0$
$$t = ?$$
Solution: Eq. 3.1: $v = v_0 + at = 200 + (-100) \times t = 0$
$$t = 2 \text{ sec} \quad \textit{Ans.}$$

How far will the particle have traveled in this time?

GIVEN: $t = 2$ sec
$$s = ?$$
Solution: Eq. 3.2: $s = v_0 t + \frac{1}{2}at^2$
$$= 200 \times 2 + \frac{1}{2}(-100) \times 2^2$$
$$= 400 - 200 = 200 \text{ cm} \quad \textit{Ans.}$$

It might be profitable at this juncture to illustrate the remark made earlier about the advantage of adhering to cgs units. In the problems just worked the acceleration is 1 meter/sec². If the number one had been used for acceleration instead of 100 the result obviously would have been different. There would have been no recognizable unit to assign to the answers. It is possible to check the correctness of units by writing a unit equation. For example,

Equation:
$$s = v_0 t + \frac{1}{2}at^2$$
Units equation: unit of $s = \dfrac{\text{cm}}{\text{sec}} \times \text{sec} + \dfrac{\text{cm}}{\text{sec}^2} \times \text{sec}^2$
$$= \text{cm}$$
If we had inserted for the acceleration 1 meter/sec:
$$\text{unit of } s = \dfrac{\text{cm}}{\text{sec}} \times \text{sec} + \dfrac{\text{meter}}{\text{sec}^2} \times \text{sec}^2$$
$$= \text{cm} + \text{meter}$$
$$= ?$$

Hence, if we adhere to cgs units, we can be assured the quantity solved for will be in cgs units; if other units are used the resulting unit may have no recognizable significance.

3.7 Uniform Circular Motion

The second method of varying the velocity suggested in §3.4 involved the variation of *direction*. If the speed is kept constant and the direction is varied uniformly, there must be an acceleration that is constant in magnitude. Such uniform variation of direction results from a particle moving with constant speed on a circle; this is known as *uniform circular motion*. The acceleration that accompanies uniform circular motion can be derived from a considera- tion of Fig. 3.2. The circle shown is the path of the moving particle, and two points P and Q are chosen along the path. At each point the velocity is tangent to the circle and of constant magnitude

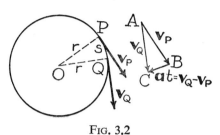

$$v_P = v_Q = v = \frac{s}{t}$$

FIG. 3.2

where t is the time interval required of the particle to move from P to Q. Though the magnitudes of v_P and v_Q are equal, their directions are different. The difference between v_P and v_Q when divided by the time t is the acceleration, even though this difference is one of direction only. Thus the acceleration multiplied by the time, at, is the closing side of the velocity triangle (Fig. 3.2). This vector diagram of velocities shows that the vector velocity change at points toward the center of the circle, if P and Q are taken close together. The velocity triangle ABC is similar to the distance triangle OPQ (which has sides r, r, and s). Hence

$$\frac{at}{v} = \frac{s}{r}$$

or

$$a = \frac{v}{r}\frac{s}{t}$$

Since the speed is constant, $s/t = v$, and we get

$$a = \frac{v^2}{r} \qquad [\,3.7\,]$$

Thus the instantaneous acceleration is directed from the particle's position toward the center of the circle and has a magnitude given by Eq. 3.7. This cen- trally directed acceleration is called the *centripetal acceleration*. Note that its magnitude is constant, but that it is continually changing its direction so as to point from the particle to the center of the circle at all times.

Example 1. If a certain particle moving on a circle of 2 meters diameter has a constant speed of 50 cm/sec, what acceleration does the particle have? What direc- tion is this acceleration?

GIVEN: Diameter = 2 meters = 200 cm; so radius = 100 cm = r

$v = 50$ cm/sec

$a = ?$

direction = ?

Solution: Eq. 3.7: $a = v^2/r$

$= (50)^2/100 = 2500/100$

$= 25$ cm/sec^2

This acceleration is toward the center of the circle, as centripetal acceleration must always be.   *Ans.*

Observe that it was necessary first to change the unit of diameter into one that is in the cgs system. To be certain that this then produces a recognizable unit for a, write a units equation:

$$a = v^2/r$$

$$\text{Units of } a = \left(\frac{cm}{sec}\right)^2/cm = cm/sec^2$$

Example 2.   A marble rolling in a circle on a roulette game board makes 30 rev/min. If the radius of the circle is 25 cm, what is the magnitude of the marble's centripetal acceleration?

GIVEN: $r = 25$ cm; $v = 30$ rev/min

$a = ?$

Solution: It is evident that v is not in cgs units, since neither revolution nor minute is a cgs unit. We convert to the desired units by remembering that the circumference of a circle is $2\pi \times$ radius. Hence, in one revolution the marble goes $2\pi 25$ cm or 50π cm; in 30 revolutions the distance is $30 \times 50\pi = 1500\pi$ cm; this requires 60 sec, so the velocity is $1500\pi/60 = 25\pi$ cm/sec $= v$.

$$a = v^2/r$$

$$= (25\pi)^2/25 = 25\pi^2 = 246 \text{ cm/sec}^2 \quad \textit{Ans.}$$

PROBLEMS

1.   An automobile covers a distance of 10 km at a uniform speed of 50 km/hr, then quickly accelerates to 80 km/hr and remains at this speed for 20 km. Neglect the brief time required for changing speeds and calculate the average speed over the 30 km.   *Ans.*   66.6 km/hr.

2.   A train traveling with a speed of 20 km/hr accelerates uniformly to a speed of 100 km/hr. What is its average speed during this period?   *Ans.*   60 km/hr.

3.   A particle has a linear acceleration of 20 cm/sec^2. If it starts from rest what is its velocity after 2 min? How far has it gone?   *Ans.*   24 m/sec; 1.44 km.

4.   A body uniformly accelerated from rest attains a velocity of 10 m/sec while traveling a distance of 2000 cm. What is its acceleration? How long was the body in motion?   *Ans.*   250 cm/sec^2; 4 sec.

5.   A particle starting from rest is uniformly accelerated to a velocity of 6 m/sec in

1 min. How far has it traveled in reaching this velocity? What was its velocity at the end of $\frac{1}{2}$ min? What was its velocity after covering one-half its total distance?

Ans.   180 m; 3 m/sec; 4.25 m/sec.

6.   A body moving with a velocity of 10 m/sec is uniformly decelerated, coming to rest in a distance of 20 m. What is its deceleration? How long a time was required for the body to come to rest?   *Ans.*   250 cm/sec²; 4 sec.

7.   A certain centrifuge has a radius of 50 cm and makes 100 rev/sec. What is the centripetal acceleration of a particle at the periphery of the centrifuge?

Ans.   1.97 × 10⁷ cm/sec².

8.   The radius of the earth at the equator is 6.4 × 10⁶ m. What is the acceleration of a body at the equator?   *Ans.*   3.4 cm/sec².

Suggested Reading

DAMPIER, SIR WILLIAM, "A History of Science," New York, The Macmillan Co., 1946.
> Pages 141–47 cover Galileo's achievements in dynamics.

GALILEO, "Two New Sciences," New York, The Macmillan Co., 1914.
> Pages 154–243 are translations of Galileo's original publication concerning the nature of velocity and acceleration in dynamics.

HARSANYI, ZSOLT, "The Star Gazer," New York, G. P. Putnam's Sons, 1939.
> A very successful fictional biography of Galileo.

MOTT-SMITH, M., "This Mechanical World," New York, D. Appleton and Co., 1931.
> Chapters VI, VII, and VIII discuss Galileo's mechanics and the role of acceleration. Easy reading.

MOULTON, F. R., and SCHIFFERES, J. J., "The Autobiography of Science," New York, Doubleday Doran and Co., 1945.
> Quotations from the writings of da Vinci, Galileo, and Newton.

Particle Dynamics—Mass and Force

4.1 The Birth of Dynamics

The first clear understanding of the motion of bodies came in the sixteenth century. Most of the credit for the early contributions goes to Galileo, who broke with the prevailing ideas of his time and spent his lifetime devising and interpreting experiments which showed the true nature of motion. He was not entirely alone in this effort; some constructive work had appeared in the preceding century. Leonardo da Vinci, whose notes were unpublished in his day, understood the form of the motions of falling bodies, and Benedetti clearly stated that falling bodies were accelerated. But it was Galileo who recognized the central role of acceleration in all dynamical motions and who put dynamics on its modern course in one sweeping generalization from experiment.

Most of the early speculation in dynamics was concerned with freely falling bodies, since these are the simplest motions which are readily observable. In Galileo's time this speculation followed Aristotle, who believed that each body had its "natural" place, heavy bodies below and light bodies above, and that it was therefore "natural" for heavy bodies to fall and seek their rightful place. Furthermore, as in accord with these natural inclinations, heavy bodies fell faster than light bodies. Such were the desires of nature. Speculation concerning more complicated motions went even further from the reasoning of modern science; projectiles engaged in "violent" motions, aided by the air. No attempt was made to give a quantitative description or to observe what really happened.

Galileo's numerous ingenious experiments which shattered these views are well known. His fabled dropping of weights from the Leaning Tower of Pisa disproved the contention that heavy bodies fall faster than do light bodies; his careful experiments with bodies moving down inclined planes showed the true circumstances which determine the velocities of all falling bodies. The important point which he found was this: the velocities of falling bodies in-

36

crease with the time of fall and with the distance fallen. In what manner does this occur, and what are the relations between the time and the distance? By analyzing his experiments he succeeded in showing that the central quantity in all falling motion is the *acceleration*. There is some property of nature which causes all freely falling bodies to fall with constant acceleration, and this acceleration is independent of the size, shape, or mass of the body. This universal acceleration alone determines the form of the motion, and the velocities and distances are secondary results which evolve in due course as the motion proceeds in time. This realization that acceleration is the root of motion is the central theme in dynamics; Galileo's contribution gave a firm starting point from which later workers could complete the study.

4.2   Newton's Laws of Motion

Galileo showed the way for advance in science by discarding speculation unfounded on observation and by insisting on testing his hypotheses by direct experiment. His approach exemplifies the statements made in Chapter 1 concerning experiments and physical laws. However, his genius did not extend to physical theory. There is no abstract underlying structure to Galileo's dynamics. This was supplied by Newton in the seventeenth century.

Newton summarized and completed the science of motion in three laws, which relate velocity and acceleration with that fundamental property of every particle which we call its mass. These laws are the foundation of ordinary dynamics and simultaneously form the basic definitions, hypotheses, and deductions of the theory. The adjective "ordinary" refers to the small but real discrepancies which appeared in Newton's theory at the turn of the present century; these discrepancies were resolved by the theory of relativity. Relativistic dynamics differs from Newton's theory only for the cases of very high velocities or for very large distances.

Since the description of motion requires a reference system, it is necessary to specify what reference system is chosen in the statement of the laws of motion. This becomes a subtle problem. The proper system for the simplest discussion of motion is the system attached to the fixed stars, stars which are so far away that our earth's orbital motion has no appreciable effect on their apparent positions relative to each other. This reference system is called an *inertial system*, and Newton's laws refer to this system. However, it is not the only inertial system. Any reference system moving *without acceleration* with respect to the fixed stars is also an inertial system. For most purposes our earth's acceleration with respect to the fixed stars is small enough so that it is effectively an inertial system for terrestrial experiments.

The statement of the laws of motion as they are applicable in an inertial system may be made as follows:

Law I   A particle under the action of no external force remains at rest or moves with constant velocity.

Law II   The resultant force on a particle is the product of its mass and its acceleration.

Law III   If two particles exert forces on each other, the force of the first on the second is equal in magnitude and opposite in direction to the force of the second on the first.

These laws are seen to involve the concepts of particle, velocity, acceleration, mass, and force, the last two of which have not been defined, and it might be objected that such definitions should precede their statement. However, mass and force are not definable independently, and indeed their fundamental relation is embodied in the laws themselves. In this sense Newton's laws are not physical laws as we have defined them as empirically discovered relations between observables, but are definitions of the basic concepts in dynamics.

4.3   Newton's First Law of Motion

To extract the full meaning from these apparently simple laws requires careful scrutiny. Let us analyze the first law. Our first thought is that it constitutes a direct denial of Aristotle's "natural" rest position. Equally "natural" is motion with constant velocity! The law simply states that bodies will always remain in uniform motion unless prevented by an outside force. (Zero motion is just a special case of uniform motion.) This characteristic of matter to persist in motion (including rest position) is not "explained" by the first law in the sense that it states *why* it happens. It simply embodies the results of observations made by Galileo and Newton that it does happen. The name *inertia* is given to that property of matter which opposes *change of motion*. It is easy to appeal to our intuitive sense to illustrate this inertial characteristic of material bodies.

It is common experience that it requires less effort to stop a light passenger car than to stop a 10-ton truck; the latter has a greater persistence to retain its motion, that is, has more inertia. Hence our intuitive sense suggests that inertia must be associated with *mass*. However, regardless of whether the inertia is large or small the first law states that neither body would have ever stopped if an outside force had not been applied. Since we do not actually find perpetually moving bodies on our earth we must assume—if we subscribe to the first law—that there is always an outside force to prevent the uniform motion. This force is the force of *friction*, which always supplies a retarding force that prohibits the observation of bodies moving on the earth free of all external forces.

4.4 Newton's Second Law of Motion

This law states that

$$\text{Force} = \text{Mass} \times \text{Acceleration}$$

or

$$\mathbf{F} = m\mathbf{a}$$

Observe that force is a vector quantity, and consequently $\mathbf{F}$ in the general case will be the *resultant* force obtained by adding vectorially all the forces acting on m. It is this resultant or unbalanced force which gives m an acceleration, and the direction of the acceleration is the same as the direction of the resultant force, according to the second law. If we assume, as we must, that mass must remain largely an intuitive concept beyond the reach of definition, then Newton's second law provides us with a working definition of force: force is that quantity which will give a mass an acceleration, and is equal to the product of the mass and the acceleration. Hence, the second law may be viewed as a definition rather than a law of nature.

Unit of Force. The cgs unit of force is found in the usual manner, by supplying the units of the quantities which define it. It is a gram-centimeter per second per second (gm-cm/sec^2). However, force is a quantity so widely encountered in physics that a special name has been given to this unit. One gm-cm/sec^2 of force is a *dyne*. Thus: *One dyne is that force which will give a one gram mass an acceleration of one centimeter per second per second.*

Concept of Equilibrium. The second law demands that wherever a resultant force acts on a particle or system of particles there must be an acceleration of that particle or system. Hence, a system on which the resultant force is zero must have zero acceleration, that is, constant velocity. Such a system is in *equilibrium*. For example, all *inertial* systems must be equilibrium systems since by definition an inertial system is a non-accelerated system. Observe carefully, that equilibrium does not demand zero motion, but rather *zero change of motion*. We now see that Newton's *first* law simply describes the motion of a body in equilibrium, the *second* law describes the motion when equilibrium is disturbed, that is when an unbalanced force exists. From this point of view the first law is just a special case of the more general second law.

4.5 Newton's Third Law of Motion

This law is often stated: "For every action (force) there is an equal and opposite reaction." This statement can be made so glibly that the profound implications are often missed. It is by no means an obvious law, and it awaited the insight of Newton for its clear establishment. Forces must always occur in pairs, never singly. However, *these pairs do not act on the same body;* rather the applied force acts on the receiving body, and the reaction force acts on the applying body. Therefore, we cannot vectorially add action and reaction forces because they do not act on the same body.

A book resting on a table exerts a downward force on the table top, and the third law declares that the table top must exert an equal and opposite (upward) force on the book. If you lean against a lamppost, exerting a lateral force on it, the lamppost is also "leaning" against you, exerting the same lateral force though oppositely directed. The shoes of a man walking push backward against the floor, and the reaction to this force pushes the man forward. In this case it is the force of friction between the shoes and the floor which allows the man to push backwards on the floor. If he were on a sheet of "ultra" ice that was completely frictionless he would be unable to press back against the ice, and thus be unable to move himself forward. A wise man caught in such an impossible situation (we carefully overlook the question of how he found himself at rest on the ice) would start hurling the contents of his pockets, for each forward force his arm gave to a mass there must be a reaction force on the body; each reaction force accelerates his motion and he travels over the frictionless ice by primitive jet propulsion. It is evident that a frictionless world would be a hazardous place indeed.

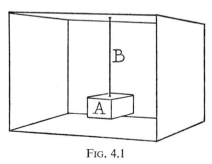

FIG. 4.1

4.6   Isolation of a System

We have used the word *system* frequently; by it we mean those physical bodies to which our attention is directed. Quite evidently the concept of a system is broad and flexible, and to make it meaningful we must always carefully state the limits of the system. This process of limiting our attention is called *isolating* the system. To illustrate, consider the situation of Fig. 4.1 in which a mass A is suspended from the ceiling of a room by a string B. We now ask what forces are acting? To make this question sensible we must rephrase it to read: in a certain system (yet to be specified) what forces are acting? Suppose we choose just the mass A as the system in question and isolate it by ignoring all forces *not* acting on A. Then the answer would be that there are two forces acting on this system, the weight (force of gravity) downward and the upward pull of the string on A; if we assume the mass is at rest, that is, the system is in equilibrium, these two forces are equal and opposite, their sum zero.

Suppose we now enlarge the system to include the mass A and the string B. The forces now acting include the gravitational force on A, the upward tension of the string on A, the third law reaction to this on B and finally the upward force of the ceiling on B. (We neglect the gravitational force on the string itself.) Quite evidently, if we continue to enlarge the system we will have to include the downward force on the ceiling, the support of the ceiling by the sidewalls which in turn are supported by the floor, which itself is supported by the earth, etc. If we consider the entire earth as our system we must then include its gravitational attraction to the sun, the effect of the moon, etc. The entire universe is the only ultimately isolated system. However, only the cosmologist makes this ultimate isolation; our efforts to analyze a problem often become simpler the more narrow our limits of isolation.

4.7   An Interpretation of the Meaning of Mass

While there exists no independent definition of mass and force, Ernst Mach at the end of the nineteenth century showed how to interpret mass in terms of the laws of motion. Neither Newton nor the early contributors to dynamics conceived of mass in the modern manner. They spoke of it as the quantity of matter in a body, a concept which is circuitous because we can no more readily define matter than mass. Mach interpreted mass in terms of the interaction of two particles and the third law of motion.

In a somewhat abridged form his argument goes like this. Consider two interacting particles A and B (see Fig. 4.2). Regardless of how they make

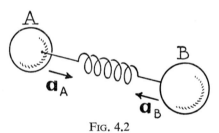

FIG. 4.2

their influence felt on each other, for example, by a connecting spring or electrical attraction, it is found experimentally that the magnitudes of the accelerations of A and B are in constant ratio, and the directions of the accelerations are exactly opposite. The ratio of the magnitude of the acceleration of A to that of B is taken to be equal to the ratio of the *mass* of B to that of A, That is,

$$a_A/a_B = m_B/m_A$$

or

$$a_A m_A = a_B m_B$$

which is just a formula for the third law of motion, where force has been defined by the second law. To complete the description of mass it is necessary to let A and B interact one at a time with a particle of unit mass $m_U = 1$. Then

$$\frac{a_A}{a_U} = \frac{m_U}{m_A} = \frac{1}{m_A}$$

That is,

$$m_A = \frac{a_U}{a_A}$$

and similarly

$$m_B = \frac{a_U}{a_B}$$

In this view the mass of a body is the ratio of the acceleration of a standard body to that of the body in question when the two are allowed to interact. This may seem incomplete and unsatisfactory and it may be argued that mass has a more fundamental nature than simply a measure of a body's relative acceleration. However, when we seek to find this mystical property we fail. Only a measurement can disclose the mass of a body, and all mass measurements involve an interaction of the type employed above.

4.8   Illustrations of the Laws of Motion

In a sense, a great deal of the remainder of this book will illustrate the interpretation and the application of Newton's laws. Often their use may become obscured by the complexity of the problem, but even more often they pass unnoticed because of our readiness to take them for granted. In any case, their simplicity of statement induces a deceptive feeling of understanding that may be dispelled by some of the following examples.

Example 1.   To a 50-gm body at rest on a frictionless horizontal table is applied a force of 1000 dynes. What is the resulting acceleration?
GIVEN: $m = 50$ gm; $F = 1000$ dynes
$a = ?$
Solution: Since the table is frictionless and horizontal, there are no frictional or gravitational forces; hence the entire applied force produces acceleration. Thus
$$F = ma$$
$$1000 = 50 \times a$$
$$a = 20 \text{ cm/sec}^2 \quad Ans.$$

Example 2.   Suppose the problem in Example 1 is changed to admit a frictional force of 200 dynes. What is the acceleration?

GIVEN: m = 50 gm; F = 1000 dynes
         f = frictional force = 200 dynes
         a = ?

Solution: There now exists an opposing force of 200 dynes; if the applied force had been 200 dynes or less there would have been no acceleration. The unbalanced force available for acceleration is $1000 - 200 = 800$ dynes. Therefore

$$F = ma$$
$$800 = 50 \times a$$
$$a = 16 \text{ cm/sec}^2 \quad Ans.$$

Example 3.   An ice skater mass 50 kg (kilograms) starts coasting with an initial velocity of 200 cm/sec; the frictional force of his skates and the ice is 1,000,000 dynes. How far does he coast?

GIVEN: m = 50 kg = 50,000 gm; v_0 = 200 cm/sec
         v = 0; frictional force = 1,000,000 dynes
         s = ?

Solution: In this case the applied force is completely one of friction and serves to decelerate the skater.

Second law: $F = ma$; $-1,000,000 = 50,000 \times a$
              $a = -20 \text{ cm/sec}^2$
Eq. 3.3: $v^2 = v_0^2 + 2as = 0$
              $0 = (200)^2 - 2 \times 20 \times s$
              $s = 1000 \text{ cm} \quad Ans.$

Example 4.   A problem often posed (Fig. 4.3) to test the understanding of the third law is the following: A tractor is dragging a log at constant speed along a horizontal path; a spring balance placed in the dragging chain shows that the tractor is pulling forward with a force of 10^8 dynes. With what force is the log pulling back on the tractor? The answer comes promptly from anyone who has just read Newton's third law: 10^8 dynes. Then if the tractor pulls forward with a force of 10^8 dynes and is pulled back by the log with the same force, why does the tractor move? It is hoped that this question constitutes no paradox for the reader of this chapter. The tractor exerts a force on the *log,* the log exerts a force on the *tractor;* we cannot add them for they act on different bodies (one is the reaction of the other).

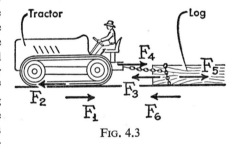

FIG. 4.3

This problem merits careful analysis. Figure 4.3 shows the system which includes the tractor, the log, and the earth. The tractor pushes along the earth's surface with a force F_1, and the reaction to this is the forward force F_2 on the tractor. The forward pull on the log by the chain is F_3 and the reaction force on the tractor is F_4.

Hence the total force on the tractor is $F_2 + F_4 = 0$. (The tractor is not accelerating.) Next consider the log. The force of friction between the log and the path is F_5 acting on the log; the reaction to F_5 is F_6 acting on the earth. (The log is trying to pull the earth along with it.) The total force on the log is $F_3 + F_5 = 0$. (The log is not accelerating.) Finally, what force acts on the earth? It is $F_1 + F_6 = 0$. (The tractor-log combination is not causing the earth to accelerate.) We have accounted for all the forces.

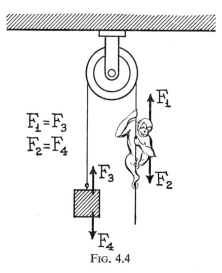

$$F_1 = F_3$$
$$F_2 = F_4$$

FIG. 4.4

Example 5. Another illustration of Newton's laws of motion is the monkey and rope problem (Fig. 4.4). A rope running through a frictionless pulley supports a clinging monkey on one side, and hanging on the other side is a weight that just balances the monkey. The monkey now decides to climb the rope. What is the motion of the weight? A great deal of argumentative heat can be engendered by this problem, but the application of the second and third laws will settle the question at once. When the monkey is at rest the rope must be exerting a force upward F_1, just equaling his weight F_2. To accelerate himself, as he must do to start moving, the monkey must exert an additional downward pull on the rope (second law), and the rope must react to this new force (third law). The pulley plays no role except to reverse the direction of the rope; hence the increased tension in the rope must be an increased force F_3 on the weight (third law), and this can only result in an upward acceleration of the weight (second law). So the weight rises at just the same rate as the monkey. Their motions are identical.

4.9   Inductive and Deductive Reasoning

Chapter 3, which discussed the relations of the space variables, distance, time, velocity, and acceleration, should logically follow the present chapter, which has been concerned with the fundamental relations between acceleration, mass, and force. We have looked at the characteristics of motion before we asked what the fundamental requirements were for the existence of this motion. Put differently, Chapter 3 constructs a theory relating certain space variables before we know whether the theory has any application to the motions actually observed in nature. This violation of logical sequence (and historical sequence, too) was done for two reasons: first, it is best to have a clear concept of acceleration to appreciate Newton's laws; second, this sequence of presentation can be used to illustrate two methods of reasoning, *deduction* and *induction*. The complete ramifications of these two divisions of logic are far too extensive for a thorough treatment here. Since, however, they play such a significant role in the methods of science, it is necessary to consider them, even if in a brief and oversimplified manner.

In reasoning by *deduction* in science one starts with a set of assumptions or premises and employs the rules of logic (or mathematics) to draw conclusions from these assumptions. By the nature of logic the conclusions are always consistent with the assumptions. However, the conclusions may or may not be consistent with reality in the physical world. Only if the assumptions are consistent with reality can we guarantee that the conclusions are similarly consistent.

In a physical theory the deductive method is followed to certain conclusions which can be tested for consistency with physical reality. However, there is no deductive method for establishing the assumptions of the theory. Thus in Chapter 3 a deductive system was constructed for the science of motion. We established a set of assumptions based on the definitions of velocity and acceleration and we assumed a form of logic—scalar and vector algebra—for the manipulation of these assumptions. The results were the formulae relating the displacement, velocity, acceleration, and time for uniformly accelerated motion. As we shall see, such motion is common in nature, but we must remember that this is a tribute to the assumptions of the theory.

In science such deductive reasoning constitutes little more than a logical exercise unless we can answer satisfactorily one question: do the assumptions made apply to any motion actually observed in nature? Stating this differently, if what happens does not agree with the assumptions used in the deduction of conclusions, then our reasoning effort remains only a study in logic without physical significance. Without a doubt this must seem markedly obvious to the student, yet for two thousand years (roughly 500 B.C. to A.D. 1500) the investigation of what actually happened in physical phenomena was considered of secondary importance and neglected by the most influential thinkers in that era. Though this pattern of scientific reasoning was not without challengers it was not until the sixteenth century that Galileo made a successful attack upon it by employing experimental observations to establish his assumptions. Galileo is often called the father of experimental science, not because he was the first to conduct experiments, but because he was the first to insist on obtaining measurements on which to formulate generalizations and had the genius to perceive those measurements which had great significance. The conclusions reached in Chapter 3 were first found experimentally by Galileo, not deductively as we have presented them.

The method of arriving at generalizations of natural behavior by starting from observation is called *induction*. Since one never observes all phenomena in a class, intuition plays a large part in this process. There is, therefore, no rule which can be followed in the inductive method. For this reason there are no simple rules in the methods of science, for induction forms a great part of scientific endeavor. This is not to say that past experience plays no part in inductive reasoning. Only the experienced experimenter can generalize his results to valid laws. The theorist likewise calls on tradition and experience in forming his assumptions. However, neither can chart in advance the way in which to proceed from observation to valid generalizations.

We thus can characterize the methods of science as a combination of inductive and deductive processes. One without the other is not complete. Pure deduction gives no assurance that the assumptions are correct or even relevant to the natural world, so that the conclusions are unlikely to be of physical value. However, deductive methods founded on valid generalizations from observation are used in much of physical theory. Together, the two methods are very powerful.

PROBLEMS

1. What force is needed to give a kilogram mass an acceleration of 40 cm/sec²?
Ans.   40,000 dynes or 40 kilodynes.

2. A force of 500 dynes is applied to a 10-gm mass over a distance of 225 cm. If the mass started from rest what is its acceleration and how long a time is required to travel the 225 cm? *Ans.*   50 cm/sec²; 3 sec.

3. A force of 2000 dynes is applied to a 100-gm mass for 10 sec. If the mass started from rest what is its velocity after 40 sec? *Ans.*   200 cm/sec.

4. It is found that a certain body, initially at rest, reached a speed of 60 cm/sec after moving 2 m. If the applied force is 1 megadyne, what is the mass of the body?
Ans.   111 kg.

5. A 500-gm book is slid across a horizontal table top with an initial velocity of 200 cm/sec; it comes to rest in 4 sec. What is the force of friction between the book and table? *Ans.*   25 kilodynes.

6. A 700-gm mass is whirling in a horizontal plane and attached to a rope 50 cm long. If it makes 10 rev/sec, what is the centripetal force on the mass?
Ans.   138 megadynes.

Suggested Reading

"A Treasury of Science," New York, Harper & Brothers, 1946.
Reprints parts of Newton's "Principia Mathematica" which treats the laws of motion.

DAMPIER, SIR WILLIAM, "A History of Science," New York, The Macmillan Co., 1946.

Chapter IV includes a historical and critical account of Newtonian dynamics.

JEANS, SIR JAMES, "The Growth of Physical Science," New York, The Macmillan Co., 1948.

Chapters V and VI give a lucid account of the development of Newtonian dynamics.

MACH, E., "The Science of Mechanics," LaSalle, Ill., Open Court Publishing Co., 1942 (translation).

Chapter II gives an authoritative historical and logical account of Newton's achievements and Mach's mass interpretation.

MAGIE, W. F., "Source Book in Physics," New York, McGraw-Hill Book Co., 1935.

Pages 30–45 reproduce excerpts from Newton's original works in dynamics.

Particle Dynamics — Gravitation

5.1 Newton's Law of Gravitation

In the year 1663 a plague which descended on England forced Newton to leave his studies at Cambridge University and to return to his family home. There he remained for two amazingly productive years during which he discovered the binomial theorem in mathematics, invented differential and integral calculus, produced a correct theory of colors, and laid the groundwork for his theory of gravitation. All this before he was 24 years old!

It was Newton's conviction that the cause for a body falling to the surface of the earth was identical with the reason for the earth and other planets adhering to nearly circular paths about the sun, or for the moon's motion about the earth. There existed a force of attraction between the sun and the earth that held the latter in its orbit; and this same kind of force caused a mass to fall to the surface of the earth. The idea of a "gravitational" force between masses had been suggested tentatively before Newton's time, but he proposed a form of the law that correlated astronomical measurements and terrestrial observations. From a simple geometrical argument employing as data the period of the moon about the earth, the radius of the moon's orbit and the radius of the earth, Newton concluded that the nature of the gravitational force could be generalized in the following statement:

There exists a force of attraction between all pairs of particles in the universe. This force is directed along the line joining the particles and has a magnitude that is proportional to the product of the masses of the particles and inversely proportional to the square of their distance apart.

In symbols this may be written

$$F = G \frac{m_1 m_2}{s^2} \qquad [5.1]$$

where m_1 and m_2 are the masses of the two particles separated by a distance s

(Fig. 5.1). G is a proportionality constant whose role is to give F the proper units, once m_1, m_2, and s have been assigned units. Later experiments (§5.7) have shown G to have the value

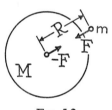

FIG. 5.1

$$G = 6.670 \times 10^{-8} \text{ cm}^3/\text{gm-sec}^2$$

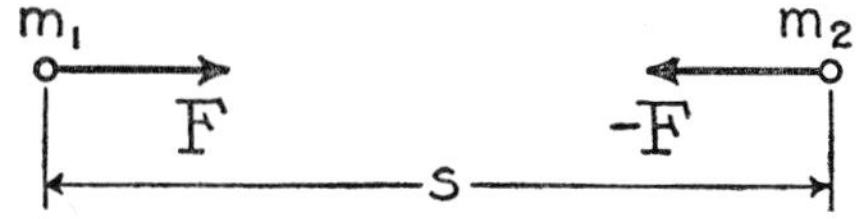

Using Kepler's data for the orbits of the planets about the sun Newton proved that the law of force was of the form of Eq. 5.1 for these cases, too.

5.2 Center of Gravity

The publication of the law of gravitation was held up by Newton for twenty years. One possible cause for this caution lay in the following question: Because of their great separations astronomical bodies can be treated as mass points to a good approximation; but will the same law apply to two masses such as the earth and any relatively small body (Fig. 5.2) falling to the surface of the earth? Employing his newly invented calculus, Newton arrived at the following conclusion: every rigid body possesses a point, called its *center of gravity*, at which all the mass can be considered to be concentrated. It is only necessary to measure the distance between the centers of gravity of the masses in order to apply the gravitational law. Furthermore, because of the complete symmetry of a homogeneous sphere, its center of gravity is located at its geometrical center. For other geometrical shapes the position of the center of gravity can be calculated with the aid of calculus.

FIG. 5.2

5.3 Gravitation on the Earth

A particle on or near the surface of the earth is attracted by all the particles making up the mass of the earth. Since the earth is approximately spherical, the resultant force on the particle is directed toward the center of the earth, and the magnitude of the force of attraction is given by Eq. 5.1, where the distance s is now the radius of the earth. (The earth's radius is some 21,000,000 ft; a few feet above the earth will add a negligible amount to this.) Since almost all terrestrial bodies are small enough to be considered as particles in comparison with the earth, the resultant gravitational force acting on the body is directed toward the center of the earth and of magnitude:

$$F = G \frac{Mm}{R^2} = \left(G \frac{M}{R^2} \right) m \qquad\qquad [\,5.2\,]$$

where M is the mass of the earth, m that of the terrestrial body, and R the radius of the earth. The mass of the body is considered as concentrated at its center of gravity. The factor in parentheses is constant over the surface of the earth, if we assume the earth to be a perfect sphere. Remembering that by Newton's second law of motion any force must be of the form of a mass times an acceleration, we see that (GM/R^2) has the units of an acceleration. It is called the *acceleration due to gravity* on the earth's surface, and a special symbol, g, is given to it. Its magnitude is given by

$$g = G \frac{M}{R^2} \qquad\qquad [\,5.3\,]$$

(Do not confuse g, the acceleration with which all bodies on the earth fall freely, with G, a proportionality constant in the gravitation law.)

The *force of gravity* on a terrestrial body is the force of Eq. 5.2. Neglecting the buoyancy of the atmosphere in which we live, we can conclude that the force of gravity is directly proportional to the body's mass, and the acceleration of gravity (Eq. 5.3) is independent of the mass of the falling body to a good approximation, since the radius R varies very little even at high altitudes. The force of gravity on any body is called the *weight* of the body. The weight, w, is thus given by

$$w = mg \qquad\qquad [\,5.4\,]$$

as is seen by combining Eq. 5.2 and 5.3. The weight of a body accelerates it toward the center of the earth—a vertical acceleration—unless some other force of non-gravitational nature is present and counterbalances it. Bodies of themselves always fall to the earth. Non-gravitational mechanisms which check this fall are frequently supplied by rigid supports such as tables and chairs. The counterbalancing force is the force of tension or compression in the supports. An ever present force which modifies falling is the frictional resistance of the air, which retards the fall and makes the actual acceleration less than g.

We may think of the force of gravity for terrestrial bodies in a slightly different way which illustrates the third law of motion. The attractive force on the body has a reaction force which operates on the mass of the earth at the earth's center. When a body falls there is an acceleration of the earth toward the body as well as the downward acceleration of the body. The interposition of a support for the body is just a mechanism for keeping these two attracting masses apart. Of course, in actuality the great difference between the masses of the earth and that of any falling body makes the acceleration of the earth negligibly small as compared with g.

5.4 Free-Fall Motion

At best it is difficult to measure directly the rapid acceleration of a freely falling body; air friction must be removed as nearly completely as possible, and quite precise timing devices must be employed. A far simpler and more accurate method employs a pendulum whose length and period can be determined with good precision (this method is discussed briefly in §10.2). The result, to a sufficient accuracy here, is

$$g = 980 \text{ cm/sec}^2$$

This value is somewhat less at high altitudes because of the increase in distance from the center of the earth. There is also a variation with latitude in the value of g. This is due to several factors. Since the earth and all masses on it are rotating, these masses must have a centripetal acceleration; this acceleration is larger at the equator than at latitudes above and below the equator. The force to maintain this centripetal acceleration must be supplied by gravitational attraction, thus reducing the free-fall acceleration. On this account g will be least at the equator and greatest at the poles of the earth. There is a second cause which has a similar effect on the variation of g; the earth is slightly flattened at the two poles, making R smaller at the poles than at the equator; since R^2 is in the denominator of Eq. 5.3 then g will have its greatest value at the poles. Finally, there are small local effects due to the presence of irregular surface features such as oceans and mountains and underground concentrations of abnormally dense or light materials. The measured values of g at sea level vary from 977.99 cm/sec² at the equator to 983.21 cm/sec² at the north pole.

The equations of linear accelerated motion obtained in Chapter 3 apply directly to freely falling bodies, since those equations were derived on the assumption of uniform acceleration, and for small altitude and latitude variations the value of g is constant to a good approximation. Therefore the equations of free-fall motion become ($a = g$, $s = h$, the height)

$$v = v_0 + gt$$
$$h = v_0 t + \tfrac{1}{2}gt^2$$
$$v^2 = v_0^2 + 2gh$$

or for

$v_0 = 0$

$$v = gt$$
$$h = \tfrac{1}{2}gt^2$$
$$v^2 = 2gh$$

Observe that the mass m of a freely falling body does not enter into these equations:

Example 1. A baseball is dropped from the top of a 50-meter tower. If friction is neglected, how long a time is required to fall, and with what velocity does it hit the ground?

GIVEN: $h = 50$ m $= 5000$ cm; $a = g = 980$ cm/sec^2; $v_0 = 0$
          $t = ?; v = ?$

Solution: $h = \tfrac{1}{2}gt^2$

$$5000 = \tfrac{1}{2} \times 980 \times t^2, \ t^2 = \frac{10,000}{980}$$

$$t = 3.2 \text{ sec} \quad Ans.$$
$$v = gt = 980 \times 3.2$$
$$= 3100 \text{ cm/sec} = 31 \text{ m/sec} \quad Ans.$$

or

$$v^2 = 2gh = 2 \times 980 \times 5000$$
$$v = 3100 \text{ cm/sec as before.}$$

Example 2. A baseball is thrown vertically upward with an initial velocity of 10 m/sec. How high will it rise? What time is required to reach its maximum height?

GIVEN: $v_0 = 10$ m/sec $= 1000$ cm/sec; $v = 0$ (at the top)
         $a = -g = -980$ cm/sec^2 (the motion is one of deceleration);
         $h = ?; t = ?$

Solution: $v^2 = v_0^2 + 2gh$
           $0 = (1000)^2 - 2 \times 980 \times h$
           $h = 511$ cm   Ans.
           $v = v_0 + gt$
           $0 = 1000 - 980 \times t$
           $t = 1.02$ sec   Ans.

It should be evident that the fall of the ball will be identical with its rise; in the analysis the only differences are: $v_0 = 0$, $a = +g$ for the fall; if it falls the same height it rose, its final velocity will be the same as its initial velocity, and its time of flight down will equal its time of rise.

5.5   The Inclined Plane

One of the major triumphs of Galileo's experimentation was to show that the acceleration due to gravity was constant. Lacking adequate timing

mechanisms to make a direct observation he used a device—the inclined plane
—to slow down the acceleration due to gravity. He succeeded in demonstrating
that if the plane could be treated as frictionless then the velocity a body possessed after sliding down the plane depended only on the height of the plane
and was independent of its length (Fig. 5.3). This is by no means intuitively
obvious. Let us analyze it. Consid-
er the ideal particle and frictionless plane of Fig. 5.4. The particle
is attracted to the earth by a force
of $F = mg$. This force produces an
acceleration of the particle down
the plane. Since the particle is constrained to slide along the plane,

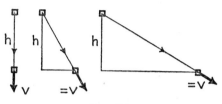

FIG. 5.3

only the component of the force which is along the plane is available for this
acceleration. It is labeled F_1 in Fig. 5.4. Evidently from Newton's second law
$F_1 = ma$, where a is the acceleration down the plane. The other component of
F is perpendicular to the inclined plane and is balanced at all times by a compressional force in the plane. The
force triangle and the inclined plane
triangle are similar (two sides mu-
tually perpendicular, remaining
sides parallel); hence

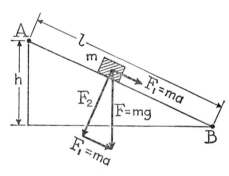

FIG. 5.4

$$\frac{F_1}{F} = \frac{h}{l} = \frac{ma}{mg}$$

or

$$a = \frac{h}{l} g$$

That is, the acceleration along the
plane is a uniform acceleration, and is the fraction h/l of the acceleration of
gravity—the acceleration of free fall.

Since the acceleration along the plane is now shown to be uniform we may
write the instantaneous velocity of the particle, using Eq. 3.6:

$$v^2 = 2as$$

where s is the distance the particle has moved from its rest point A along the
plane. Upon reaching the foot of the inclined plane the particle will have
attained a velocity

$$v^2 = 2al$$

But

$$a = \frac{h}{l} g$$

SO

$$v^2 = 2\frac{h}{l}gl = 2gh \qquad\qquad [5.5]$$

Now if the particle had been *dropped* from A it would have freely fallen with an acceleration g through a distance h. Its final velocity would then be

$$v^2 = 2gh$$

Thus, the particle's velocity along the plane is the same as the vertical velocity of a particle which has fallen freely from rest through the same vertical distance.

5.6 Weight Units versus Force Units

By definition, the cgs unit of force is a dyne. Thus, the force of gravity on a one gram mass is 980 dynes ($F = ma$ and $a = g = 980$ cm/sec²). Unfortunately, there exists a derived unit of force which is more commonly used outside of physics; it is unfortunate because the name of the derived unit is identical with the name of the cgs unit of mass. Thus, we speak, illogically, of a force of 100 gm; this force may be due to a coiled spring or to a gas under pressure or to many other non-gravitational forces. Yet by a force of 100 gm is meant a force equal to the gravitational attraction on a 100-gm mass, that is, 100×980 dynes. The custom arose from the practice of comparing all forces to their equivalent gravitational forces. Confusion should not arise if the following is remembered:

The gram is a unit of mass; when used as a force unit it must be multiplied by the acceleration due to gravity to obtain the cgs unit of force.

This statement is valid regardless of the nature of the force; we multiply by g and its unit to obtain the *unit* of force.

Example 1. To a body weighing 1 kg is applied a horizontal force of 250 gm; if the body is free to move on a horizontal, frictionless plane what will its acceleration be?

   GIVEN: Applied force $F = 250$ gm; weight of body $w = 1$ kg $= 1000$ gm.
       $a = ?$

   Solution: Newton's second law: $F = ma$. The applied force F is 250 gm, by which is meant a force equal to the gravitational attraction on a 250-gm mass. Hence this force is $250 \times 980 = 245{,}000$ dynes. The mass that is being accelerated is 1000

gm (remember that 1000 gm of weight is the gravitational force on 1000 gm of mass).
So

$$245,000 = 1000 \times a$$
$$a = 245 \text{ cm/sec}^2 \quad Ans.$$

Example 2.   A kilogram weight lying on a horizontal frictionless table is attached by a string running over a pulley to a 200-gm weight hanging on the other end of the string (Fig. 5.5). What is the acceleration of the 1-kg weight?

GIVEN: $m_1 = 1 \text{ kg} = 1000 \text{ gm}$; $m_2 = 200 \text{ gm}$
                $a = ?$

Solution: The applied force which is causing acceleration is the 200-gm weight. Hence $F = 200 \times 980$ dynes. The mass that is being accelerated includes *both* weights, since they must move together. So

$$m = m_1 + m_2 = 1000 + 200 = 1200 \text{ gm}$$
$$F = ma; \text{ or } 200 \times 980 = 1200 \times a$$
$$a = 163 \text{ cm/sec}^2 \quad Ans.$$

This is the acceleration of both weights, since they move together.

A 1-gm mass weighs 1 gm on the earth's surface, that is, there is a gravitational force of $F = mg = 980$ dynes on it. Remembering that a gram mass is about two one-thousandths of a pound (454 gm = 1 lb) we recognize that a *dyne* is a very small force indeed. Roughly, it is about the force which must be exerted to support a postage stamp! Ordinary forces that we encounter are measured in millions of dynes— megadynes.

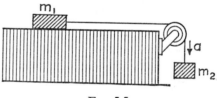

Fig. 5.5

Finally, we should note that the *mass* of a body is independent of gravitational attraction, but its *weight* depends directly on the value of g. Hence, a 100-gm mass will always be a 100-gm mass whether at the equator, the poles, or on a high mountain. Its weight will vary with these positions, though, and a coiled spring used to suspend the 100-gm mass would be extended by an amount varying with g.

5.7   The Cavendish Experiment for the Determination of G

There is no straightforward way of measuring the gravitational constant G which occurs in Newton's law of gravity (Eq. 5.1) unless the earth's mass is known (see Eq. 5.3). There is no direct way to measure this mass, and so another method has to be used in finding the value of this important constant.

Cavendish in 1798 reported an experiment which showed directly the gravitational attraction of bodies and measured the value of the constant G.

His experimental arrangement is shown in Fig. 5.6. The masses m were small lead balls, fixed on a light wooden beam L which was hung by a wire from a solid support. When the large masses M were swung into the position shown

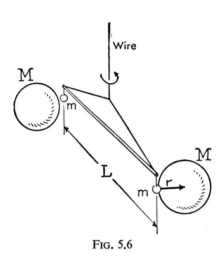

in Fig. 5.6, the wire was twisted by the gravitational attraction of each small ball for the large ball nearby. The amount of twist was noted and was transferred into a value for the force causing the twist by an auxiliary experiment which calibrated the wire. This was done by causing the masses m and their supporting beam to oscillate in a horizontal plane and noting the rate of the oscillation. This rate is related to the force required for a certain angle of twist of the wire. The observed attractive forces between each pair of masses were then equated to GmM/r^2 and G was computed since m,

FIG. 5.6

M, and r were known. The Cavendish values of G were not very accurate, since the forces between the attracting balls were extremely small and hard to measure. Modern measurements using refined techniques, give a value of G of

$$G = 6.670 \times 10^{-8} \text{ cm}^3/\text{gm-sec}^2$$

Notice that when this value is substituted into Eq. 5.3

$$g = G \frac{M}{R^2}$$

where g = 980 cm/sec², R = radius of earth = 6.37×10^8 cm, that the mass of the earth may be found. It is

$$M = \frac{R^2g}{G} = \frac{(6.37 \times 10^8)^2 \times 980}{6.67 \times 10^{-8}}$$
$$= 5.96 \times 10^{27} \text{ gm}$$

or about 6×10^{21} tons. This might be said to be a direct measurement of the mass of the earth. It is essentially a measurement of the acceleration of the earth $a = (m/M)g$ produced by a known force $F = G (Mm/R^2)$, and the deduction of the earth's mass from the second law of motion.

The average density (mass divided by volume) of the earth from the above calculation is

$$\frac{M}{\frac{4}{3}\pi R^3} = 5.5 \text{ gm/cm}^3$$

This average density is somewhat greater than that of samples gathered from the surface of the earth and shows that the earth possesses a core of dense material.

5.8 Compounded Motion—The Projectile

The path, or "trajectory," of a particle projected with an initial velocity forward and upward, after which the particle is subject only to the force of gravity, is the result of compounding two motions. Galileo was the first to

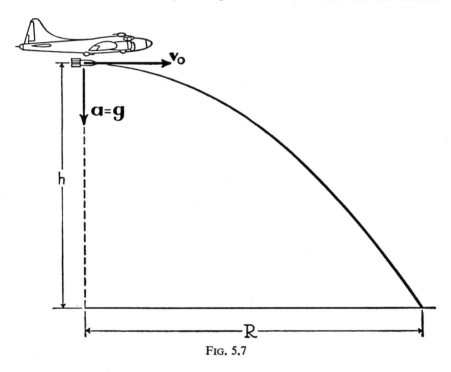

FIG. 5.7

understand fully this somewhat complicated motion, a proof of his clear comprehension of the laws of falling bodies.

The actual motion of projectiles such as bullets and gun shells is greatly complicated by the presence of the atmosphere, the rotation of the earth, and other factors. We shall assume these factors to be negligible, and further to simplify the approach we shall treat only the case of *horizontal* initial velocity.

This problem is illustrated by the motion of a bomb released from a airplane flying on a horizontal course (Fig. 5.7). The result usually desired is the range, R, which is the distance traveled forward, measured along the horizontal. That two motions are involved is clear at once: the forward motion due to the initial velocity, v_0, continues uniformly (neglecting air resistance), and is compounded with the falling motion due to the force of gravity. The *time* the bomb spends in the air is just the time to fall vertically through the height, h. This time is found from the equations of free fall motion (§5.4). Here v_0 is zero (there is no initial *vertical* velocity), so

$$h = \tfrac{1}{2}gt^2$$

or

$$t = \sqrt{2h/g}$$

During this time the bomb is moving forward with a uniform horizontal velocity, v_0. The distance, R, it travels in time t is

$$R = v_0 t$$

Substituting the value for t:

$$R = v_0 \sqrt{2h/g}$$

Example. An airplane flying horizontally with a speed of 240 mi/hr (385 km/hr or 107 m/sec) releases a bomb from a height of 1000 m. How long will the bomb spend in the air and what is its horizontal range?

GIVEN: $v_0 = 107$ m/sec $= 10700$ cm/sec
              $h = 1000\ m = 100,000$ cm;
              $t = ?\ R = ?$

Solution: Neglecting air friction (a rather serious neglect in this case), then
$$h = \tfrac{1}{2}gt^2 \quad \text{or} \quad 100,000 = \tfrac{1}{2} \times 980 \times t^2$$
$$t^2 = 204$$
$$t = 14.3 \text{ sec}$$

During this time it is moving forward with a speed of 107 m/sec; hence
$$R = v_0 t$$
$$= 10,700 \times 14.3$$
$$= 153,000 \text{ cm} = 1530 \text{ meters} \qquad Ans.$$

Observe, that as long as we neglect air friction, the range is independent of mass—a heavy bomb would have the same trajectory as a light bomb.

PROBLEMS

1. Calculate the gravitational force between two kilogram masses whose centers are 10 cm apart.   *Ans.*   0.00067 dynes.

2. The mass of the moon is approximately 7.5×10^{25} gm, its radius is 1.7×10^8 cm. How much would you weigh on the moon?
                                    Ans.   About one-sixth your earth weight.

3. A body weighs 1 kg. What is the gravitational force on it?

Ans. 0.98 megadynes.

4. What force is necessary to give a kilogram mass which lies on a horizontal frictionless table an acceleration of 50 cm/sec²? *Ans.* 50 kilodynes.

5. How long will it take a body starting from rest to slide down a frictionless inclined plane that is 2 m long and 5 cm high? *Ans.* 4 sec.

6. A 200-gm mass lying on a horizontal frictionless table is attached by a string running over a pulley to a 200-gm mass hanging on the other end of the string. What is the acceleration of the system? *Ans.* 490 cm/sec².

7. Over a frictionless pulley attached to a ceiling is looped a string; on one end of the string is a 500-gm mass, on the other a 700-gm mass. What is the acceleration of either mass when the pulley is allowed to rotate? *Ans.* 163 cm/sec².

8. A man enters an elevator and steps on spring scales; he observes a reading of 80 kg. The elevator now accelerates uniformly upward 100 cm/sec², while the man remains on the scales. What is the reading of the scales during this acceleration? If on the return trip the downward acceleration is also 100 cm/sec², what will the scales read? *Ans.* 88 kg; 72 kg.

9. A 500-gm mass is whirled at the end of a 10-cm string in a vertical plane; if it makes 2 rev/sec, find the maximum and minimum forces on the string.

Ans. 1.28 and 0.30 megadynes.

10. A golf ball is driven horizontally over the edge of a 100-m cliff; the initial velocity is 20 m/sec. How long is the ball in the air, and how far from the base of the cliff does the ball land (neglecting air friction)? *Ans.* 4.5 sec; 90 m.

Suggested Reading

GALILEO, "Two New Sciences," New York, The Macmillan Co., 1914.
Page 181 gives Galileo's original views on projectile motion.

MAGIE, W. F., "Source Book in Physics," New York, McGraw-Hill Book Co., 1935.
Pages 105–10 are an excerpt from Cavendish's original paper on the measurement of the gravitational constant.

MOTT-SMITH, M., "This Mechanical World," New York, D. Appleton and Co., 1931.
Chapters XIII and XV discuss the law of gravity and the distinction between mass and weight.

SHAPLEY, H., and HOWARTH, H. E., "A Source Book in Astronomy," New York, McGraw-Hill Book Co., 1939.
Page 77 gives excerpts from Newton's "Principia" concerning gravitation.

SHAPLEY, H., WRIGHT, H., RAPPORT, S., "Readings in the Physical Sciences," New York, Appleton-Century-Crofts, Inc., 1948.
Pages 161–65 present a popular account of modern measurements of the gravitational constant (weighing the earth).

Work and the Conservation of Energy

6.1   An Argument on "Quantity of Motion"

Toward the end of the seventeenth century a famous dispute arose among scientists. What quantity would best measure how much "motion" a moving body had? Today, we would probably look askance at this question, feeling that it was imprecise and required first a definition of motion. Yet the argument contributed signs of a dawning comprehension of a principle which, more than any other, pervades all physics—the principle of the conservation of energy.

To Newton the term "quantity of motion" meant the product of the mass and the velocity of the body. Descartes likewise subscribed to this view and was its most active proponent. The crux of Descartes' argument was this: Two bodies had the same amount of motion if equal forces acted upon them for equal times. With this proposition granted, he could easily show that mass times the velocity for each body was a measure of the force acting. For, suppose we have two different forces, each acting for the same time interval. Then

$$\frac{F_1}{F_2} = \frac{m_1 a_1}{m_2 a_2} = \frac{m_1 a_1 t}{m_2 a_2 t} = \frac{m_1 v_1}{m_2 v_2}$$

and mv would thus be a measure of the force, and equally a measure of the quantity of motion, according to Descartes.

The most vocal opponent of this view was Leibnitz in Germany. He observed that it requires the same effort (he called it "force") to lift a 1-kg weight through a height of 4 meters as it does to lift a 4-kg weight through 1 meter. If, in these two cases, the body is allowed to freely fall from its height, it is the *square* of the velocity that is proportional to the height ($v^2 = 2gh$); hence the effort to lift them must be measured by the product of the mass and the square of the velocity the body has upon falling; this should measure the "quantity of motion." It is difficult for us today to appreciate fully the intensity of this kind of controversy; it is revealed by the lengthy title of a two-page treatise emanating from the Leibnitz camp:

> "A short Demonstration of a Remarkable Error of Descartes & Others, Concerning the Natural Law by which they think the Creator always preserves the same Quantity of Motion; by which, however, the Science of Mechanics is totally perverted."

As so often happens, the confusion in this argument was one of terms; Descartes' use of mv as his measure of quantity of motion is correct for a force acting for a certain *time*; Leibnitz' insistence of mv^2 is correct for a force acting through a certain *distance*. Both quantities are exceedingly fruitful in dynamics. The first one we now call *momentum*, and it will be discussed in the next chapter. Leibnitz' quantity when multiplied by one-half is called *kinetic energy*. However, the full significance of these quantities was only appreciated 150 years later. It was not necessary for the science of dynamics to make a choice between these points of view; instead, dynamics incorporated both of them into its structure. This process began when it became evident that not only was force important in the analysis of motion, but even more significant was the cumulative effect of a force acting on a body in moving it through a distance and acting for a given time. The study of this cumulative effect gave a new insight into dynamics and supplied a simple method of solving many dynamical problems. This method involved an understanding of the relations between work and energy.

6.2 Work

Work is defined as the product of the displacement produced by a force acting on a particle and the component of the force parallel to this displacement, i.e., force × distance. In symbols, using W for work, s for displacement, and F_s for the component of F along s, it is

$$W = F_s \times s$$

It is important to note that it is only the component, F_s, of the force, along s that is used in the calculation of work. Of course, if a particle is not constrained in its motion, that is, if its motion results solely from the action of a single applied force, then the displacement produced will be along the force and the whole force contributes to the work done. If, however, the particle is constrained to move at some angle with respect to the applied force then the work is less than the product of the total force and the displacement since only the component F_s acts along the displacement.

Though it is not evident from its definition *work is a scalar quantity*. In

mowing a lawn it does not matter in what directions the swaths are cut by the
mower (if the lawn is flat); a 50-ft cut taken east-west requires the same work
as the same cut made north-south. However, though work has no direction,
it does have a sign—it can be either positive or negative. If the displacement s
is in the *same* direction as the force F_s on the body, the work is positive; if s is
in the *opposite* direction the work is *negative*. Thus to set a body in motion
positive work is done *on* the body, and F_s and s are in the same direction.
But to stop a moving body negative work is expended since now the force on
the body must oppose the motion. In this sense the force of friction always
works negatively on a body for it always opposes the direction of motion.

As a dictionary will verify, the word work is used with many connota-
tions; in physics, however, it has one and only one meaning. A man who holds
a 50-lb weight in one position for several hours would undoubtedly claim that
he was working, but in the physical sense he has done no work at all, because
there was no displacement of the weight. Muscular fatigue is not to be con-
fused with dynamic work.

Units.   The unit of work is found in the usual manner. In the cgs system it
is a dyne-centimeter (observe that this is a dyne times a centimeter, not a dyne
per centimeter); the unit dyne-cm is renamed an *erg*, and a frequently used
derived unit is 10,000,000 (10^7) ergs which is called a *joule*. Thus:

**One erg is the work done by a force of 1 dyne moving through a distance of
1 cm; one joule is 10^7 ergs.**

Example 1. How much work is required to lift a 10-kg mass to a height of 3 m?
GIVEN: Mass $= m = 10$ kg $= 10^4$ gm; $h = 3$ m $= 300$ cm
Solution: $W = F_s \times s$; here the force (weight) is parallel to the vertical dis-
tance h; hence

$$F_s = F = mg = 10^4 \times 980 \text{ dynes}$$
$$s = h = 300 \text{ cm}$$
$$W = 10^4 \times 980 \times 300$$
$$= 294 \times 10^7 \text{ ergs} = 294 \text{ joules} \quad Ans.$$

Example 2.   A force parallel to a frictionless inclined plane pushes a mass m up
the plane at a constant velocity. Find the work done in moving the mass from B
to A along the plane (Fig. 6.1).
GIVEN: $w = mg$; $s = l$
$W = ?$
Solution: The reason that work must be done is due to the fact that the
weight is being lifted against the force of gravity. Quite evidently the force due to the
weight is not parallel to the inclined plane, so it is necessary to obtain the component of $F = mg$ that is along the plane. This is F_1 in the figure. Since there is no

acceleration or friction, the applied force need be just enough to equal F_1, that is, $F_s = F_1$. So $W = F_s l$. But as we noted before with inclined planes, the force triangle and the triangle formed by the plane are similar. Therefore,

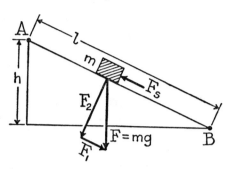

$$\frac{F_1}{mg} = \frac{h}{l}$$

or

$$F_s = F_1 = \frac{h}{l}mg$$

and

$$W = F_s l = \frac{h}{l}mgl$$

$$W = mgh \quad Ans.$$

That is, if there is no friction, the work to push the mass up the plane with uniform velocity is just the same

FIG. 6.1

as the work to lift it vertically at a uniform rate. It requires the same work to go from B to A by lifting vertically as it does by pushing along the plane; but the *force* required is *not* the same. Along the plane only a component of the weight, namely, $F_s = (h/l)mg$, need be exerted. The fact that the use of an inclined plane to lift an object requires less force than if the object were lifted vertically is expressed in the statement: The inclined plane has a mechanical advantage h/l.

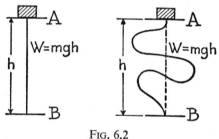

FIG. 6.2

The analysis of Example 2 permits us to generalize: Work done against gravity is dependent only on the vertical distance of the path, and the actual path is immaterial

(Fig. 6.2). This is seen by remembering that gravity is a vertical force so that the work is done against gravity only by the vertical component of the applied

force, and this component moves through a distance h. A circuitous route up a mountain side may be less fatiguing than a vertical climb, but it saves no work in the physical sense of the word.

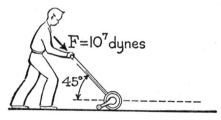

FIG. 6.3

Example 3. In mowing a lawn a man exerts a force along the direction of the handle of 10 million dynes (Fig. 6.3). If the angle of the handle is 45°, how much work does he do in mowing a 10-m strip?

GIVEN: $F = 10^7$ dynes; $\theta = 45°$; $s = 10^3$ cm
$\quad\quad\quad W = ?$

Solution: By the Pythagorean Theorem:

$$F_s = F/\sqrt{2} = \frac{10^7}{\sqrt{2}} \text{ dynes}$$

$$W = F_s \times s$$
$$= \frac{10^7 \times 10^3}{\sqrt{2}} \text{ ergs } = 707 \text{ joules} \quad\quad Ans.$$

Example 4. A 1000-kg automobile moving horizontally with a speed of 10 meters/sec is brought to rest in a distance of 20 meters by the application of a steady frictional force. What is the value of this force, and how much work was done on the car in bringing it to rest?

GIVEN: $m = 1000$ kg $= 10^6$ gm; $v_0 = 10$ m/sec $= 10^3$ cm/sec
$\quad\quad\quad v = 0; s = 20$ m $= 2 \times 10^3$ cm
$\quad\quad\quad F = ?; W = ?$

Solution: It is necessary to find the deceleration; Eq. 3.3:
$$v^2 = v_0^2 + 2as; 0 = (10^3)^2 + 2a \times 2 \times 10^3; a = -250 \text{ cm/sec}^2$$
then

$$F = ma = -10^6 \times 250 = -2.5 \times 10^8 \text{ dynes}$$
$$W = Fs$$
$$= -2.5 \times 10^8 \times 2 \times 10^3$$
$$= -5 \times 10^{11} \text{ergs} = -5 \times 10^4 \text{ joules} \quad\quad Ans.$$

6.3 Energy

If a weight is lifted from the floor to a table top, work is done on the weight in overcoming the gravitational attraction of the earth; but if the table is removed and the weight falls to the floor it can do work on any object in its path of fall. By lifting the weight we have given it a property which it had not possessed, namely, the ability to do work by virtue of its new position. To take another example, we know that to set a shuffleboard disk in motion requires work, and by virtue of this motion given to the disk it is now capable of doing work on anything in its path. The disk has been endowed with a capacity it otherwise had not possessed. It is necessary to investigate this capacity more carefully, for it is found to be of tremendous significance in nature. (It was the crux of the Descartes-Leibnitz argument.)

The name given to the capacity for doing work is *energy*. If energy is manifested by dynamical motion—either actual or possible—it is called *dynamical energy*. All the examples so far presented have been of dynamical energy. There are, however, many other forms of energy. We know that there is some property possessed by dynamite which will cause a violent expansion, an explosion. Such a property is found to be due to the molecular nature of dynamite and is called chemical energy. A metal rod when heated will expand and push on any structure that is constraining its expansion; this is thermal (heat) energy. We shall study means of annihilating mass with a consequent release of dynamical energy—a case of mass energy. A list of the kinds of energy is long for there are many evidences of the ability to do work.

6.4 Dynamical Energy—Potential and Kinetic

Our present task is to investigate in what ways we can endow a particle with energy, the energy to be revealed by the motion it can produce. The discussion in §6.3 gave two examples. The weight which was lifted through a height was given the ability to do work because of its new position. The ability to do work because of *position* is called *potential energy*. The particle potentially can do work even though it is not actually doing so. The amount of potential energy the body has is just the amount of work that had to be done to give it its new position. Thus

$$W = F_s \times s = mgh$$

So

$$\text{P.E.} = mgh$$

Since energy is the ability to do work, the units of energy must be just those of work itself, namely, the erg and joule.

The second example cited in §6.3 was the sliding shuffleboard disk, which could do work because it was moving. The ability to do work because of *motion* is *kinetic energy*. To calculate the amount of kinetic energy a body has due to its velocity v, we must calculate how much work was done on it to give it this velocity. Evidently, to set the body in motion a force was required to accelerate it. Hence if s is the distance the body has moved in acquiring its velocity, we have

$$W = F_s \times s = ma \times s$$

But (Eq. 3.6)

$$v^2 = 2as \quad \text{or} \quad as = \frac{v^2}{2}$$

So

$$W = m\left(\frac{v^2}{2}\right) = \tfrac{1}{2}mv^2$$

and therefore,

$$\text{K.E.} = \tfrac{1}{2}mv^2$$

(Except for the factor $\tfrac{1}{2}$, this is the expression Leibnitz advanced in the argument of §6.1.) It might be well at this point to check the units of K.E., even though we have declared they must be the same as those for work. Writing a units equation:

$$\text{Units of K.E.} = \text{gm (cm/sec)}^2 = \text{gm} \times \frac{\text{cm}}{\text{sec}^2} \times \text{cm}$$

$$= \text{dyne-cm} = \text{erg}$$

6.5   The Conservation of Dynamical Energy

To lift a mass m from B to A (Fig. 6.4) work must be done on the mass, this work appearing as potential energy of the body lifted. When the mass falls, it is now capable of doing work because of its kinetic energy. The question arises logically; do we get as much work back from the mass as we put into it? When m is in position A it has acquired potential energy, P.E. = mgh, and has no kinetic energy (it is at rest). Suppose m is released and we ask what dynamical energy it possesses.

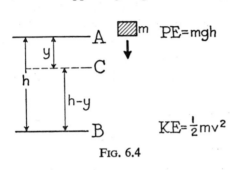

FIG. 6.4

Its potential energy has been reduced to $mg(h - y)$, but it now possesses kinetic energy. Its velocity at point C is due to the fact that the mass has moved through a distance y while being accelerated by the force of gravity:

Hence
$$v^2 = 2as = 2gy$$

and
$$\text{K.E.} = \tfrac{1}{2}mv^2 = \tfrac{1}{2}m(2gy) = mgy$$

The K.E. gained is just the P.E. lost; the sum of the two is unchanged. Finally when m reaches the level B it has given up all of its P.E. The K.E. at B is $\tfrac{1}{2}mv^2$ where now

$$v^2 = 2as = 2gh$$

or
$$\text{K.E.} = \tfrac{1}{2}mv^2 = \tfrac{1}{2}m(2gh) = mgh$$

We could summarize this as follows:

At A $W = \text{P.E.} + \text{K.E.} = mgh + 0 = mgh$
At C $W = \text{P.E.} + \text{K.E.} = mg(h - y) + mgy = mgh$
At B $W = \text{P.E.} + \text{K.E.} = 0 + mgh = mgh$

To illustrate this further, let us turn to our much-used inclined plane (see Fig. 6.1). Suppose the mass, m, slides down the plane from A to B. Along the frictionless plane the force on it is

$$F_s = \frac{h}{l}mg = ma$$

So

$$a = \frac{h}{l}g$$

at B

$$v^2 = 2as = 2\left(\frac{h}{l}g\right)l = 2gh$$

at B

$$\text{K.E.} = \tfrac{1}{2}mv^2 = \tfrac{1}{2}m(2gh) = mgh$$

But this is just the potential energy at A. Hence

(P.E. at A) = (K.E. at B), neglecting friction

The same conclusion was previously reached. We can reasonably conclude that the *sum* of the dynamical energies remains constant. Of course, this is true only if we consider just the earth and the mass; if we included air friction, or if we introduced some other force such as a cross-wind on the falling mass, our conclusion would be incorrect unless we extended our system to include these new forces. This can be restated by saying that we are dealing with an *isolated* system (the earth and the mass), that is, one free of all external forces.

With this restriction we can generalize our conclusions in a law known as the *conservation of dynamical energy:*

The total amount of dynamical energy (kinetic and potential energy) in an isolated system remains constant in time.

Any system which is thus isolated is called a *conservative system,* because the energy in such a system is conserved.

Example. Consider the motion of a pendulum bob (Fig. 6.5) that swings from A to C through the path ABC. At A it is momentarily at rest and all its energy is potential. It is clear that this P.E. is just mgh, where h is the vertical height of A above B. At point B the bob has exhausted its potential energy and now has an equal amount, according to the conservation law, of kinetic energy. By the time C is reached, the energy has once again been converted, this time from kinetic back to potential. Therefore, if we neglect friction, we find a continuous exchange of potential and kinetic energy as the pendulum repeats its motion. We now ask how high the bob would rise if at point P we insert a pin that effectively shortens the length of the pendulum for all its left-of-center swings. Before introducing the pin P the conservative system consisted of the pendulum, its support, and the earth (friction neglected); now we must broaden the system to include the pin P, which can exert a lateral force on the pendulum. In this system, as well as in the first one, energy must be conserved; therefore the K.E. at B must equal the P.E. at A, and the P.E. at D (the point of momentary rest for the foreshortened pendulum) must equal the K.E. at B. Our conclusion from this is straightforward: The P.E. at D

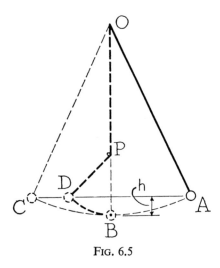

FIG. 6.5

must equal the P.E. at A, and the bob rises to exactly the same height as if the pin were absent. This is not an obvious conclusion, and it was in puzzling over this type of motion that Galileo arrived at some insight to the nature of dynamical energy.

6.6 Dissipative Forces

The examples above illustrate the principle of the conservation of dynamical energy. We have seen that to apply it a restriction is necessary. The system being considered must be *isolated*, in the sense that no external forces act on the bodies comprising the system. If external forces exist they will in general do work or extract energy as the bodies carry out their motions, and the total kinetic + potential energy in the system will not be constant in time. If, however, the system is broadened to include the bodies which give rise to the external forces, then these become internal forces, and the new expanded system may display dynamical energy conservation as a whole. However, there is a special kind of external force which is most troublesome and which cannot be eliminated by this procedure. This is the force of *friction;* it is called a *dissipative force*, a term used for any force which always *extracts* dynamical energy from a system. Indeed, no dynamical system is entirely free from dissipative forces, and the dynamical energy is constantly decreasing as the motion proceeds. Therefore, we have the added restriction to the use of the law of conservation of dynamical energy: The dissipative forces must be absent. We are now led at once to the question: Is it possible to expand the law to include the energy extracted from the system by dissipative forces? The full realization of an affirmative answer to this question came only about one hundred years ago.

6.7 The Conservation of Energy

To expand from the particular—dynamical energy—to the general—all forms of energy—required a vast amount of experimental evidence that will in part be illustrated by the remainder of this book. For the present, it will be necessary to anticipate the results of this evidence, and we shall reverse our method of step-by-step progress from evidence to law, by presenting the law and subsequently supporting it with its evidence. This violation of the inductive method is employed as a device to simplify the remainder of the discussion in this book. It has no historical and little logical justification.

The expanded generalization is known simply as the *law of the conservation of energy*. It states:

In an isolated system the sum of all forms of energy remains constant in time, though the amount of each form may change.

A less illuminating statement is often given: "Energy can be neither created nor destroyed," that is, the total amount remains unchanged. Without a doubt, this conservation law is the most sweeping generalization in all science. The use of the expression "*all* forms of energy" immediately removes the law from the realm of proof; for how will we ever know that we have accounted for all the energy in a system; in fact, how do we know that we have ever catalogued *all* the forms of energy in nature? The answer is, of course, that we do not know. Yet so deeply believed is this principle of the conservation of energy that when a new phenomenon seems to show an unaccountable dissipation in the total energy of a system the physicist has postulated a new form of energy to preserve the balance; and in every case thus far, these new forms of energy have been later discovered. Even the relativity theory, which modifies Newtonian dynamics for extreme cases, and the quantum theory, which alters our concepts of the exchange of energy, both lean heavily on the conservation of energy principle.

For our study of dynamics the new element that has been introduced by the generalized conservation of energy principle is the possibility that dynamical energy may be changed to some other form of energy. If we look for such forms we immediately encounter the obvious one, energy dissipated by friction. It is common experience that friction produces heat. Hence, in a system containing friction, there will be a dissipation of dynamical energy into heat or thermal energy. This is the most prevalent dissipative force found in nature. Yet many systems encountered can be treated to a more-or-less good approximation as conservative of dynamical energy. Recognition of this approximation accounts for the frequent use of the phrase "neglecting friction" or "frictionless." There are other, less common, dissipative forces that occasionally weaken the approximation. If flint and steel are rubbed together abruptly, not only is heat produced from the friction, but also light and sound; usually these latter dissipative forces are small and can be neglected.

6.8   Degradation of Energy

We will close this discussion with a few brief comments on the efficiency of energy exchange and the "degradation" of energy. This subject has little direct bearing on atomic physics, but it may serve to emphasize the importance in science of the concept of energy.

We live in a world surrounded by many forms of energy. A major task of the scientist is to obtain a thorough understanding of these forms and the means of effecting exchanges from one form to another. The problem usually reduces to one of efficient conversion of a kind of energy which exists in abundance in nature to a form which is more usable for the purpose of man.

To illustrate, let us trace backwards the energy transformations necessary to obtain light from an electric lamp. We shall ignore all the branch operations in making the filament, the glass, etc., and concentrate only on the chain of energy transformations directly responsible for the light. To act as a source of light the filament must be hot; the heat and light energy comes from the flow of electrons through the metal filament, and about 10% of this electron kinetic energy produces light, 90% produces heat. To give the electrons energy, a generator somewhere is being forced to rotate; if we assume a hydroelectric generator, this energy of rotation comes from a waterfall; and finally the waterfall derives its kinetic energy from the potential energy given it by the evaporation from one level and condensation (rain) at a higher level, through the agency of the sun's heat. The beginning and the end of our chain is chiefly heat! Actually, of course, there is no beginning or end; we should ask what causes the sun's heat, and what happens to the heat of the electric lamp.

However we trace energy transformations we encounter one form of energy that is always present—heat. The characteristic feature of these encounters is that heat usually appears as a dissipator of dynamical energy. In the case of the lamp it carries off more than 90% of the energy supplied to the filament by the electron current. We shall learn in Chapter 9 that the term heat is simply a synonym for molecular kinetic energy. When a body is heated, the individual molecules in the body gain kinetic energy. However, molecules can readily lose their increased kinetic energy by collisions with other, slower moving molecules, a process called heat flow. Consequently, it is virtually impossible to retain within one body any appreciable excess of molecular kinetic energy over its neighboring bodies; the flow of heat tends to dissipate most of the energy. Nor have we ever found an efficient mechanism for reversing this heat flow, that is, to concentrate heat in one body at the expense of its cooler neighbors. True, there exist heat engines which will perform this function, but they require external forces for their operation, and their efficiency of concentration of heat is low. We might feasibly look about us and ask if there is no agency in nature which will concentrate heat for us, instead of allowing it to dissipate continually to other bodies.

The results of such a search in nature have yielded no such agency. In fact, there exists a law, unproved but never yet found violated, called the second law of thermodynamics, which says in effect: Without the aid of external forces it is impossible to transfer heat to a body from a cooler body. In other words, any dynamical energy (to take just one form) that is dissipated into heat energy is eternally lost as dynamical energy; the heat energy into which it was transformed will spread throughout the matter in the system and its neighboring bodies, and there is no way of regaining it, short of paying with more dynamical energy through the use of heat engines. This phenomenon is called degradation, that is, energy is being demoted to a less useful and less available form. It has occurred to many people that the oceans contain a vast amount of heat energy; if some mechanism could be found to lower their average temperature only a few degrees the energy thus released would be tremendous. But the second law of thermodynamics states that this can be done only by using up some other form of energy, and that process is inefficient. Most of the energy content of our earth is unavailable to us. Nor has the more recent discovery of mass energy greatly alleviated this situation, though here we are on less sure grounds.

6.9   Power

It is well known that to accelerate an automobile from 10 mi/hr to 50 mi/hr in 10 sec requires a more powerful motor than if the same change in speed took 10 min. The kinetic energy acquired is the same in both cases, but the *rate* of acquiring this energy is different. This is expressed in the term power. *Power* is defined as the *rate of doing work*. In symbols, using P for power,

$$P = \frac{\text{Work}}{\text{Time}} = \frac{W}{t}$$

As is evident from this defining equation, the cgs unit of power is the *erg/second*. Another commonly employed unit is the *watt*. It is one joule/sec or 10^7 ergs/sec. An even larger power unit, used especially in electricity, is the kilowatt. Evidently a kilowatt is 1000 watts, or 10^3 joules/sec or 10^{10} ergs/sec.

Example. How much power must a person spend to lift a 25-kg mass to a height of 1 meter in 2 sec?

GIVEN: $m = 25$ kg $= 25{,}000$ gm; $h = 1$ m $= 100$ cm; $t = 2$ sec

$P = ?$

Solution: $P = W/t$

$W = mgh = 25{,}000 \times 980 \times 100 = 24.5 \times 10^8$ ergs

$P = \dfrac{24.5 \times 10^8}{2}$

$= 12.2 \times 10^8$ ergs/sec

$= 122$ watts   *Ans.*

PROBLEMS

1. A kilogram mass is lifted vertically to a height of 10 m. How much work is done? *Ans.* 98 joules.

2. How much work is required to push a 10-kg mass up a frictionless inclined plane whose length is 3 m and whose height is 0.5 m? *Ans.* 49 joules.

3. If in Problem 2 there is a force of friction between the mass and the incline plane of 0.7 megadynes, how much work is done in moving the mass up the plane? *Ans.* 70 joules.

4. In pulling a loaded sled along the horizontal a man exerts a force of 10 megadynes at a 45° angle with the sled. How much work does he do in moving the sled a distance of 1 km? *Ans.* 70,700 joules.

5. A 3-kg pendulum bob is pulled away from its center position until it has risen a height of 20 cm; it is then allowed to swing. Find its velocity as it passes through center position. *Ans.* 199 cm/sec.

6. A 5-kg body, initially at rest, is accelerated 20 cm/sec² over a distance of 1 m. What is its kinetic energy at the end of the 1 m? *Ans.* 1 joule.

7. What power is required to accelerate an automobile weighing 2000 kg to a velocity of 25 m/sec in 20 sec? *Ans.* 31.2 kw.

Suggested Reading

MACH, E., "Popular Science Lectures," Chicago, Open Court Publishing Co., 1895. Pages 136–85 give a critical account of the principle of energy conservation.

MAGIE, W. F., "Source Book in Physics," New York, McGraw-Hill Book Co., 1935. Page 51, excerpts from Leibnitz's views of kinetic energy.

MOTT-SMITH, M., "This Mechanical World," New York, D. Appleton and Co., 1931. Chapter XVII on dynamical energy is simply written.

SHAPLEY, H., WRIGHT, H., RAPPORT, S., "Readings in the Physical Sciences," New York, Appleton-Century-Crofts, 1948. Page 304, on energy in its various forms.

SWANN, W. F. G., "The Architecture of the Universe," New York, The Macmillan Co., 1934.
Chapter V is an interesting account of the concepts of energy and its degradation.

CHAPTER 7

Momentum and Its Conservation

7.1 The Limitation of Energy as a Dynamical Concept

The vast importance of the concept of energy lies in its property of conservation, a property possessed not only by dynamical energy, but by all forms of energy found in nature. The conservation law is a generalization that embraces the entire physical universe. As we noted in the last chapter, the law is without proof, nor has a violation ever yet been found. If the physical system under observation has negligible dissipative forces, we found that we could restrict the more general principle to one immediately applicable to forms of dynamical energy only. Finding the exchange of dynamical energy in such a system is a fruitful method for analyzing the motions within the system.

However, because energy is a scalar quantity, its use in problems of motion leaves one important characteristic undetermined, namely, the *direction* of the motion. To complete the description of the motion we need a quantity which is a vector, and which, like energy, is also conserved. For those problems in which the magnitude of the motion is desired the application of the conservation of energy is often sufficient. If we wish to treat systems in which the direction of the motion is important we must turn to the other half of the Descartes-Leibnitz argument, this time giving our attention to Descartes' quantity *mv*.

7.2 Momentum and Conservation of Momentum

The *momentum* of a particle is defined as the product of its mass and its velocity. To obtain a symbol for this quantity we resort to the Greek equivalent of its initial letter m, which is μ (mu). Then

$$\mu = m\mathbf{v}$$

As indicated, momentum must be a vector, for it is a vector, $\mathbf{v}$, multiplied by a scalar, m. Since it depends on velocity, momentum is a strictly dynamical quantity. We shall prove from Newton's laws of motion that in any dynamical system momentum must be conserved. To this law there are no exceptions; momentum, unlike energy, *cannot be lost* from a dynamical motion to some other form, for there are no other forms of momentum. Hence, the conservation of momentum, though a more restricted principle than the conservation of energy, supplies a simple and rigorous method for studying dynamical motions. When it is possible to use both the conservation laws, that is, when dynamical energy is also conserved, we have an exceedingly powerful method available.

Proof of the Conservation of Momentum. In contrast with the inductive concept of conservation of energy, we can show that the conservation of momentum can be derived at once from Newton's laws of motion. The proof is valid for a system having any number of particles in it. For the sake of simplicity, we shall assume only two particles, and identify them by subscripts 1 and 2. Let us suppose that there are forces of some kind operating between the two particles; these forces may be caused by connecting springs, or gravitational attraction, or even by some unknown agent. The only restriction imposed is that they be *internal forces*, arising completely from within the system. We shall suppose the system is isolated, that is, there are no external forces operating on the particles. If there is no external force, then the system must be in equilibrium, and we can write

$$m_1 a_1 + m_2 a_2 = 0$$

The total momentum of the system is the vector sum of the momentum of each particle or

$$\mu = m_1 v_1 + m_2 v_2 \qquad [7.1]$$

Now suppose that due to internal collisions, or any other cause, the velocities of the two particles changed; will the total momentum of the system change? In other words, will the momentum for the system be conserved? For the instant, let us assume that the total momentum does change to some new value μ', due to the new velocities v_1' and v_2'. (The primes simply represent some value other than that of the unprimed.) Then

$$\mu' = m_1 v_1' + m_2 v_2' \qquad [7.2]$$

If Eq. 7.2 is subtracted from Eq. 7.1 and then divided by the time, the left-hand side represents the time rate of change of momentum:

$$\frac{\mu - \mu'}{t} = m_1 \frac{v_1 - v_1'}{t} + m_2 \frac{v_2 - v_2'}{t}$$

$$= m_1 a_1 + m_2 a_2$$

But, according to Eq. 7.1, the condition for an isolated system is

$$m_1 a_1 + m_2 a_2 = 0$$

Therefore,

$$\frac{\mu - \mu'}{t} = 0$$

The time rate of change of momentum is zero, which is the same as saying that momentum does not change with time in an isolated system. Thus we have proved the *conservation of momentum:*

The total momentum of a system of particles isolated from external forces remains constant with time.

Internal forces and motions may redistribute the momentum but cannot cause it to increase or decrease. Note carefully, by total momentum is meant the *vector* sum of the momenta.

7.3 Momentum Changes and Force

In §7.2 we showed that if the external force on a system of particles was zero, then the total momentum of the particles was unchanged. Evidently if the force had not been zero the momentum would have changed, and so there must be a relation between force and momentum.

Consider a *single* particle of mass m acted on by a force **F**. By Newton's second law

$$\mathbf{F} = m\mathbf{a}$$
$$= m\frac{\mathbf{v}' - \mathbf{v}}{t} = \frac{m\mathbf{v}' - m\mathbf{v}}{t} \qquad [7.3]$$

where **v** is the particle velocity at time $t = 0$ and **v**' the velocity at time t. Equation 7.3 states, therefore, that the force is equal to the change in momentum divided by the time required for the change. This is an alternative statement of Newton's second law of motion: *The time rate of change of momentum of a body is equal to the external force acting on it.* This statement can be made to apply to a system of interacting bodies equally well, in which case the conservation of momentum of §7.2 is the special case of zero force acting on the system.

7.4 Collision Problems, Head-On Collisions

One of the common ways in which momentum is internally redistributed is by collisions between particles in the system; the application of the conservation of momentum is most directly applied to this type of problem.

All collisions between two bodies can be classified in two categories: (1) *head-on collisions* in which all the motion involved lies along the same straight line, and (2) *glancing collisions* for which the paths of the colliding particles are at an angle other than zero. We shall take up each of these cases, but only the head-on collision will be treated in detail. In addition to this distinction based on the direction of motion, it is necessary to make one on the basis of the dynamical energy of the system. Here we introduce two terms: (I) *Elastic collisions* occur when there is *no loss of dynamical energy;* (II) *inelastic collisions* occur when the total amount of dynamical energy (K.E. and P.E.) is reduced in the collision process, this loss reappearing as some other form of energy such as heat, deformation, light, or sound. (Remember that the total of *all* energy must remain constant if the system is isolated.) If such dissipative forces are negligible we can treat the collision as elastic to a good approximation. For example, collisions between billiard balls or steel spheres are, to a good approximation, elastic.

Case I: Elastic Head-On Collisions. Consider a particle of mass m_1 and velocity v_1 striking a particle of mass m_2 at rest ($v_2 = 0$). After head-on-collision the particles move with new velocities v_1' and v_2' (Fig. 7.1). Positive velocities

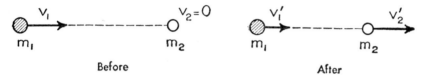

Before   After

FIG. 7.1

are measured to the right, negative to the left. From the conservation of momentum we have that

Momentum before collision = Momentum after collision

$$m_1 v_1 + 0 = m_1 v_1' + m_2 v_2' \qquad [7.4]$$

Since we are assuming the collision to be elastic, then dynamical energy (K.E. in this case) is conserved.

K.E. before collision = K.E. after collision

$$\tfrac{1}{2} m_1 v_1^2 + 0 = \tfrac{1}{2} m_1 v_1'^2 + \tfrac{1}{2} m_2 v_2'^2 \qquad [7.5]$$

If we solve Eq. 7.4 for v_1, substitute it into Eq. 7.5, and then solve for v_1' we get

$$v_1' = v_2' \frac{m_1 - m_2}{2m_1} \qquad [7.6]$$

If we solve for v_1' in Eq. 7.4 and substitute it into Eq. 7.6 we get another useful relation,

$$v_1 = v_2' \frac{m_1 + m_2}{2m_1} \qquad [7.7]$$

Now v_2' must always be positive in a head-on collision; therefore we see in Eq. 7.6 four possible situations for v_1':

(1) m_1 is greater than m_2 (a billiard ball hitting a marble): Eq. 7.6 says that v_1' is positive also and the billiard ball follows along after the marble, but with reduced velocity.

(2) m_1 is less than m_2 (a marble hitting a billiard ball): since $(m_1 - m_2)$ is now negative, v_1' is to the left—the marble bounces back in the collision.

(3) m_1 is equal to m_2 (two similar billiard balls); $m_1 - m_2 = 0$. So $v_1' = 0$; the first billiard ball stops completely, the second one carries on with all the energy originally possessed by the first ball (Eq. 7.5). Such a head-on elastic collision between like masses played a significant role in the discovery of the neutron (Chapter 26).

(4) m_1 very much smaller than m_2 (a ball-bearing hitting a massive steel plate). If we neglect m_1 as compared with m_2 in the numerator of Eq. 7.7 we get

$$2m_1v_1 = m_2v_2' \qquad [7.8]$$

approximately. Thus, v_2' is much smaller than v_1 (by the ratio $2m_1/m_2$). By Eq. 7.4

$$m_1v_1 - m_1v_1' = m_2v_2'$$

By comparing this with Eq. 7.8 we see that $v_1' = -v_1$. Thus the ball bounces back with a speed equal to the speed of approach. From Eq. 7.8 we see that the momentum of the steel plate after collision is *twice* the momentum of the incident ball. This situation is closely duplicated when a gas molecule collides with the wall of a container, and we shall use this result in Chapter 9.

Case II: Inelastic Head-On Collisions.   As the name suggests, these are collisions in which dynamical energy is never conserved. The simplest example to

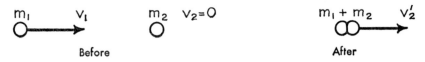

Before   After

Fig. 7.2

treat is the head-on collision in which the incident particle does not rebound at all, but instead adheres to the particle with which it collides; a rifle bullet shot into a wooden block, or a putty ball hurled against the wall are examples of inelastic collisions. Though dynamical energy is not conserved, momentum must be, because there are no ways for momentum to change into anything except momentum. If the two particles stick together we then have (Fig. 7.2):

$$m_1 v_1 = (m_1 + m_2) v_2' \qquad [7.9]$$

Though it is not conserved, we can calculate how much kinetic energy is retained in the system.

$$\text{K.E. before collision} = \tfrac{1}{2} m_1 v_1^2$$
$$\text{K.E. after collision} = \tfrac{1}{2}(m_1 + m_2) v_2'^2$$

If we form the ratio

$$\frac{\text{K.E. after}}{\text{K.E. before}} = \frac{\tfrac{1}{2}(m_1 + m_2) v_2'^2}{\tfrac{1}{2} m_1 v_1^2}$$

Using Eq. 7.9, this reduces to

$$\frac{\text{K.E. after}}{\text{K.E. before}} = \frac{m_1}{m_1 + m_2}$$

Since $m_1/(m_1 + m_2)$ must always be less than unity, the kinetic energy after collision must always be less than before collision. The loss of energy goes into the colliding bodies as energy of deformation and as heat (with a small amount being given off as sound and possibly light).

There is little more to be said about the dynamics of inelastic collisions. The major significance in a study of atomic physics appears when we try to find the manner and form in which kinetic energy was not conserved; in this search we shall discover the means by which internal energy can be given to the atom and its nucleus.

7.5 Glancing Collisions

The most likely collisions between particles are glancing. The conservation of momentum law demands that the *vector* sum of the momenta be the same before and after collision (Fig. 7.3) regardless of the individual paths of the particles. If the collision is elastic, dynamical energy is likewise conserved. The analysis of such elastic glancing collisions requires trigonometry and will be foregone here. However, one special case can be analyzed readily, the elastic glancing collision of two particles of the *same* mass. Using primes for the after-collision velocities, we have from the conservation of momentum

$$m\mathbf{v}_1 = m\mathbf{v}_1' + m\mathbf{v}_2'$$

or

$$\mathbf{v}_1 = \mathbf{v}_1' + \mathbf{v}_2' \qquad [7.10]$$

Since the collision is elastic, kinetic energy is conserved. Hence

$$\tfrac{1}{2}mv_1^2 = \tfrac{1}{2}mv_1'^2 + \tfrac{1}{2}mv_2'^2$$

or

$$v_1^2 = v_1'^2 + v_2'^2 \qquad\qquad [7.11]$$

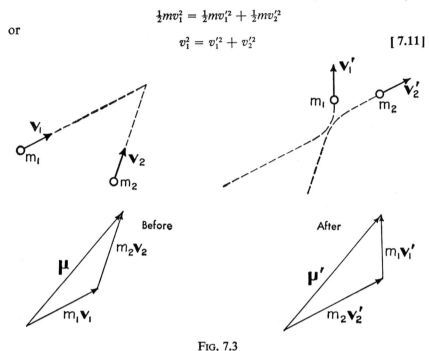

FIG. 7.3

Equation 7.11 demands that the vector triangle of Eq. 7.10 be a right-angle triangle (Pythagorean theorem). One possibility is shown in Fig. 7.4. Thus,

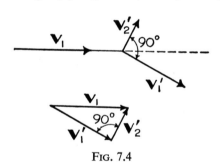

FIG. 7.4

when a moving particle strikes a particle of the same mass at rest, the two rebound along paths which are perpendicular to each other (Fig. 7.4). The velocity is divided between them in any proportion consistent with Eq. 7.10 and Eq. 7.11 and depends only on the degree of glancing. A head-on collision makes $v_1' = 0$, and the triangle closes to make $v_1 = v_2'$. As the collision becomes more glancing, larger and larger values are assumed by v_1', until for a "side-swipe" v_2' becomes almost zero. The most probable collision for random aiming is one in which $v_1 = v_2'$; for this case the momentum triangle is a right triangle with 45° angles.

7.6 More About Collisions

Ordinarily when we speak of a collision we visualize a solid impact of one material body on another. However, there is nothing in the theory of momentum conservation which demands such proximity, nothing which restricts the nature of the forces operating between the colliding bodies. As we have already seen, gravitational force acts at a distance from the masses concerned; a comet moving toward the sun is influenced by the sun's gravitational force long before the two bodies come in contact; in fact they rarely if ever do come in contact. For such a case the conservation of momentum principle must apply, even though there is not a "collision" in the usual sense of the word. In the scale of atomic physics intimate contact between the colliding bodies seldom occurs, for there are usually strong electrical or specifically atomic forces which take hold of the bodies well before they collide in the usual sense. Gas molecules may not strike the walls of a container, but turn back at distances comparable to the size of the molecule. The high-speed particles which are used to produce transmutation and radioactivity in atomic nuclei are scattered from their nuclear targets most of the time and seldom make the desired intimate contact required for penetration into the nucleus. Slow moving electrons in gases are deflected from their straight paths at distances which are many times the size of the deflecting atoms. Yet in every case the principle of momentum conservation is valid and is a valuable aid in dealing with these collision problems.

7.7 Guns and Rockets

It may seem a distant cry from atoms to rockets, yet their motions are equally well described by the conservation of momentum principle. It is possible to measure the energy of an ejected nuclear particle by measuring the recoil momentum of the nucleus from which it was ejected; it is equally possible to measure the velocity of a gun bullet by measuring the recoil momentum of the gun.

Let us consider a loaded gun at rest relative to the earth (Fig. 7.5). The momentum of the gun and its shell is zero before the shell is fired, and there-

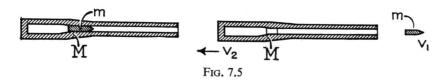

FIG. 7.5

fore the sum of the momenta must be zero after firing. If the bullet moves to the right with a velocity v_1, then the gun must recoil to the left with a velocity v_2, where

$$0 = mv_1 - Mv_2$$

or

$$mv_1 = Mv_2$$

and

$$v_2 = \frac{m}{M}v_1$$

The following example is for the U.S. Army M1 rifle.

Mass of the bullet $= m = 180$ grains $= 0.0257$ lb
Muzzle velocity $\quad = v_1 = 2690$ ft/sec
Mass of the gun $\quad = M = 9.5$ lb

$$v_2 = \frac{0.0257 \times 2690}{9.5} = 7.3 \text{ ft/sec} = 2.2 \ m/\text{sec}$$

This is the recoil velocity if no provision is made for anchoring the gun. If the marksman's shoulder serves this purpose the recoil velocity is further reduced by his mass and the friction between his feet and the earth. The "kick" is the rapid acceleration of the gun butt due to its recoil velocity as the bullet leaves the muzzle. In some guns the force of recoil is reduced by allowing the gun barrel to push against a spring, thus prolonging the period of acceleration and reducing the impulse force for a given recoil momentum.

The problem of rocket propulsion is interesting, because it adds a new possibility to the use of the conservation of momentum. In §7.2 this law was proved by assuming that the system of particles underwent changes in velocity only; however, momentum is the product of mass and velocity, and our derivation would have been valid if we had assumed that the particles changed both mass and velocity (though the derivation in this case is more involved). This case is illustrated by rocket or jet motors. Their propelling force is obtained from the recoil momentum produced when a high-speed jet of gas is

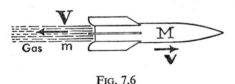

FIG. 7.6

emitted from a nozzle in the tail of the rocket. The gas is produced at high pressure by the rapid combustion of a fuel or explosive and is allowed to expand in a flared nozzle in order to reach a high velocity as it leaves the nozzle exit. In the case of rockets, the oxygen for combustion is carried along, and since the recoil is in no way dependent on the presence of the atmosphere, rockets fly most efficiently in high altitude where the air resistance is least, and in fact, are inherently capable of interplanetary flight. Jet engines use atmospheric oxygen for combustion, but otherwise operate on the same principles.

The elementary equations for rocket flight are easily derived. We will use the following symbols (see Fig. 7.6):

M = mass of the rocket and its fuel
m = mass of the fuel ejected (as gas)
v = velocity of the rocket relative to the earth before ejection of gas
V = velocity of the gas ejected relative to the rocket
t = time interval during which fuel is being ejected
a = acceleration of the rocket during this interval (assumed constant)
$R = m/t$ = rate of gas ejection

At $t = 0$ the momentum of the rocket and its contents is $\mu = Mv$. If fuel is now ejected for a time t, the rocket will recoil and be accelerated; if t is taken short enough, the increased velocity will be just $v + at$. To add up all the momentum after time t we must bear in mind that the rocket is now lighter by an amount of mass, m, and its velocity has increased by an amount at; furthermore, the gas now has momentum, due to its velocity V (assumed constant), relative to the rocket, or $[(v + at) - V]$ relative to the earth. Hence, at the end of the interval t we have

$$\mu' = (M - m)(v + at) + m(v + at - V)$$

So, by conservation of momentum,

$$\mu' = \mu$$

or

$$Mv = (M - m)(v + at) + m(v + at - V)$$

giving

$$Mat = mV$$

or

$$Ma = \frac{m}{t}V = RV$$

[7.12]

We see that if the acceleration of the rocket is to be large, the gas velocity and the rate of its expulsion must be as large as possible. However, a large final velocity for a given amount and type of fuel does not depend on the rate of burning, since the final rocket velocity is determined only by the *total* recoil momentum. We will not derive the equation for the final velocity of the rocket, since the acceleration a in Eq. 7.12 is not uniform (because the mass, M, of the rocket varies as the fuel is ejected), and the treatment of non-uniform accelerations is well beyond the mathematical scope of this book. The result of such a derivation is particularily interesting in showing that a rocket can move faster with respect to the earth than the gas velocity, V. In other words, to an observer on earth the gas appears to follow the rocket rather than recoil from it.

PROBLEMS

1. A 1000-gm moving body has 2 joules of kinetic energy. What is its momentum?

Ans. 2×10^5 gm-cm/sec.

2. A 20-gm body moving with a velocity of 90 cm/sec makes an elastic head-on collision with a 40-gm body at rest. After collision the 40-gm body has a velocity of 60 cm/sec to the right. What is the velocity of the 20-gm body?

Ans.   30 cm/sec to the left.

3. Two billiard balls of equal mass, one in motion, one at rest, undergo a head-on collision. After collision the one that had been at rest is observed to have a speed of 50 cm/sec. Find the initial and final velocity of the other billiard ball.

4. An atom with an unknown velocity and a mass of 1.66×10^{-24} gm collides head on with a second atom at rest and of mass 6.64×10^{-24} gm. The second atom is observed to have a velocity of 100 km/sec. Find the initial velocity of the first atom, assuming the collision elastic.   *Ans.*   250 km/sec.

5. A 10-gm bullet is shot from a rifle into a 10-kg wood block and is embedded in the block. As a result of the impact the block gains a velocity of 250 cm/sec. Find the velocity of the bullet.   *Ans.*   2500 m/sec.

6. Calculate the kinetic energy before and after the collision of Problem 5. What accounts for the loss of K.E.?

Suggested Reading

MACH, E., "The Science of Mechanics," La Salle, Ill., Open Court Publishing Co., 1942.
    Pages 396–421 give a logical and historical account of the momentum concept in impact problems by Huygens and others.

MOTT-SMITH, M., "This Mechanical World," New York, D. Appleton and Co., 1931.
    Chapter X on conservation of momentum.

CHAPTER 8

Atomism and the Laws of Gases

8.1 The Atomic Idea

Dynamics represents the great contribution of physics in the seventeenth and eighteenth centuries. Not only did it give a means of analyzing the motions of terrestial bodies, but combined with Newton's law of gravitation it reached out to the solar system and the universe at large, forming a strict order of force and motion in the whole realm of material bodies. Dynamics was developed for the world of perceptible bodies where mass, velocity, and acceleration are directly susceptible to measurement, but its influence has gone far beyond its origins and particularly into the world of sub-perceptible matter—the fundamental atoms and molecules which make up all matter. That is to say, it was possible and fruitful to apply mechanical ideas to the description of the internal constitution and motions in matter as well as to the motions of bulk matter. This mechanical description of molecular motion was one of the principal achievements of physical science in the nineteenth century.

To understand the nature and the growth of this mechanics of sub-perceptible matter it is necessary to consider two basic questions. What is the evidence regarding the atomic constitution of matter, and what are the measurable quantities which can be described by the mechanics of these constituent atoms? The first question takes us briefly into nineteenth century chemistry; the second question brings in the mechanical theory of heat, particularly of the heat in gases, where the original theory gives a fairly complete answer.

The atomic idea is generally attributed to Democritus, a Greek philosopher of the fifth century B. C. Democritus did not originate atomism, but as the leader of the movement he coordinated and extended its influence. In modern eyes his views are purely speculative in the tradition of Greek philosophy. In essence, he argued that the world was composed of minute, indestructible parts, the atoms, lodged in a void or vacuum, and that these were the primary constituents of nature. The evidence was the logic and simplicity of the notion, hardly a basis for what we now consider as scientific evidence. Greek atomism is of scientific importance chiefly because of its influence in Europe during the Renaissance; it provided a tradition on which to build modern atomism.

Modern atomism began with the advance of chemistry in the late eighteenth and early nineteenth centuries. During this period chemical reactions were first systematically studied, and certain substances, the *elements*, were found which were chemical entities, incapable of being decomposed by chemical means. These elements form compounds which have definite chemical and physical properties; the fundamental particles of the compound are *molecules*, while the chemically irreducible constituents of each molecule are its *atoms*. Thus compounds (the usual form of all matter) are molecular, elements are atomic. The names of Lavoisier, Priestley, Davy, and others are associated with the discovery of the common elements in this period. By 1800 perhaps twenty chemical elements were generally recognized, and several chemical compounds of each were known. As such studies proceeded from qualitative descriptions of the reactions to quantitative measurements of the materials involved in the reactions, certain regularities of importance to atomic theory were revealed.

8.2   The Dalton and Avogadro Laws

Two highly significant contributions to the growth of the atomic theory of matter were made in the early nineteenth century by Dalton and Avogadro. In 1808 Dalton announced his famous law of multiple proportions which states that elements combine in certain fixed proportions by *weight* to form compounds.* In the same year Gay-Lussac published evidence which showed that the chemical combination of *gases* involve integral proportions *by volume*. To Avogadro this meant, when coupled with Dalton's law of multiple proportions, that equal volumes of all gases must contain numbers of atoms bearing simple ratios to each other. The simplest form of Avogadro's law, stated in 1813, is that equal volumes of gases (at the same temperature and pressure) contain the same number of molecules. The data on which the conclusions of Dalton and Avogadro were made were considerably improved in the next five decades, so that by 1858 Cannizzaro was able to demonstrate

---

* In atomic theory the terms weight and mass are used almost interchangeably, e.g., atomic weights, atomic masses. This is in direct conflict with our distinctions of Chapter 5 where *weight* was defined as a force, the force of gravity on a body. Part of this practice stems from the chemists' comparison of masses by the balance, where weights are truly being compared. To avoid confusion we shall not use the term weight in referring to the masses of atoms even in certain places where common usage is otherwise.

their validity with good precision. Let us illustrate their significance using present day knowledge and terminology.

Dalton's Law.   Atoms always combine in fixed mass ratios to form molecules. Thus 16 gm of oxygen combine with 2 gm of hydrogen to form water (H_2O); 12 gm of carbon combine with 16 gm of oxygen to produce carbon monoxide (CO); 14 gm of nitrogen combine with 16 gm of oxygen to form nitric oxide (NO). Or to take a slightly more complicated case, 1 gm of hydrogen combines with 12 gm of carbon and 14 gm of nitrogen to form hydrogen cyanide (HCN). Now if the molecule of carbon monoxide, for example, is truly just one atom of carbon attached to one atom of oxygen, then 12 gm of carbon must have exactly the same number of atoms as 16 gm of oxygen; consequently the mass of a carbon atom must be $\frac{12}{16}$ of the mass of the oxygen atom. Likewise a certain number of nitrogen atoms has a mass of $\frac{14}{16}$ of an equal number of oxygen atoms, so that the nitrogen atom must have a mass of $\frac{14}{16}$ of the oxygen atom.

Avogadro's Law.   Equal volumes of gases (at the same temperature and pressure) contain the same number of molecules. This statement was based on the observation of Gay-Lussac that gases combined in simple volume ratios to form compounds. Thus a *volume* of nitrogen gas combines with an exactly equal *volume* of oxygen gas to form nitric oxide (NO); furthermore, the resulting nitric oxide occupies a volume of twice that of either the nitrogen or the oxygen (we assume the pressure and temperature are held constant). This latter comes about because both nitrogen and oxygen when existing in the free state are themselves diatomic (2-atom) molecules. Hence

$$N_2 \ + \ O_2 \ \rightarrow \ 2NO$$
(1 vol)   (1 vol)   (2 vols)

For the case of water it is observed that two volumes of hydrogen (which is diatomic) combine with one volume of oxygen to produce just two volumes of water vapor. This must uniquely establish the atomic content of the water molecule:

$$2H_2 \ + \ O_2 \ \rightarrow \ 2H_2O$$
(2 vols)   (1 vol)   (2 vols)

Such a chemical equation depends directly on the validity of Avogadro's law, for two volumes of hydrogen or two volumes of water vapor must have *twice* the number of molecules contained in one volume of oxygen; in other words, equal volumes of gases have equal number of molecules, whether they happen to be combining or not. (Note, however, that Dalton's law demands that equal volumes of different gases will have different masses.) Avogadro had the insight to recognize that for a given pressure and temperature of a gas its volume depended only on the number of molecules of the gas.

8.3 The Concept of Atomic and Molecular Masses

The steady recurrence of certain mass ratios in chemical combinations which are approximately the ratios of small integers suggests that these integers may have a fundamental atomic significance, the integers being proportional to the actual masses of the atoms. On this basis the chemical system of atomic mass numbers is built up.

An arbitrary unit of mass, called the *mass unit* (mu) is defined such that the mass of a single oxygen atom is exactly 16 mu. The number 16 is called the *atomic mass* of oxygen. Then, in accordance with the observed mass ratios in the formation of chemical compounds carbon is given an atomic mass of 12, nitrogen 14; the molecule CO has a molecular mass of $12 + 16 = 28$, NO is 30, O_2 is 32. On this scheme we must assign an atomic mass of 1 to atomic hydrogen since in the compound HCN 1 gm of atomic hydrogen combines with 12 gm of atomic carbon and 14 gm of atomic nitrogen. Since 2 gm of hydrogen gas (H_2) combines with 16 gm of oxygen gas (O_2) to form water, there must be two atoms of hydrogen and one of oxygen in the water molecule (H_2O). This confirms the conclusion already reached with the aid of Avogadro's law.

It must be remembered that the atomic mass is simply a number which represents the mass of an atom in arbitrary units. The actual mass of a single atom is (mass number) $\times$ (mass in grams of 1 mu). There is, however, another mass whch figures importantly in atomic theory, the *gram-atom*, which is a mass in grams of an element equal to its atomic mass number. For molecules a similar unit is defined, the *mole* or *gram-molecule*, which is a mass in grams of the compound equal to the molecular mass number. Thus 32 gm of oxygen gas is a gram-molecule, or mole, of oxygen.

Though to the uninitiated this may seem to be a kind of numerology, it is actually of great fundamental importance in the whole of chemistry and atomic physics. With its aid we can restate Dalton's law more simply: Atoms always combine in proportion to their atomic masses to form a molecule. With the aid of these combining masses all the known elements have been assigned atomic masses. Some elements have atomic masses that are very nearly whole numbers; others deviate from whole numbers (chlorine is 35.5). However, improved accuracy has shown deviations, though often slight, for all the atomic masses; hydrogen is 1.0081, carbon is 12.0040, etc. Considerable emphasis will be put on these values in studying nuclear physics in the last part of this book.

8.4   Pressure and Its Measurement

Throughout the first half of the nineteenth century atomic ideas in chemistry gained wider favor and scientists became accustomed to thinking of matter in atomic terms. During the same period Gay-Lussac and Avogadro's ideas about gases were extended and served as a basis of a mechanical theory of heat. In the latter half of the century this theory assumed the form of the present *kinetic theory of gases*. In explaining this development we shall need to review the main facts concerning the measurable properties of confined gases. This will take us briefly into the measurement of *pressure* and of *temperature*.

Confined gases exert forces against the walls of their containers, since forces are necessary to compress such gases. If a cylinder containing a gas is closed at one end with a piston (Fig. 8.1) and a force F is exerted on the piston, the gas is compressed, and by this compression it generates a force opposing F until finally the piston is in equilibrium under the action of two equal forces. Since the gas presses on all parts of the piston, it is profitable

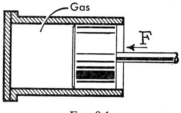

FIG. 8.1

to think of it as exerting a certain force per unit area on the piston. This is defined as the *pressure* of the gas:

$$\text{Pressure} = \frac{\text{Force}}{\text{Area}}$$

Writing P for pressure,* A for area, this is

$$P = \frac{F}{A} \text{ dynes/cm}^2$$

The force, F, must be perpendicular to the area, A.

A simple method for measuring pressure rests on the fact that confined liquids exert pressure due to their weight. In Fig. 8.2 a cylindrical column of liquid above which there is a vacuum has a cross-sectional area of A; we wish to calculate its pressure on the bottom of the container. The force exerted by the liquid on the bottom of the container is just the gravitational force on the liquid, mg, where m is the total mass of the liquid; then, the pressure must be

$$P = \frac{mg}{A}$$

Instead of dealing with the mass of the liquid it is more convenient to speak of

---

* The same symbol was used for power (§ 6.9); it is difficult to avoid duplication of symbols in physics. In this case no confusion should arise since power and pressure will not be discussed simultaneously.

the ratio of its mass to its volume; this ratio is its *density*, symbolized by ρ (rho). If V designates volume (we retain the symbol v for velocity) we thus define density as

$$\rho = \frac{m}{V} \text{ gm/cm}^3$$

(This definition applies to all states of matter, gases, liquids, and solids.) In terms of its density the mass of the liquid in Fig. 8.2 is $m = \rho V$; since the column is a cylinder, $V = Ah$. Hence

$$P = \frac{mg}{A} = \frac{\rho V g}{A} = \frac{\rho A h g}{A}$$

or

$$P = \rho g h \hspace{3cm} [\,8.1\,]$$

Thus the pressure due to the column of liquid is proportional to the height, h, of the column and the density of the liquid; it does *not* depend on the area of the

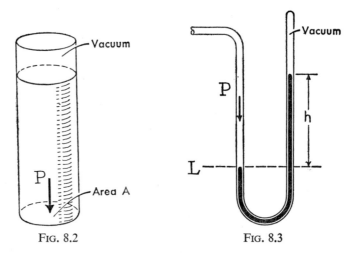

FIG. 8.2   FIG. 8.3

column, even though the definition of pressure does include the area. Since Eq. 8.1 bears little resemblance to the definition of pressure, it might be useful to stop and check our units.

$$P = \rho g h$$

$$\text{Units of pressure} = \frac{\text{gm}}{\text{cm}^3} \times \frac{\text{cm}}{\text{sec}^2} \times \text{cm}$$

$$= \frac{\text{gm-cm}}{\text{sec}^2} \times \frac{1}{\text{cm}^2} = \frac{\text{dyne}}{\text{cm}^2}$$

Equation 8.1 suggests a convenient method of measuring pressure in terms of the length of liquid column supported. Such a pressure measuring device is called a *manometer*; the liquid is usually mercury, and the tube is usually bent into a U shape. One end of the tube is evacuated and closed, and the other end is attached to a gas chamber in which the gas pressure is to be measured (Fig. 8.3). The liquid moves until it is in equilibrium under the action of the pressure of the gas and the force of gravity. At level L the downward gas

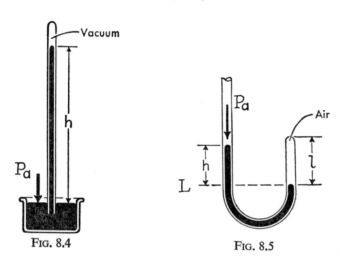

FIG. 8.4   FIG. 8.5

pressure P is on the liquid in the tube on the left and $\rho h g$ on the right. The liquid below L is in equilibrium under the action of these pressures. Hence

$$P = \rho g h$$

which is the same as Eq. 8.1. If the outside gas pressure is zero, the liquid levels are the same on the left and right sides, i.e., $h = 0$. As the pressure P increases, h increases. When such a manometer is used to measure the pressure of the atmosphere, it is called a *barometer*, as indicated in Fig. 8.4, where a dish open to the atmosphere is substituted for the U tube. On an average day at sea level the atmospheric pressure on the liquid surface raises the mercury in the barometer tube to a height of 76.0 cm. The density of mercury is 13.6 gm/cm³ so that the atmospheric pressure (P_a) is

$$P_a = \rho g h = 13.6 \times 980 \times 76.0$$
$$= 1.01 \times 10^6 \text{ dyne/cm}^2$$

The value 76 cm of mercury, or its cgs value 1.01×10^6 dyne/cm² is taken to be "normal" atmospheric pressure.

8.5 Boyle's Law

Boyle in 1662 discovered the law which bears his name; he used a manometer tube which differed from that of Fig. 8.3 in that air was contained above the mercury in the closed tube. The apparatus is shown in Fig. 8.5. By adding mercury to the open tube he could vary the height h and hence the pressure of the trapped air sample. This pressure is

$$P = P_a + \rho gh$$

since this is the pressure at level L necessary to balance the mercury column h and the atmosphere P_a bearing down on it. As mercury was added, the air sample was compressed and the degree of compression noted by observing the length l. The volume of the compressed gas is

$$V = Al$$

Boyle found that this volume varied inversely as the pressure of the gas, i.e., that P is proportional to $1/V$, or

$$PV = \text{Constant} \qquad\qquad [\,8.2\,]$$

He also found that this was only strictly true provided that the temperature of the room did not change and that the compression was done slowly or time given for the temperature to regain its original value after each compression.

8.6 Temperature and Its Measurement

Temperature is a measure of the intensity of heat, the "warmness" of a body. Common experience serves to show that heat and temperature are not the same. It requires much more heat to raise the temperature of a gallon of water by 10° than is needed to raise the temperature of a cup of water the same amount. As we shall see, heat is the kinetic energy of molecules and temperature is proportional to the amount of energy which the molecules possess.

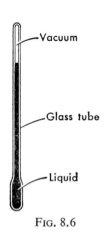

FIG. 8.6

A thermometer ordinarily consists of an evacuated glass tube containing mercury or colored alcohol (Fig. 8.6). When placed in a cold environment the liquid level drops; when heated it rises. This results from the greater contraction or expansion of the liquid as compared with the contraction or expansion of the glass stem. The change of dimensions of the glass is small enough to be negligible for ordinary purposes. A thermometer is calibrated in degrees in the following way. It is immersed in a cold bath (usually melting ice) and then in a hot bath (usually steam). The two liquid levels are noted and arbitrarily given numerical values as follows:

Melting ice level called 0° on centigrade scale or 32° on the Fahrenheit scale.

Steam level called 100° on centigrade scale or 212° on the Fahrenheit scale.

The stem is then divided into a number of equal length intervals between these two marks and each interval corresponds to a certain temperature interval. On the centigrade scale there are 100 equal intervals or degrees between the 0° and the 100° marks. By extrapolation the scale can be extended above 100° and below 0°.

This is an arbitrary calibration, and one may object that we have assumed that the expansion of the mercury is strictly proportional to the temperature, and this is truly what is done. In fact, the temperature is defined to be proportional to the expansion, and this is the observational definition of temperature. However, the standard temperature scale does not use either mercury or alcohol as the expanding substance, for there are more suitable substances on which to base the primary standard of thermometry. These are the permanent gases. This choice is based partly on theory and partly on internal consistency. A number of gases such as hydrogen, nitrogen, helium, argon, and oxygen give the same thermometer scales to a very high precision when the temperatures at which they liquefy are not too closely approached. That is, these gases all expand by the same relative amount per degree rise in temperature, and this amount is the same at all points on the temperature scale.

8.7 The Gas Thermometer and Absolute Zero

Since a change in volume of a gas in general will produce a change in pressure, a gas thermometer is somewhat more elaborate than a mercury thermometer where the mercury always has a free surface and is not compressed. In one type of gas thermometer the *volume* is kept constant and temperature rise noted as a rise in pressure. In another type the volume varies and the *pressure* is kept constant. This latter type is shown in Fig. 8.7 for the case where the pressure is kept at P_a, i.e., atmospheric pressure. The tube on the left contains the gas, and on raising its temperature the gas expands downward and raises the level at L. However the piston can be lowered to bring the two levels to the same height, thus keeping the bulb pressure at P_a. The change in volume is recorded as a change in length l of the gas column.

In an actual constant-pressure gas thermometer the diameters of the mercury
tubes are small and the gas bulb large in
order to magnify the level change caused
by the expansion.

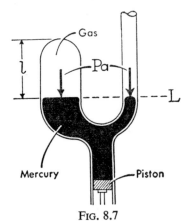

FIG. 8.7

It was observed by Charles and several
others that the *fractional* increase in volume
for a unit increase in temperature was constant, and in fact the same constant was
found for many different gases. Its value
was $\frac{1}{273}$ for each degree centigrade change in
temperature. Likewise, Charles reported
that if the volume was kept fixed and the
pressure variation noted, then the fractional increase in pressure for each degree
centigrade change in temperature was also
$\frac{1}{273}$ for many gases. Mathematically these two laws of Charles may be stated
as follows:

$$V = V_0 + V_0\frac{t}{273}, \quad P \text{ constant}$$

$$P = P_0 + P_0\frac{t}{273}, \quad V \text{ constant}$$

where the subscript 0 refers to the value of V or P when t, the centigrade
temperature, is 0°C. Figure 8.8 shows a plot of the volume variation with
temperature, the pressure held fixed. Evidently if $t = -273$°C then $V = V_0 -$
$V_0 = 0$ and $P = P_0 - P_0 = 0$. Physically however, this is not observed, since
all gases liquefy before reaching this temperature. At atmospheric pressure
nitrogen liquefies at -196°C, hydrogen at -253°C, and lowest of all,
helium liquefies at -269°C. However, the laws of Charles do imply that
-273°C *is the lowest temperature possible*, since even if the gas did not
liquefy—a so-called perfect gas—its volume or pressure would be zero at that
temperature, and what is more important as we shall see, its molecular energy
is zero. For this reason the temperature $t = -273$°C is called *absolute zero*,
and a natural thermometer scale is often used which starts with zero at this
point. This is called the *Kelvin* or *absolute scale;* its degree (°K) is of the same
size as the centigrade degree, so that an absolute temperature T is related to a
centigrade temperature t by the equation

$$T = t + 273°K$$

(We shall consistently use t for the centigrade scale, T for the Kelvin scale.)
On this temperature scale Charles' laws are written as

$$V = V_0 + V_0\frac{(T - 273)}{273} = V_0\frac{T}{273}$$

$$P = P_0 + P_0\frac{(T - 273)}{273} = P_0\frac{T}{273}$$

Designating as T_0 ($= 273°K$) the temperature $t = 0°C$ these laws may be written more symmetrically as:

$$\frac{V}{T} = \frac{V_0}{T_0}, \quad P \text{ constant} \qquad\qquad [8.3]$$

$$\frac{P}{T} = \frac{P_0}{T_0}, \quad V \text{ constant} \qquad\qquad [8.4]$$

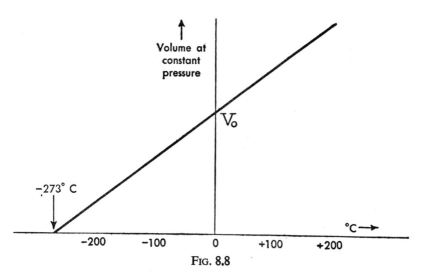

Volume at
constant
pressure

V_0

−273° C

−200   −100   0   +100   +200

°C →

FIG. 8.8

8.8 The General Gas Law

Boyle's law (Eq. 8.2) and the two forms of Charles' law (Eq. 8.3 and 8.4) may be combined into a single equation which relates the temperature, pressure, and volume of a given sample of gas. This equation is called the *general gas law* since it describes the three quantities, pressure, temperature, and volume in relation to each other and is the most general relation between the three simple observables of confined gases. Such an equation may be derived by analyzing a gas sample under changes of pressure and temperature one at a time, but it is simpler to write down the result and show that it unambiguously includes the three other equations. The result is

$$\frac{PV}{T} = \frac{P_0 V_0}{T_0} \qquad\qquad [8.5]$$

where P_0, V_0, T_0 are taken at some starting point, usually 0°C and 76 cm Hg of pressure. Clearly if T (absolute temperature) is constant, we have Boyle's law and understand Boyle's observation that his law applies only when the temperature is constant. If the volume is kept constant, V_0 cancels V in Eq. 8.5 and we have Eq. 8.4, Charles' law for constant volume. If the pressure is kept constant Eq. 8.5 reduces to Eq. 8.3, the constant pressure form of Charles' law. Hence we have shown that Eq. 8.5 contains the other three as special cases, and that these special cases hold under the conditions stated in the experimental laws.

It is possible to evaluate the right-hand side of Eq. 8.5 by arbitrarily agreeing on certain standard conditions. The convenient value for P_0 is that of normal atmospheric pressure, 76 cm of Hg or 1.01×10^6 dynes/cm²; likewise T_0 is most simply taken at 0°C, or $T_0 = 273°$K. This pressure and temperature are therefore called "normal pressure and temperature" and abbreviated N.T.P. The question of a "normal" volume is not so obvious, since the volume at P_0 and T_0 will depend on the mass of the gas. However, as we have seen, Dalton's and Avogadro's laws suggest strongly that, at least for chemical combinations, the gram-molecule or mole (gram-atom if the substance is monatomic) is of fundamental significance. Therefore, we shall choose as our "normal" *mass* 1 mole of gas. Dalton's law has shown that a mole of any substance has the same number of molecules as a mole of any other substance and Avogadro's law states that equal numbers of molecules of a gas occupy equal volumes; hence the *volume* of a mole of a gas is a fixed number that is easily measured—one simply obtains 32 gm of oxygen or 2 gm of hydrogen or 28 gm of nitrogen, etc., and observes its volume at N.T.P. The result is called the *molar volume* and is 22,400 cm³. It is this value we choose for V_0. Hence, giving the ratio P_0V_0/T_0 the symbol R, we have

$$R = P_0V_0/T_0 = 1.01 \times 10^6 \times 22{,}400/273 = 8.31 \times 10^7 \text{ erg/}°\text{K}$$

R is called the *molar gas constant*, and its unit ergs/°K is verified by writing the usual units equation:

$$R = \frac{P_0V_0}{T_0}$$

$$\text{Units of } R = \frac{\text{dyne}}{\text{cm}^2} \times \text{cm}^3 \times \frac{1}{°\text{K}} = \text{dyne-cm/}°\text{K} = \text{erg/}°\text{K}$$

In making a choice of normal quantities in the general gas law we have restricted V_0 to 1 mole of gas, hence the left side of Eq. 8.5 is likewise so restricted. This is an unnecessary limitation that can be removed by multiplying R by the fraction of a mole actually present. Calling this molar fraction f and writing the temperature T on the right side of the equation we have

$$\text{For 1 mole of gas} \quad PV = RT$$
$$\text{For } f \text{ moles of gas} \quad PV = fRT$$

[8.6]

Equation 8.6 is the most common form of the general gas law.

Example 1. What is the density of oxygen gas at N.T.P.? By definition, density is mass/volume, and 1 mole of O_2 (or any gas) occupies one molar volume at N.T.P.; so

$$\rho = \frac{m}{V} = \frac{32}{22,400} = 1.43 \times 10^{-3} \text{ gm/cm}^3 \quad \textit{Ans.}$$

Example 2. A certain gas has a volume of 200 cm³ when its pressure is 76 cm of Hg and its temperature is 10°C. It is allowed to expand to a new volume of 1000 cm³, at a new pressure of 10 cm of Hg. What is its temperature?

$P_0 = 76$ cm of Hg; $V_0 = 200$ cm³; $T_0 = 273 + 10 = 283°K$
$P = 10$ cm of Hg; $V = 1000$ cm³
$T = ?$

$$\frac{PV}{T} = \frac{P_0 V_0}{T_0}$$
$$\frac{10 \times 1000}{T} = \frac{76 \times 200}{283}$$
$$T = 186°K = -87°C \quad \textit{Ans.}$$

Example 3. What is the volume of 10 gm of oxygen of N.T.P.?

We know that 1 mole (32 gm) occupies 22,400 cm³ at N.T.P. Hence the volume of 10 gm is

$$\frac{10}{32} \times 22,400 = 7000 \text{ cm}^3 \quad \textit{Ans.}$$

Example 4. A flask of nitrogen (N_2) has a volume of 1000 cm³; the gas pressure is 2 atmospheres, its temperature 20°C. What is the mass of the gas?

$$PV = fRT$$

$P = 2 \times 1.01 \times 10^6$ dynes/cm²; $V = 1000$ cm³; $T = 293°C$, $R = 8.31 \times 10^7$
then

$$2 \times 1.01 \times 10^6 \times 10^3 = f \times 8.31 \times 10^7 \times 293$$
$$f = 0.083 \text{ moles}$$
$$1 \text{ mole of } N_2 \text{ is 28 gm; so } m = 0.083 \times 28 = 2.3 \text{ gm} \quad \textit{Ans.}$$

PROBLEMS

1. Each of the ice skates worn by a man weighing 75 kg has a length in contact with the ice of 15 cm. If the skate runners are 6 mm wide find the pressure on the ice due to either skate (one skate on the ice).   *Ans.* 8.15 megadynes/cm².

2. A solid steel post (density of 7.8 gm/cm³) of 2 m height, 20 cm diameter is resting on a horizontal floor. What pressure does it exert?
                                                         Ans. 1.53 × 10⁶ dynes/cm².

3. If "normal" atmospheric pressure will support a column of mercury ($\rho = 13.6$ gm/cm³) of 76.0 cm length, what column of water ($\rho = 1$ gm/cm³) will it support?

Ans. 10.3 m (34 ft).

4. At 0°C the volume of a certain gas is 500 cm³. What is its volume at -80°C if its pressure is unchanged?   *Ans.* 354 cm³.

5. A certain gas at N.T.P. occupies a volume of 500 cm³. Its temperature is raised to 50°C, and its pressure changes to 100 cm of Hg. What is its volume under these conditions?   *Ans.* 450 cm³.

6. Using Table C in the Appendix, determine what mass forms a mole of each of the following molecules: O_2, H_2O, HCN, NaCl, H_2SO_4, UF_6.

7. What is the volume of 5 moles of helium at 100°C and atmospheric pressure?

Ans. 153,000 cm³ or 153 liters.

8. What is the pressure of 0.2 moles of hydrogen whose volume is 100 cm³ and temperature -20°C?   *Ans.* 4.2×10^7 dynes/cm².

Suggested Reading

BRAGG, SIR WILLIAM, "Concerning the Nature of Things," London, G. Bell and Sons, 1925.

First lecture is a popular description of atomism. Entertaining.

DAMPIER, SIR WILLIAM, "A History of Science," New York, The Macmillan Co., 1946.

Pages 225–31 give a historical account of nineteenth century atomism.

GREGORY, J. G., "A Short History of Atomism," London, A. & C. Black, 1931.

Chapters I–IV treat the early history of the atomic concept. Chapters VII–VIII give Dalton's atomic theory.

HECHT, SELIG, "Explaining the Atom," New York, Viking Press, 1947.

Chapter I reviews in simple terms the evidence for atoms.

MOTT-SMITH, M., "Heat and its Workings," D. Appleton and Co., New York, 1933.

Chapters I–III are a good elementary account of the temperature concept and the behavior of gases.

MOULTON, F. R., and SCHIFFERES, J. J., "The Autobiography of Science," New York, Doubleday Doran and Co., 1945.

Pages 15–16 quote Lucretius and his ideas of atomism.

Heat Energy and the Kinetic Theory of Gases

9.1   Early Ideas

The birth of the mechanical theory of heat cannot be localized to any particular year. From early times friction and compression were known to produce heat, but no systematic theory of heat and molecular motion was possible until the atomic constitution of matter had been established. Daniel Bernoulli, who derived Boyle's law from a theory of motion of gas particles some hundred years before the full development of kinetic theory, also mentioned that such a theory could account for an increase in gas pressure on heating. This theory found no great acceptance and during the eighteenth and nineteenth centuries, heat was supposed to be a substance called "caloric" which actually flowed from one body to another. Caloric was a massless and colorless fluid and otherwise inaccessible to observation. When a flame was applied to a body, caloric was supposed to flow into the body from the flame. Friction was supposed to bring caloric up to the rubbed surfaces and heat them.

This kind of theorizing on the nature of heat bore a resemblance to the Greek speculative method in science, but its effort to flourish were in an era when inductive reasoning was shaping the progress of physics; caloric was made to stand the rigid test of experiments, and it failed. Bernoulli had already questioned it, and many others followed him in the effort. Count Rumford (an American Tory in the employ of the Elector of Bavaria) questioned how a boring tool could supply an unlimited amount of caloric to a cannon barrel, and concluded that heat was some form of motion of particles in the barrel. The final blows to the caloric theory came from the experiments of Joule and Kelvin. At about the same time Clausius and Maxwell developed a satisfactory theory of the behavior of gases based on the motions of molecules.

9.2   Joule's Experiment for the Energy Equivalent of Heat

The concept of this experiment is simple and straightforward. If heat is a form of motion of the molecules in a body, then to *increase* the heat mechanical work must be done. If a paddle-wheel is at rest in a container of water and at the same temperature as the water, then there should be no exchange of heat—either on the caloric theory or on the kinetic theory of heat. However, if the paddle-wheel is now rotated in the water, the caloric theory declares there will still be the same total amount of caloric, hence there will be no temperature increase; the kinetic theory demands that the water and paddle-wheel must heat up, because dynamical work is being expended on the system by friction between the water and paddle-wheel. This work must reappear as increased kinetic energy of the molecules; the amount of this increase will be indicated by the amount of temperature rise. Joule devised an experiment not only to show that mechanical work could be changed into thermal energy but also to measure the amount of work required to produce a certain amount of heat.

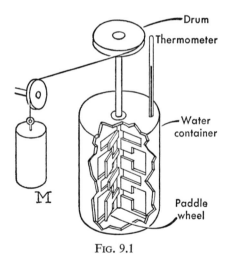

Drum

Thermometer

Water container

Paddle wheel

M

FIG. 9.1

Figure 9.1 is a schematic drawing of Joule's equipment. A mass M is attached to a cord which is wound around a drum. As the mass falls the drum rotates a paddle-wheel which is attached to it. The paddle-wheel is in a water bath that is well insulated from the room, to avoid all possible heat escape. The amount of mechanical work is just the loss in potential energy suffered by the mass in falling a distance h, that is, Mgh. If the amount of water is large compared to the mass of the stirrer and the container, we can neglect the small amount of heat they absorb. A temperature rise of the water bath will then be a measure of the heat gained by the water. The result Joule obtained was this:

Qualitatively: The temperature rise was directly proportional to the energy expended by the paddle-wheel.

Quantitatively: To raise the temperature of one gram of water by one degree centigrade requires 4.2×10^7 ergs (4.2 joules) of energy. (This amount of energy is called a calorie.)

Joule's experiment and many others which have followed it have given a firm experimental basis for the kinetic concept of heat. The next step is to ask if a theory can be devised which will include explanations for other heat phenomena such as the pressure a gas exerts when its temperature is increased, or the vaporization and boiling of a liquid, or the melting of a solid. Such a theory has been developed, but except for the part pertaining to gases the complexity makes it inappropriate to our study of atomic physics. This kinetic theory of gases was first worked out by Clausius and Maxwell. It is based completely on the dynamical idea of heat.

9.3 The Kinetic Theory of Gases

As with any theory in science arrived at inductively we must first review the experimental evidence on which to make our assumptions and test the theory. The main features of this evidence may be itemized as follows:

1. Heat is a form of molecular motion.
2. Temperature, a measure of the intensity of heat, must be proportional to the heat energy.
3. All gases obey (to a good approximation) the general gas law

$$PV = fRT$$

4. Gases obey Avogadro's law: Equal volumes of gases at N.T.P. have equal numbers of molecules.

To prevent the theory from becoming unwieldy we shall make certain simplifying assumptions (their validity must be investigated later) about confined gases:

1. The volume of the molecules themselves is negligible compared with the volume of their container.
2. All collisions made by the molecules with each other or with the walls of the container are *elastic* (K.E. is conserved).
3. There are no intermolecular forces except those involved in the collisions between molecules.

A gas obeying the above set of assumptions is said to be a "perfect gas." At ordinary temperatures and pressures most gases act as perfect gases to a good approximation.

With this evidence and set of approximations let us set up a model on which to make calculations. Suppose we have a cube (Fig. 9.2) of dimensions l cm on a side containing a total of n similar molecules, each of mass m gm. We suppose that these molecules are in motion, but do not require them all to have the same velocity; in fact, we shall assume that all velocities from zero to very large values are present. According to Newton's first law of motion any single molecule will move with constant velocity in a straight line until acted upon by an external force; this external force is produced by a collision either with another molecule or with a wall. Let us consider the effect of wall collisions; to eliminate molecular collisions we shall remove all the molecules but one and watch its motion. This molecule, number 1, will have a velocity of

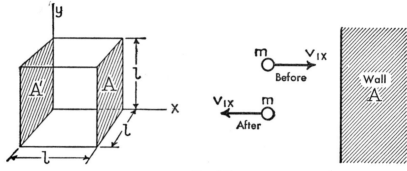

FIG. 9.2

v_1, with components v_{1x}, v_{1y}, v_{1z} along the three coordinate axes x, y, and z. If we further confine our attention to only the x direction, the time required by the molecule to go from wall A to wall A' and back to A along the x direction is just

$$t = \frac{2l}{v_{1x}} \text{ sec}$$

In this round trip molecule 1 hits wall A once; hence the number of collisions with wall A per second is just the reciprocal of the time per collision:

$$\frac{v_{1x}}{2l} \text{ collisions per sec}$$

These collisions are elastic by assumption, and are of the form discussed in §7.4, that is, a very light mass hitting a very heavy mass (the wall). As we saw there, the change of momentum received by the molecule is $2mv_{1x}$ (Eq. 7.8), and by the conservation of momentum this same amount (though opposite in sign) must have been imparted to the wall by the collision. The total amount of momentum received by the wall per second is then:

$$2mv_{1x} \cdot \frac{v_{1x}}{2l} = \frac{mv_{1x}^2}{l} \text{ gm-cm/sec}^2$$

But the change of momentum per second is just the force (see §7.3) on the wall due to molecule 1. If we now include the rest of the n molecules, each one will have an x-component motion which will produce its force on wall A; therefore the total force in the x direction due to the n molecules is

$$F_x = \frac{mv_{1x}^2}{l} + \frac{mv_{2x}^2}{l} + \cdots + \frac{mv_{nx}^2}{l} = \frac{m}{l} (v_{1x}^2 + \cdots + v_{nx}^2)$$

If we treat the y and z components of velocity of the molecules in the same way, we have

$$F_y = \frac{m}{l} (v_{1y}^2 + v_{2y}^2 + \cdots + v_{ny}^2)$$

$$F_z = \frac{m}{l} (v_{1z}^2 + v_{2z}^2 + \cdots + v_{nz}^2)$$

Now there is no experimental evidence to show that a gas exerts greater force in one direction than in any other. Hence we must assume that

$$F_x = F_y = F_z = F$$

where F without a subscript is the force on *any* wall due to the motion of the gas molecules. Thus $F_x + F_y + F_z = 3F$. Forming this sum:

$$3F = \frac{m}{l} (v_{1x}^2 + v_{1y}^2 + v_{1z}^2 + \cdots + v_{nx}^2 + v_{ny}^2 + v_{nz}^2)$$

In §2.5 it was pointed out that the value of a resultant vector in terms of its x, y, and z components is

$$v^2 = v_x^2 + v_y^2 + v_z^2$$

Therefore we can write the force equation in terms of these resultant speeds:

$$3F = \frac{m}{l} (v_1^2 + v_2^2 + \cdots + v_n^2)$$

As we have stated, the speeds of the molecules may have all values. However, we do not know the values of all these speeds; we must replace the individual speeds by an average speed. Since the speed appears in the force equation as a squared term it seems most logical to define an *average square*. We define this just as any average is defined: the sum divided by the number of quantities being added. Applying this, we have

$$\overline{v^2} = \frac{v_1^2 + v_2^2 + \cdots + v_n^2}{n}$$

This average is called the *mean-square speed*, and its square root, $\sqrt{\overline{v^2}}$, is called the *root-mean-square speed* (often abbreviated as rms speed). Using the mean-square speed we have

$$3F = \frac{m}{l} n\overline{v^2} \quad \text{or} \quad F = \tfrac{1}{3} \frac{m}{l} n\overline{v^2}$$

If we divide by l^2, we then have on the left-hand side the force per area on any wall, that is, the pressure on the wall

$$P = \frac{F}{l^2} = \tfrac{1}{3}\frac{m}{l^3}\,n\overline{v^2} = \tfrac{1}{3}\frac{m}{V}\,n\overline{v^2}$$

where $l^3 = V$, the volume of the cube. Rewriting, we have:

$$PV = \tfrac{1}{3}nm\overline{v^2} \qquad\qquad\qquad [9.1]$$

Equation 9.1 is one of the principal results of the kinetic theory of gases. It relates the measurable quantities pressure and volume on the left-hand side to the dynamical quantities of molecular mass and mean-square velocity on the right-hand side.

9.4 Molecular Speeds

A simple deduction from Eq. 9.1 allows us to calculate the root-mean-square speeds of molecules of various gases. Consider the factor mn; it is just the total mass of gas in the box; hence nm/V is the density of the gas, i.e.,

$$\rho = \frac{nm}{V}\ \text{gm/cm}^3$$

so that

$$P = \tfrac{1}{3}\frac{nm}{V}\overline{v^2} = \tfrac{1}{3}\rho\overline{v^2}$$

or

$$\text{Root-mean-square speed} = \sqrt{\overline{v^2}} = \sqrt{\frac{3P}{\rho}} \qquad\qquad [9.2]$$

For nitrogen gas ρ is 0.00126 gm/cm^3 at N.T.P. (0°C and 1.01×10^6 dynes/cm^2). Thus the rms speed of nitrogen molecules is

$$\sqrt{\overline{v^2}} = \sqrt{\frac{3 \times 1.01 \times 10^6}{0.00126}} = 4.93 \times 10^4\ \text{cm/sec}$$

This is about 1100 mi/hr! Table 9.1 shows the rms speeds of the molecules of several gases at N.T.P.

Table 9.1

GAS	RMS SPEED
Hydrogen	18.39×10^4 cm/sec
Helium	13.10
Water vapor	6.15
Nitrogen	4.93
Oxygen	4.61
Argon	4.31

In the case of hydrogen and helium the root-mean-square speeds are close to the speed necessary for a body to escape from the earth's field of gravity, which is some 1.1×10^6 cm/sec or about 7 mi/sec. We shall see that many of the molecules in a gas are moving faster than the rms speed, so that some fraction of them will escape from the earth. For the light gases this fraction is quite appreciable, as is borne out by the almost total lack of hydrogen and helium in the earth's atmosphere. Probably some billions of years ago both of

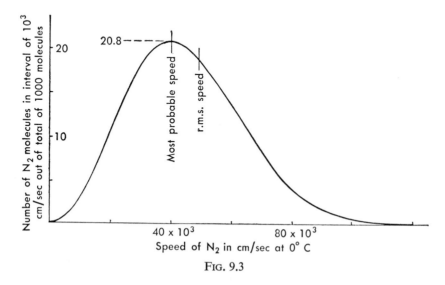

FIG. 9.3

these gases made up a sizable part of our atmosphere. On bodies such as the moon (where the velocity of escape is only 2.4×10^5 cm/sec) a good fraction of all the molecules in Table 9.1 would have sufficiently high velocities to escape. It is well known that the moon has no atmosphere.

We have thus far used only the rms speed of the molecules, without stating how the speeds are distributed about this value. The calculation of this distribution is mathematically too complex for this book. The result can best be shown by a graph drawn from the distribution formula of Maxwell and Boltzmann which is derived from the laws of probability as applied to a kinetic-theory gas. The curve of Fig. 9.3 drawn for 1000 nitrogen molecules at 0°C shows the result of their formula. For any other kind of gas or different temperature a curve of similar shape will be obtained. The height of the curve represents the number of molecules having velocities in a certain small range (a range of 10^3 cm/sec in Fig. 9.3) so that where the curve has a large height many molecules cluster about that speed. We see that the curve of Fig. 9.3

is highest for a speed of 40×10^3 cm/sec. This is called the most probable speed. The rms speed of Eq. 9.2 lies somewhat to the right of this most probable speed (greater than the most probable speed by a factor 1.225).

The height of the curve can also be interpreted as the probability or chance that a single molecule has a speed lying in a certain range. We see that this probability falls off rapidly on both the high and low sides of the most prob-

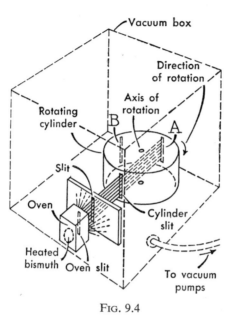

able speed. For example, the probability that a molecule has a speed twice the most probable value is only 20% as great as its having the most probable value, and a speed of three times the most probable value is too small to be seen on the graph of Fig. 9.3. Consequently, nearly all molecules have speeds which differ by only a small factor from either the root-mean-square or the most probable values.

The distribution formula of Fig. 9.3 has been verified by several direct experiments. The arrangement used by Zartman is shown in Fig. 9.4. Bismuth metal is boiled in a vacuum oven. A thin beam of bismuth atoms emerges from the system of two

FIG. 9.4

slits. A hollow, slitted cylinder rotates at high speed on an axis which is in line with and parallel to the slits. Once in each revolution the atom beam enters the cylinder. The atoms in the beam, being entirely free from the cylinder, do not rotate with it but strike at the point on the cylinder surface which is in line with the beam direction when they have completed their trip across the cylinder diameter. Fast-moving atoms strike near the point A which was in line with the slits when the atoms entered the cylinder; slower atoms strike farther along the cylinder toward point B. If the cylinder is very cold, the atoms stick where they hit and build up a layer of bismuth metal which is thicker at the points on the wall corresponding to the speeds of greater probability. In fact, the layer thickness at any point is proportional to the number of atoms having a speed which carries them across the cylinder at the time at which that point is in line with the slits. By measuring the layer thickness along AB Zartman obtained a curve like Fig. 9.3, plotting the length along the cylinder circumference on the horizontal axis and the layer thickness vertically. Because of the very large values of molecular speeds (about 3×10^4 cm/sec for the most probable speed of bismuth atoms at Zartman's oven temperature) the cylinder must rotate at high speeds in order to give a layer of appreciable length. Zartman used rotational speeds of some 240 rev/sec.

9.5   The Brownian Movement

The basic assumption of kinetic theory that the molecules of a gas are in rapid motion and are undergoing random collisions with each other and the walls gains experimental support from the analysis of the *Brownian movement* of microscopic particles. This phenomenon was discovered in 1827 by the botanist Brown who observed that small particles suspended in a medium, such as smoke particles in air, seem to possess a completely randon but continual motion whose paths might be indicated as in Fig.

(a)   (b)

FIG. 9.5

9.5a. Some 50 years elapsed before the significance of the Brownian move-ment was understood. Though a smoke particle large enough to be seen in a microscope will consist of a cluster of several thousand molecules, it is being bombarded steadily by collisions with individual molecules of the gas (Fig. 9.5b); since these collisions are random, at any given instant there will not be an equal number of molecules hitting the particle from all sides. Consequently, an unbalanced force must exist under which the particle moves. The next instant this distribution of bombarding molecules may be completely shifted, and the particle will move in some other direction. Careful observation of these motions reveals that the particle has a mean kinetic energy equal to that of the gas in which it is suspended—in confirmation of the kinetic theory of gas.

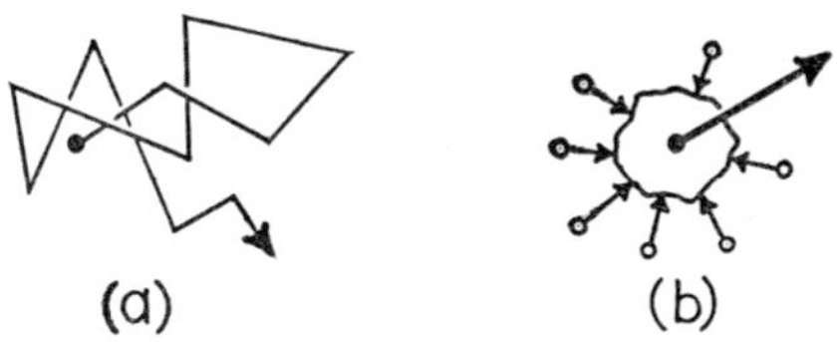

9.6   The Energies of the Molecules

To test the validity of the kinetic theory of gases it must be subjected to the tests of experiments. Its prediction of molecular velocities was well verified by the Zartman experiment, and the theory supplied a plausible explanation for the absence of an atmosphere on the moon and for the Brownian move-ment. We now ask how it can justify the general gas law: $PV = fRT$. If we turn to Eq. 9.1 of the theory we find

$$PV = \tfrac{1}{3}nm\overline{v^2}$$

Hence, according to this,

$$\tfrac{1}{3}nm\overline{v^2} = fRT$$

Now f is the number of moles of the gas at N.T.P., or n/f is the number of gas molecules per mole. This ratio is known as *Avogadro's number N:*

$$N = \frac{n}{f} = \text{Number of molecules per mole of substance}$$

It's value has been experimentally determined to be (see §13.6)

$$N = 6.02 \times 10^{23} \text{ molecules per mole}$$

Hence

$$\frac{nm\overline{v^2}}{3f} = RT$$

or

$$\tfrac{1}{3}Nm\overline{v^2} = RT$$

giving

$$T = \tfrac{1}{3}\frac{Nm\overline{v^2}}{R} = \tfrac{2}{3} \cdot \frac{1}{R} (\tfrac{1}{2} Nm\overline{v^2}) \qquad\qquad [9.3]$$

$$= \tfrac{2}{3} \cdot \frac{1}{R} \cdot (\text{mean kinetic energy of the molecules})$$

That is, the absolute temperature is nothing more than a measure of the mean kinetic energy of the molecules. At absolute zero this mean kinetic energy is zero; it is evident that there must be an absolute zero of temperature because kinetic energy cannot be less than zero (that is, negative).

Thus, the kinetic theory of gases is in agreement with the two items of evidence listed as 2 and 3 in §9.3, namely, the relation between heat energy and temperature and the general gas law. It may be illustrative to calculate the total heat energy content of a given gas. Suppose we consider 1 mole of a gas at normal pressure and at room temperature ($21°C = 294°K$). Rewriting Eq. 9.3,

$$\begin{aligned}
\text{K.E. of gas} &= \tfrac{3}{2} RT \\
&= \tfrac{3}{2} \times 8.31 \times 10^7 \times 294 \\
&= 3.66 \times 10^{10} \text{ ergs} = 3.66 \times 10^3 \text{ joules}
\end{aligned}$$

This is the amount of energy that would be needed to heat up a mole of gas (observe it does not matter what kind of gas) from absolute zero to room temperature.

9.7   Avogadro's Law

Finally, the kinetic theory must corroborate Avogadro's law: Equal volumes of gases at N.T.P. contain equal numbers of molecules. Suppose we have two kinds of gases, one indicated by subscript 1, the other by subscript 2. We write Eq. 9.1 twice:

$$P_1V_1 = \tfrac{1}{3}n_1m_1\overline{v_1^2} \qquad P_2V_2 = \tfrac{1}{3}n_2m_2\overline{v_2^2}$$

Let both gases have the same pressure and volume, so $P_1V_1 = P_2V_2$; therefore,

$$\tfrac{1}{3}n_1m_1\overline{v_1^2} = \tfrac{1}{3}n_2m_2\overline{v_2^2}$$

also let the gases have the same temperature, that is,

$$\tfrac{1}{2}m_1\overline{v_1^2} = \tfrac{1}{2}m_2\overline{v_2^2}$$

so

$$n_1 = n_2$$

which is just Avogadro's law.

9.8   The Significance of Avogadro's Number N

The value of Avogadro's number to atomic physics is considerably greater than its rather inconspicuous appearance in kinetic theory would indicate. If we couple with it the value of the molar volume the significance may be pointed up in the following statement:

There are 6.02×10^{23} (N) molecules in 1 mole of any substance; and if that substance is a gas at N.T.P. 6.02×10^{23} molecules occupy a volume of 22,400 cm^3.

(Remember that if the substance is monatomic then the word "atoms" replaces "molecules" and "gram-atom" replaces "mole.") Several striking calculations can be made with this information.

Mass of a Molecule.   A mole of hydrogen (H_2) is 2 gm and this mass contains $N = 6.02 \times 10^{23}$ molecules. Therefore, one hydrogen molecule has a mass of $2/(6.02 \times 10^{23}) = 3.32 \times 10^{-24}$ gm, or an *atom* of hydrogen is just one-half of this, 1.66×10^{-24} gm. In the same way an atom of uranium (atomic mass number 238) has a mass of $238/(6.02 \times 10^{23}) = 395 \times 10^{-24}$ gm.

Number of Molecules.   How many molecules has 1 cm^3 of oxygen gas at N.T.P.? A molar volume of *any* gas is 22,400 cm^3 and contains 6.02×10^{23} molecules. So 1 cm^3 of *any* gas contains $(6.02 \times 10^{23})/22,400 = 2.69 \times 10^{19}$ molecules. Or, how many molecules are contained in 1 gm of oxygen? We know that 32 gm (1 mole) contains 6.02×10^{23} molecules; so 1 gm has $\tfrac{1}{32} \times 6.02 \times 10^{23} = 1.88 \times 10^{22}$ molecules.

Size of the Molecules (Roughly). Molecules of a gas move about with great freedom, as we have seen; the extension of the kinetic theory to liquids and solids indicates that molecules in a liquid move with much less freedom, whereas molecules in a solid are nearly touching. Actually x ray and other evidence shows that most solids possess a symmetrical array of atoms, that is, are crystals, but if for the instant we choose to overlook this fact and assume the atoms of a solid such as aluminum are packed tightly together and furthermore that these atoms are spherical in shape, we can make a calculation of their radius. The density of aluminum is 2.7 gm/cm³, its atomic mass number is 27; hence 1 cm³ of aluminum is 0.1 gram-atom, therefore has $0.1 \times 6.02 \times 10^{23} = 6.02 \times 10^{22}$ atoms. If each of these is a sphere of volume $\frac{4}{3}\pi r^3$, then crudely

$$6.02 \times 10^{22} \times \tfrac{4}{3}\pi r^3 = 1 \text{ cm}^3$$

or

$$r = 3.4 \times 10^{-8} \text{ cm}$$

We can place little reliance on this figure other than as an order of magnitude, namely, the atomic radius is a few times 10^{-8} cm.

9.9 Validity of the Kinetic Theory Assumptions

We have gone to some length to demonstrate the successes of the kinetic theory, but have not mentioned its limitations. Most of the latter rest in the assumptions we listed earlier. If a gas is very dense, as for instance under high pressure, the volume of the molecules themselves must be considered. Furthermore, intermolecular forces do exist and become an appreciable factor when the molecules are forced very close together; it is partly for this reason that the kinetic theory for liquids and solids is much more complicated than for gases. The assumption that all collisions are elastic ignored the fact that molecules and atoms have an internal structure, and some energy may be given to the components of this structure.

9.10 Philosophical Implications of Kinetic Theory

The most striking aspect of Newton's dynamics is the great precision with which it describes mechanical motions. This success made it popular to assume that all nature operated within a strictly dynamical structure; it only remained for the scientist to ferret out and properly analyze the forces and motions responsible. Such a philosophy of nature is often termed "mechanistic." It presumes that there is a fixed and definite, though undoubtly highly complicated, plan under which all natural events must inevitably occur. If we are unable to predict properly the course of such events, it is not because nature is unpredictable, but rather because man's mentality is limited and his measuring instruments inaccurate. To a superman nature would be completely knowable—the plan and the structure exist to be known. Some less cautious philosophers went further to extend these beliefs to animate nature; thus the exact dimensions, position, and rate of growth of a leaf of a tree was part of some great natural plan—and the leaf could not have grown differently.

In one stroke kinetic theory both aided and questioned this mechanistic philosophy of nature. It demonstrated that heat is completely a mechanical phenomenon and molecular processes obey Newton's laws of motion. In this respect the kinetic theory of gases was a great triumph for the concept of a mechanical universe. On the other hand, the kinetic theory introduced ambiguity, for it offered no way of determining what energy a single molecule had; it could only name the most probable energy. In fact, a molecule undergoing several billion collisions per second could scarcely be identified with any particular amount of energy. The question of how much energy a single molecule has makes very little sense. If nature has a plan for every single natural event it must be fantastically complex even for such a simple thing as a cubic centimeter of gas.

This concept of probability rather than certainty in the ways of natural events immediately simplifies, at least in principle, the problem of analyzing atomic and molecular phenomena. It abandons all ideas of describing the motion of a single sub-perceptible particle, since in all likelihood the particle's motion alters too frequently to allow description even if we were able to concentrate our attention on it. We lose our assurance that there is ever a possibility of *completely* describing single-particle motion, even if we were equipped with perfect measuring instruments. Our study of atoms and their constituent parts will bring more light on this philosophical problem; the kinetic theory was the first inkling that the problem even existed.

PROBLEMS

1. A molecule having a velocity of 500 m/sec bounces between two walls which are 10 cm apart, always hitting the walls perpendicularly. What is the time between collisions as measured at one of the walls? How many collisions occur at this wall per second?   *Ans.* 4×10^{-4} sec; 2500 collisions/sec.

2. Steel shot from a group of air rifles are fired at a fixed steel plate. Each shot weighs 10 gm and hits the plate with a velocity of 100 m/sec. Calculate the force on the steel plate (assuming elastic impacts) if the plate is hit by 1000 shot/sec.
                                      Ans. 2×10^{8} dynes.

3. The components of the velocity of a certain particle are observed to be: 30

cm/sec in the x direction, 60 cm/sec in the y direction and 20 cm/sec in the z direction. Find the velocity of the particle.   *Ans.*   70 cm/sec.

4.   The density of helium is 1.76×10^{-4} at N.T.P. What is the rms velocity of the helium atoms?

5.   What is the total kinetic energy of the molecules of 2 gm of hydrogen (H_2) at N.T.P.?   *Ans.* 3.40×10^{10} ergs or 3400 joules.

6.   How much energy must be removed from the gas of Problem 5 to reduce its temperature to 1°K?   *Ans.*   3387 joules.

7.   How many molecules of hydrogen (H_2) are in one cubic centimeter at N.T.P.? What is the mass of this volume of H_2? What is the mass of each molecule?
                Ans. 2.7×10^{19} molecules; 8.9×10^{-5} gm; 3.3×10^{-24} gm.

8.   The best vacuum yet attained in the laboratory is a pressure of 10^{-9} cm of Hg. How many molecules still remain in one cm³ in this so-called vacuum?
                                    Ans.   354 million molecules.

9.   If a hole is made in an ordinary light bulb of 500 cm³ volume that had been completely evacuated, and molecules of nitrogen are allowed to pass in at the rate of one million per second, how long would be required to fill the bulb to atmospheric pressure?   *Ans.* 1.34×10^{16} sec, or 426 million years.

Suggested Reading

BORN, MAX, "The Restless Universe," London, Blackie & Son, 1935.
    Chapter I is an excellent discussion on the background of kinetic theory.

DAMPIER, SIR WILLIAM, "A History of Science," New York, The Macmillan Co., 1946.
    Pages 245–57 treat the mechanical theory of heat and kinetic theory of gases.

EDDINGTON, SIR ARTHUR, "The Nature of the Physical World," New York, The Macmillan Co., 1933.
    Chapter IV contains an excellent treatment on the meaning of probability and the availability of heat energy. Readable.

JEANS, SIR JAMES, "The Mysterious Universe," New York, The Macmillan Co., 1937.
    Chapter VII reviews the history of the development of kinetic theory.

MAGIE, W. F., "Source Book in Physics," New York, McGraw-Hill Book Co., 1935.
    Page 203, excerpts from Joule's experiments on the mechanical equivalent of heat. Page 247, Bernoulli's early (1738) treatment of the kinetic theory of gas pressure. Page 146, Rumford's experiments on heat production.

MOTT-SMITH, M., "The Story of Energy," New York, D. Appleton-Century Co., 1934.
    Chapters VII through XV contain a very understandable discussion of heat and energy.

CHAPTER 10

Periodic Motions and Waves

10.1 Periodic Motions

Generally speaking it is possible to divide mechanical motions into two classes: those which proceed from a start to a finish, such as the motion of a falling body, and those which repeat themselves, such as the motion of the moon around the earth. Of the repeating kind, the simplest and indeed the commonest have a certain regularity of repetition; they repeat in a fixed time interval and during every interval the motion is the same in all respects. These

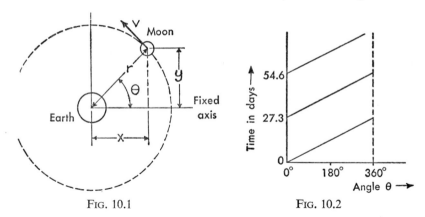

FIG. 10.1   FIG. 10.2

motions are called *periodic*, and the time interval for repetition is called the *period* of the motion. The motion of the moon is such a periodic motion; its period is the 27.33 days required to make one revolution around the earth, and as we know the motion has repeated itself with this same period for at least the several thousands of years of astronomical records.

To simplify further and specify repeating motions we should inquire as to the exact form of motion during a period. As an example we will consider the motion of the moon (Fig. 10.1). The moon's orbit results from the gravitational attraction of the earth which gives rise to a constant centripetal ac-

113

celeration v^2/r where both v, the moon's speed in its orbit, and r, the distance from the center of the earth to the center of the moon, are approximately constant. In describing the periodic character of the motion we must decide upon some measurable quantity and consider its variations in time. In such problems the choice of this variable is quite important since only certain choices give a simple answer. In the moon problem one choice is the angle θ between the earth-moon line and some axis fixed in space and lying in the plane of the moon's orbit. This angle evidently increases uniformly with time, as in Fig. 10.2, where time is counted from the instant when $\theta = 0$.

Another choice is the distance x (Fig. 10.1) which is the projection of the moon's instantaneous position on the fixed axis. This is also a suitable variable since there is only one value of x having the same direction of change, i.e., increase or decrease, for each position of the moon. Now x does not simply increase uniformly with time during each period as does θ. Rather, x satisfies the equation.*

$$x = \sqrt{r^2 - y^2}$$

Graphically, x varies with θ, the angle, and with t, the time, as in Fig. 10.3. Surprisingly, this choice of x as the variable is more useful in many cases than

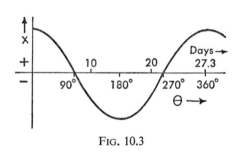

FIG. 10.3

the angle θ, even though x does not increase uniformly with time. In fact, motions in which the variable changes with time in the way shown in Fig. 10.3 are extremely common. They are called *simple periodic motions* (and the variation with time is said to be "sinusoidal").

Some insight into these motions can be had by considering the forces in the moon problem from a slightly different point of view. As we know, the force on the moon is a constant earthwardly directed force caused by the gravitational attraction. This force may be resolved into two components at any instant, one along x, F_x, and one along y, F_y, neither of which is in itself constant in time, though the magnitude of their vector sum remains constant in time. Consider F_x at the instant depicted in Fig. 10.4. It bears the same relation to F as x bears to r. Hence

$$\frac{F_x}{F} = \frac{x}{r}$$

* A better formula uses trigonometry, writing $x = r \cos \theta$, where θ increases uniformly with time.

or

$$F_x = \frac{F}{r} x$$

Since F does not change with time, F_x is proportional to x. A similar relation holds for F_y. We may, therefore, think of the motion as resulting from two forces, one along x and one along y, each varying in time so that it is propor-

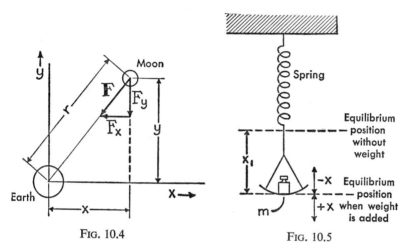

FIG. 10.4   FIG. 10.5

tional to the displacement x or y, and each pointing toward the origin of the axes, the earth. The two forces add, of course, at every instant to give the true earthwardly directed gravitational force. However, the moon's motion could equally well be due to two such forces.

10.2   Hooke's Law Forces

In a problem like the one discussed, the introduction of the two perpendicular forces certainly produced no simplification. However, if only *one* of the inwardly directed forces proportional to the displacement was present, the displacement would vary exactly as does x in the moon problem. That is, a single force of such a type (one whose magnitude is proportional to the displacement) produces simple periodic motion along the line on which the force acts.

So-called elastic forces are of this type. They are described by *Hooke's law* which states that the forces due to elastic connections (springs, solid deformable bodies, certain types of electrical attractions, intramolecular forces, etc.) are directed toward the point of connection and are proportional to the displacement from the equilibrium position (the amount of "stretch"). Thus when a spring is used as a balance (Fig. 10.5) for determining weights, the spring stretches an amount x_1, which is proportional to the weight put on to the pan. Since this weight is mg and the system is in equilibrium, the spring must generate an upward force mg which is proportional to x_1. It is clear that such a force is just like the x-component force in the moon problem. It is a force proportional to displacement. Therefore, if the weighted pan is stretched an additional amount x from the new equilibrium position and released, the pan will move from $+x$ to $-x$ and back just as in Fig. 10.3, except for a difference in the period. If M is the total mass of pan and weight, the period p of the motion (the time for one *complete* vibratory motion) can be calculated to be

$$p = 2\pi \sqrt{\frac{M}{k}} \ \text{sec}$$

where k, the so-called spring constant is the force in dynes necessary to stretch the spring 1 cm, or generally the stretching force per centimeter. A stiff spring has a large k and so a small period for a given attached weight as compared with a soft spring.

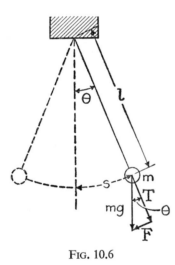

Another well-known machine which exhibits simple periodic motion is the simple pendulum (a mass swinging at the end of a massless rod). Here the angle θ (Fig. 10.6), between the pendulum and the vertical, is chosen as the variable. The force of gravity on the pendulum bob is resolved into a component T, balanced by the tension in the rod and a force F which is directed along the path of the motion. For small angles F is proportional to θ, hence is also proportional to s, the displacement. The period p is the time for a complete swing, from right to left and back again. Since both g and l

FIG. 10.6

are easily kept constant to a high degree, a pendulum has a fixed period and is often used for keeping time. Or, by measuring p and l it may be used to find the acceleration due to gravity g. Its period can be shown to be

$$p = 2\pi \sqrt{\frac{l}{g}} \ \text{sec}$$

10.3   Wave Motion

The transmission of a periodic motion through a medium or empty space is called a *wave*. There are many kinds of waves in physics, differing in the kind of stimulus which is transmitted, but the same in several respects. One important kind is observed in the motions of bulk matter along the course of the wave; waves on ropes, water waves, and sound waves are of this type. These are the most easily visualized. In another type of wave electric and magnetic forces are transmitted through matter or empty space; these are called electromagnetic waves, of which light and radio waves are examples. Still another type are the waves associated with atomic particles, the de-Broglie waves which give the probability of observing the particle at a certain position. These are perhaps the most difficult to visualize.

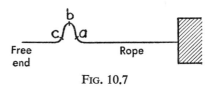

FIG. 10.7

Waves and periodic motion are intimately related; indeed a wave is observed by the periodic motion which it induces on a particle. A water wave passes along the surface of a lake and causes a cork to bob up and down in a periodic motion, and it is the bobbing cork or other reference particle which assures us of the wave's existence. A radio wave strikes an antenna and induces periodic motions of the electrons in the antenna and the wires and vacuum tubes in the radio receiver. A neutron having just the right deBroglie wave length induces a periodic disturbance in an atomic nucleus which tears it apart, while another neutron "out-of-tune" with the nucleus passes through without effect.

10.4   The Concept of a Wave

The wave concept is more abstract than a mechanical motion of a particle, since a wave is not a "thing" but a disturbance which is propagated.

Consider, for example, a stretched rope with a free end and suppose that this end is quickly jerked up and back to its original position (Fig. 10.7). Instead of merely displacing the entire rope along some sort of smooth curve, this procedure produces a pulse which moves along the rope. The particles at some distance from the free end do not immediately receive the information that the motion has occurred but only at a later time when the pulse is completed, so that point (a) on the "bump" tells first of the early upward part of the pulse, (b) of the greatest upward excursion, and (c) of the return. The pulse is a type of wave, a disturbance which is propagated down the rope.

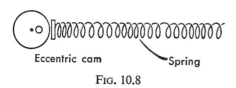

FIG. 10.8

A similar situation occurs when the free end of a coiled spring is suddenly stretched and then returned to its original position. A stretching or compressional wave is sent along the spring (Fig. 10.8).

Such single wave disturbances or pulses are less common in nature than a *continuous train of waves* originating from a continuous oscillation. If the stretched rope is steadily moved up and down with periodic motion, waves are continuously sent from the driven end and follow each other down the rope. If the oscillating source follows simple periodic motion the waves are also simple periodic. That is, each particle of the rope oscillates with a simple periodic motion similar to that of the driven end, though successive particles

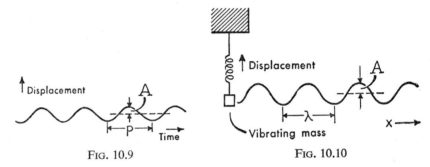

FIG. 10.9   FIG. 10.10

undergo their motion in sequence as the wave travels down the rope. Furthermore, at a particular instant of time the displacement varies in an oscillating manner as one goes along the rope. The curve of Fig. 10.9 shows the variation of the displacement with time *for a particular rope particle*. As in simple periodic motion, p is the period. Figure 10.10 shows the displacement of the rope particles *at a particular instant* as a function of the distance along the rope. The "period" in *distance* along the rope in Fig. 10.10 is called the *wave length* λ (lambda, the Greek *l*). The maximum disturbance labeled A is called the *amplitude*. The wave is periodic in both time and space; if one could "freeze" the medium (the rope in this case) for an instant of time, the disturbance along the medium would be periodic; or if attention is concentrated on only one particle of the medium, the motion of that particle is periodic. This double periodicity is characteristic of all waves whether in ropes or springs, sound waves, electromagnetic waves, or the deBroglie waves of atomic particles.

10.5   The Wave Velocity

By reference to Figs. 10.9 and 10.10 we see that at a particular instant two particles along the wave path are undergoing identical motions if they are separated by a distance λ, the wave length. And, since in a time p a single particle has completed a whole oscillation and is about to begin the next, we may define the wave velocity as

$$v = \frac{\lambda}{p}$$

i.e., the velocity of the disturbance which moves a distance λ in the time p. This is more frequently written as

$$v = \lambda \nu \qquad\qquad [\,10.1\,]$$

where ν (nu, Greek n) is called the *frequency* of the wave. The frequency is defined as the number of oscillations per second; quite evidently $\nu = 1/p$. Equation 10.1 applies to all kinds of wave motion.

Example 1. A tuning fork vibrating at a frequency of 100 cycles/sec sets up a wave in a string. The wave length is measured to be 12 cm. What is the wave velocity?

GIVEN: $\lambda = 12$ cm; $\nu = 100$ cycles/sec

$\qquad v = ?$

Solution: $v = \lambda \nu$

$\qquad\qquad = 12 \times 100 = 1200$ cm/sec   *Ans.*

Example 2. A broadcasting station is "tuned in" at 750 kilocycles/sec on the radio dial. Radio waves travel at a velocity of 3×10^{10} cm/sec. What is the wave length?

GIVEN: $\nu = 750 \times 10^3$ cycles/sec; $v = 3 \times 10^{10}$ cm/sec

$\qquad \lambda = ?$

Solution: $\lambda = \dfrac{v}{\nu}$

$\qquad\qquad = \dfrac{3 \times 10^{10}}{7.5 \times 10^5} = 4 \times 10^4$ cm $= 400$ meters   *Ans.*

10.6 Kinds of Waves

In §10.4 a distinction was made between a wave pulse, in which a single disturbance is propagated, and a wave train, in which a continuous series of disturbances is propagated; more particularly, we simplified the problem of the wave train by assuming the source of the disturbance was moving with simple periodic motion, thus allowing us to assign to the resulting wave a period, a frequency and a wave length. Yet we recognize from Figs. 10.7 and 10.8 that there are two ways in which a wave pulse or a wave train might be propagated. In Fig. 10.7 (and Figs. 10.9 and 10.10) the motion of the medium is perpendicular (transverse) to the direction of propagation; such a wave is called a *transverse wave*. On the other hand, Fig. 10.8 shows a situation in which the motion is along the direction of wave propagation; such a wave is called a *longitudinal wave*. All waves found in nature can be classified in one or the other of these divisions, or in a combination of the two. Water ripples, vibrating strings, electromagnetic waves (light) are examples of transverse wave motion while compression waves in springs, shock waves (from an explosion), and sound waves are longitudinal in character.

In a study of atomic physics the nature of electromagnetic waves is of prime importance, and consequently the remainder of this discussion will be concentrated on transverse wave motion in general and light waves in particular. In so narrowing our attention we are promptly confronted with a question:

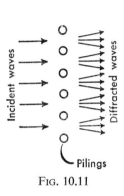

FIG. 10.11

How do we know light is a wave? The detection of wave motion is simple enough for rope and water waves; we see the wave propagating, and we can directly measure its frequency and velocity. Propagating sound waves can also be studied by observing the frequency with the aid of a thin diaphragm placed in the path of the waves; the bulk motion of the air caused by the wave will displace the diaphragm, and the displacement can be measured either directly or by the electrical impulse it can produce (the microphone); the velocity of a sound wave is sufficiently small (some 340 m/sec) to measure with the help of a measured distance and a stop-watch. However, light eludes all such simple approaches; neither its frequency nor its velocity is sufficiently low to allow a simple mechanical method of measurement, and deBroglie waves are the most elusive of all. We shall see later that they are so abstract that only the most indirect experiments reveal their presence. Yet we have declared that light *is* a wave, and that deBroglie waves do exist; the evidence for this assurance arises from two special characteristics of all waves: *diffraction* and *interference*. These two phenomena are so closely associated that we shall treat them under the same heading.*

10.7 The Diffraction and Interference of Light Waves

When in a homogeneous medium free of obstacles light travels in straight lines. This statement is also true for all other kinds of waves, but a little thought will make apparent that the phrase "free of obstacles" is essential. Consider what happens when water waves approach a row of obstacles such as dock pilings (Fig. 10.11); the waves seem to bend somewhat

---

* A third characteristic, polarization, determines uniquely if a wave is transverse or not; its elaboration takes us too far afield for the purposes of this book.

about the pilings, and the smaller the space between pilings the more marked is this bending. A similar phenomenon occurs with sound waves—we can hear sound that enters through door or window cracks without being directly in line with the door or window; the sound spreads out as it emerges from such openings. The bending of a wave about an obstacle is called *diffraction*. We have little difficulty observing the diffraction of water or sound waves, but its detection in the case of light waves depends on the phenomenon of interference.

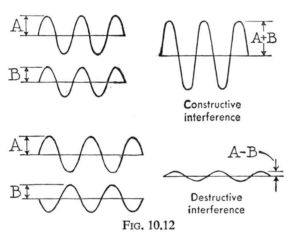

Fig. 10.12

Interference is the addition (either positive or negative) of two or more similar waves that have crossed each other's path in space. The waves may aid or destroy one another, that is, they may *constructively* or *destructively* interfere. If continuous trains of waves are to interfere they must have exactly the same wave length, though trains of waves having nearly the same wave length may interfere momentarily or even periodically. The requirement for interference between wave trains is evident from Fig. 10.12. If the two waves of amplitudes A and B have the same wave length and if they are exactly *in step* (the peaks and valleys superimpose) constructive interference is the result; if B is *out of step by one-half wave length* relative to A, the two waves destructively interfere. Evidently if the amplitudes A and B are equal, the result of constructive interference is a wave of double amplitude, while destructive interference leaves no wave at all.

10.8 Young's Double-Slit Experiment

To understand how the phenomenon of interference reveals the diffraction of light let us review the definitive experiment performed by Young in

1790. Incidentally, it was this experiment that ended a long standing controversy over the wave nature of light. The essential components of Young's experiment are shown in Fig. 10.13a. Light traveling through the single slit S_3 falls upon a pair of narrow slits* S_1 and S_2 which lie close together. (The

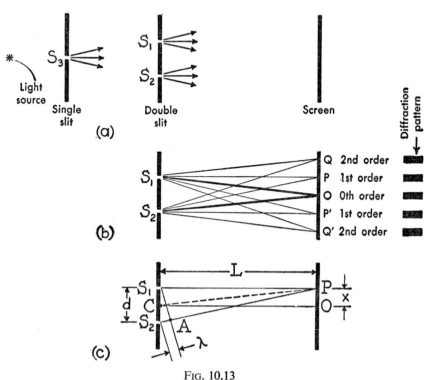

FIG. 10.13

slit widths and separation are exaggerated in Fig. 10.13; a reasonable slit width is 0.1 or 0.2 mm, with a slit separation of 0.4 or 0.5 mm.) The light leaving S_1 and S_2 is diffracted, and two possible rays of light are S_1O and S_2O (Fig. 10.13b), where O is a point on the screen opposite the slit separation; but the paths S_1O and S_2O are exactly the same length, and the two rays must therefore arrive at the screen exactly in step, producing constructive interference. Hence there should be light at point O. Now consider a point P a distance x along the screen from O (Fig. 10.13c); the ray S_1P has traveled a distance L cm, but S_2P has traveled a distance *greater than* L by an amount S_2A. If this increased path length S_2A is just *one* wave length then the ray

---

* Young used pin-holes. The experiment is similar and somewhat easier to describe if slits are used.

S_2P should be back in step with the ray S_1P, and constructive interference is again possible. Finally, we should be able to find a third point Q on the screen where the path difference is *two* wave lengths, another point R where it is *three* λ, etc. Of course, since diffraction is a symmetrical phenomenon there must be a second set of bright images below point O for which S_1P', etc, is the path that is longer than S_2P', etc.

Our reasoning allows us to conclude: If diffraction takes place at the slits S_1 and S_2 then on the screen there should be a symmetrical pattern of *diffraction bands* (remember we are dealing with slits of light, not points) which result from the constructive interference of certain diffracted light rays, separated by regions of less light which are caused by destructive interference. This is exactly the pattern that is observed. The central band is called the zero *order*, the first bright region on each side is the first order, the next the second order, etc. Furthermore, it is possible to use Young's experiment to measure the wave length (λ) of light. Consider Fig. 10.13c: the triangle S_1AS_2 is similar to the triangle CPO (remember the spacing S_1S_2 is grossly exaggerated in the figure); therefore

$$\frac{S_2A}{S_1S_2} = \frac{OP}{CO}$$

But S_2A is just 1λ or 2λ or 3λ, etc., if P is a bright region. We can express this by putting $S_2A = n\lambda$ where $n = 1, 2, 3$, etc. and is called the *order number;* also we put $S_1S_2 = d$, the slit separation, $CO = L$, the slit-screen distance, and $OP = x$, the diffraction image distance from center image. Then in these symbols our triangle relationship becomes

$$\frac{n\lambda}{d} = \frac{x}{L}$$

or

$$n\lambda = \frac{dx}{L} \qquad\qquad [\,10.2\,]$$

Now d, x, and L can all be measured easily; n is of course the result of counting; hence λ can be calculated.

Example. It is observed that the second order image produced by a pair of slits 0.5 mm apart is 2 mm away from the zero order; the screen is 1 m from the slits. Find the wave length of the light.

Here $n = 2$, $d = 0.5$ mm $= 0.05$ cm; $x = 2$ mm $= 0.2$ cm; $L = 100$ cm; therefore,

$$n\lambda = \frac{dx}{L}$$
$$2\lambda = 0.05 \times \frac{0.2}{100}$$
$$\lambda = 5 \times 10^{-5} \text{ cm} \qquad Ans.$$

10.9 The Diffraction Grating

From the above example it is seen that the diffraction pattern observed with double slits is spread out very little (x was only 2 mm for the second order). A device which will increase this spread and so allow more accurate measurements to be made is the diffraction *grating*. In essence it is simple; it contains thousands of closely spaced slits instead of just the two in Young's experiment. A good grating may contain 100,000 slits over some 15 cm, each slit being about 5 cm long (Fig. 10.14). It may be made by ruling many parallel

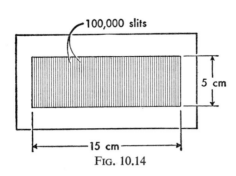

100,000 slits
5 cm
15 cm
Fig. 10.14

scratches on glass with a diamond point mounted in a special engine; the spaces between the scratches correspond to the open slits.

We shall make no effort to analyze the diffraction and interference properties of a grating, but simply state without proof that the double-slit diffraction equation (Eq. 10.2) holds for the grating,* and in fact, is usually known as the "grating equation." The quantity d in that equation—the slit separation—is obtained either by learning from the manufacturer the number of grating slits per centimeter, or by measuring the separation directly with a good microscope. The grating-screen separation L is usually several meters.

Example. Light of $\lambda = 5 \times 10^{-5}$ cm is diffracted by a grating of 2000 lines to the centimeter; the screen is 3 meters from the grating. Where does the first order image come?

$$n\lambda = \frac{dx}{L}$$
$$1 \times 5 \times 10^{-5} = (1/2000)(x/300)$$
$$x = 30 \text{ cm from the zero order.} \qquad Ans.$$

It should be noted that for a given grating and its mounting d and L are constant; then in a given *order*, n is fixed, and x varies directly with λ. Con-

---

* Equation 10.2 is approximate, depending on x being small compared with L. The exact expression is $n\lambda = d \sin \theta$, where θ is the diffraction angle measured from the zero order.

sequently, different wave lengths will occupy different points on the screen, that is, the light is diffracted by amounts according to the wave lengths present in the light. The grating *disperses* the various wave lengths of the light; or put differently, the grating produces a *spectrum* of the light, revealing all its component wave lengths, and of course this spectrum is repeated in each order other than the zero order.

10.10 The Significance of Diffraction and Interference

We have gone to considerable effort to show that light can undergo diffraction and interference. Since we know no way in which either of these phenomena can be evidenced by particles or "corpuscles" or any other entity of limited extension, we perforce take their existence in light as proof that light is a wave. This procedure gains additional support from the fact that other waves of the sort we can see directly (water waves) or indirectly (sound waves) can be made to diffract and interfere. It is a reasonable extension of logic that any other entity that can be subjected to diffraction and interference must have a wave nature. This test for the existence of waves is important and will be employed in several instances in our study of atomic and nuclear phenomena.

PROBLEMS

1. What is the period of a pendulum 1 m long? *Ans.* 2.0 sec.

2. A certain pendulum 70 cm long is found to have a period of 1.68 sec. What is the acceleration of gravity in the region of the pendulum? *Ans.* 978 cm/sec².

3. A mechanical vibrator attached to one end of a taut string oscillates 50 times per second. The length of the wave set up is 125 cm. What is the velocity of the wave in the string? *Ans.* 6250 cm/sec.

4. Radio waves travel with a velocity of 3×10^{10} cm/sec. What is the wave length of such a wave whose frequency is one megacycle/sec? *Ans.* 300 meters.

5. Like radio waves, light velocity is also 3×10^{10} cm/sec. What is the frequency of light whose wave length is 6×10^{-5} cm? (This is yellow light.)
Ans. 5×10^{14} vibrations/sec.

6. In an experimental setup of Young's experiment the two slits are 0.1 mm apart and separated from the viewing screen by 10 m. If yellow light is used ($\lambda = 6 \times 10^{-5}$ cm), what is the separation between the central bright image and the first diffracted image on either side of it? *Ans.* 6 cm.

7. A diffraction grating having 1000 lines per cm produces a first order slit image that is 25 cm from the central image. The screen is 5 meters from the grating. Find the wave length of the light. *Ans.* 5×10^{-5} cm.

Suggested Reading

DAMPIER, SIR WILLIAM, "A History of Science," New York, The Macmillan Co., 1946.
>Pages 238–42, early history of wave theory of light.

MAGIE, W. F., "Source Book in Physics," New York, McGraw-Hill Book Co., 1935.
>Page 308, excerpts from Young's original paper on the interference of light (1807). Page 365, part of Rowland's account of the making and use of diffraction gratings (1882).

MICHELSON, A. A., "Light Waves and Their Uses," Chicago, University of Chicago Press, 1903.
>Lectures I and IV on wave motion and interference are particularly lucid.

PART TWO

The Electrodynamics of Particles

CHAPTER 11

Electric Charge

11.1 The Nature of Electric Charge

Most of our study thus far has been with particle dynamics and its applications. We have seen that it describes many of the phenomena of the perceptible world and even heat, which is the dynamics of the sub-perceptible molecules. Yet even to the nineteenth century physicist who viewed the world as a great dynamical system, there was another set of phenomena and theory as fundamental in nature as the dynamical properties of matter. These were the electrical interactions of particles.

All electrical phenomena are dependent on a fundamental property of the particles of matter which is called *electric charge*. Like mass, electric charge is too fundamental in nature to be adequately defined in terms of more elementary concepts, and can be understood only in the light of the phenomena which it correlates. Unlike mass, however, we discover particles with *two* kinds of charge in nature; and in addition there are fundamental particles with no charge at all. Further, these two kinds of charge have opposite senses (like positive and negative numbers) and can combine to neutralize each other and to form composite particles which are chargeless; and at least one case is known in which two charges combine to annihilate each other—charge, mass, particles, and all. Like energy, electric charge is always *conserved* in physical processes. A charge can be neutralized by another change, but a single charge cannot be created by any known process.

Electricity is usually considered by the layman to be mysterious. The fact that we can see and touch matter lulls us into a deceptive sense of understanding which does not include electrical phenomena. Perhaps this is fortunate, since it allows us to approach the subject without false preconceptions.

Ultimately, the object of the science of electricity is to construct a kind of dynamics which includes all the usual laws of force, mass, and motion in addition to the interactions of particles which are peculiar to their electrical properties. The result, which is named *electrodynamics*, is rather complex. It introduces many new concepts and a rather elaborate set of fundamental laws. About a hundred years of sustained effort preceded its final systematic treatment by Maxwell in the 1870's. And today Maxwell's theory is called "classical" electrodynamics to distinguish it from the new quantum-electrodynamics which is being evolved for electrical phenomena on the atomic scale where the enormous velocities and minute particles demand both an atomic and a relativistic theory.

The simplest electrical phenomena concern electric charges at rest, or *electrostatics*. Here a simple law of force describes the interaction of electric charges, and the phenomena are readily explained by the nature of this force. Electrostatics was also the first branch of the subject to be investigated and understood.

11.2   Frictional Static Electricity

A set of remarkably simple experiments will yield a great deal of insight to the problems of electricity. The first is this: Rub one end of a hard-rubber rod with a piece of wool or fur, and then suspend the rod by a fine thread (Fig. 11.1); if a second hard-rubber rod is likewise rubbed and brought near the first one there will be exhibited a force which repels the suspended rod. This phenomenon was discovered by the ancient Greeks who employed pieces of amber instead of hard rubber. The Greek word for amber is *elektra*, from which we have derived our term electricity.

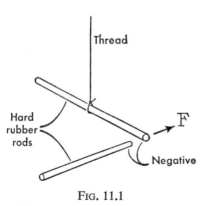

FIG. 11.1

If the experiment is repeated using silk to rub glass rods instead of the hard-rubber rods, an identical result is found—there is a repulsive force. However, if one rod is rubber rubbed with fur, and the other is glass rubbed with silk a new phenomenon occurs. There is an attractive force between the two. Now all three of these experiments can, with some technical difficulties, be repeated in a vacuum. The results are the same. We have a new kind of force. Like gravitational force it requires no medium for its transmission. Unlike gravitational force, it can be either attractive or repulsive, whereas gravitational force is always attractive. It is called an *electrostatic force*, or a *Coulomb force*.

The property which the fur-rubbed rubber rod and silk-rubbed glass rod possess is called electric charge. It seems evident that there are two kinds of charge, for rubber effects rubber differently than it does glass. We shall arbitrarily designate the charge on the glass rod as *positive charge*, that on the hard-rubber rod as *negative charge*. (This terminology is due to Benjamin Franklin.) We can restate our findings from the three basic experiments as follows: Negative charge repels negative charge; positive charge repels positive charge; but positive charge attracts negative charge. This can be simplified to state: *Like charges repel each other; unlike charges attract each other.*

11.3   Coulomb's Law of Electrostatic Force

It is inevitable in physics that the discovery of the existence of a new type of force will lead to an attempt to formulate quantitatively a force law. This was done at about the same time by Coulomb and by Cavendish who employed apparatus identical in principle with that used by Cavendish to determine the law of gravitational force (§5.7). Very light-weight spheres (pith balls coated with a thin layer of gold or silver are usually used) were suspended on a cross-arm by a thin wire (Fig. 11.2). A third sphere mounted on a rigid rod was brought near one of the suspended spheres. Charges of the same sign were placed on A and C, and the amount of twisting of the fiber due to electrostatic repulsion was observed. By means of a separate calibration this angle of twist could be converted to dynes of force, just as was done in the Cavendish experiment. The results were remarkably

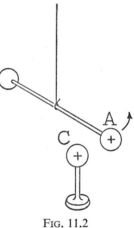

FIG. 11.2

similar to Newton's gravitational law which Cavendish had verified experimentally.

Coulomb found that the repulsion force depended on the charge on A, the charge on C, and the square of their distance of separation. Calling the charge on A, q, and that on C, q', then

$$F \propto \frac{qq'}{s^2}$$

(Newton's gravitational law: $F \propto mm'/s^2$.) The proportionality constant is usually written as $1/\epsilon$ (epsilon): So

$$F = \frac{1}{\epsilon} \frac{qq'}{s^2}$$

The gravitational law and the electrostatic law are both "inverse square" laws; they are both concerned with fundamental properties of matter, and can act through empty space. It is probably no accident that the force laws of such essentially basic properties of particles are similar, though the complete significance of this fact is not yet thoroughly understood.

11.4   Electrostatic Unit of Charge

So far nothing has been said about the unit in which charge is measured. Coulomb's law provides the means for defining a unit. Since the units of both q and ϵ are undetermined we shall arbitrarily set $\epsilon = 1$ for a vacuum and make it dimensionless, i.e., a pure number, and define the unit of q by making $q = q'$, $s = 1$ cm, $F = 1$ dyne. This unit is given no proper name, we refer to it simply as the electrostatic unit (or esu) of charge. In words it is defined by: *One esu of charge is that charge which when placed 1 cm from a like charge in a vacuum experiences a force of repulsion of 1 dyne.* Experiment has shown that for air at N.T.P., $\epsilon = 1.0006$, and hence can be considered as unity to a very good approximation. Then

$$F = \frac{qq'}{s^2} \qquad [11.1]$$

for air or vacuum.

11.5   The Mechanism of Frictional Charge

To explain *how* an insulating rod acquires a charge when rubbed confronts us with a historical dilemma which has already been encountered in this book. It is this: The correct explanation arose from modern atomic theory which came much later than the study of electrostatic phenomena. We will reverse the logical and historical order of these discoveries in order to understand electrical phenomena as we encounter them.

All matter can be reduced to a collection of molecules and these in turn to combinations of atoms. The atom itself possesses structure. It contains a central core or *nucleus* which represents virtually all the mass of the atom and possesses a positive charge. Surrounding the nucleus is a cluster of exceedingly light-weight particles called *electrons*, each of which carries exactly the same negative charge. This charge has been measured and found to be -4.8×10^{-10} esu. As normally found in nature, an atom has a number of electrons whose total charge just balances the positive charge on the nucleus (Fig. 11.3), leaving the atom as a whole electrically neutral. However, it is possible by various means to disturb this balance. Electrons can be removed from the atom, leaving it with a predominant positive charge of one or more electron charges. Or in some cases one or more electrons can be added to the atom giving it a net negative charge. An electrically unbalanced atom is called an *ion*, the process of the unbalancing is *ionization*. If the atom loses electrons it becomes a positive ion; if it gains extra electrons it becomes a negative ion.

Although atoms as normally found are electrically neutral, there exist processes for ionizing them either positively or negatively. Many atoms undergo this electrical unbalancing very read-ily; whether they become negative or positive ions depends on the partic-ular atom, the atoms surrounding it, and the ionizing process. For a given substance and method of ionization, each species of atom, i.e., each ele-ment, acts consistently. This is like-wise true of molecules, which are stable groups of atoms. When the molecules forming a hard-rubber rod are brought in close contact with the molecules forming a piece of fur, a rubber molecule readily takes an elec-tron from a fur molecule. If enough

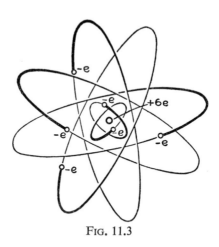

Fig. 11.3

fur is brought in close contact with enough rubber, this electron exchange occurs many billions of times. After separation of the fur and rubber, the rubber is left with this excess of electrons, and we observe that the rod is negatively charged. If we likewise investigate the fur, we find that it is posi-tively charged due to its deficit of electrons. Further, the negative charge on the rubber is numerically equal to the positive charge on the fur. Charge has not been produced but has only migrated. The argument for the glass-silk contact is similar. Glass tends to lose electrons to the silk; the glass becomes positively charged and the silk negatively charged. The only purpose of rub-bing the two together is to obtain the closest possible contact of a large num-ber of molecules. It is to be noted carefully that we have discussed only the migration of electrons. In frictional charging the much heavier ions are unable to move. If they did there would be a transfer of weighable material from one of the bodies to the other. Frictional forces are too weak to effect this. In summary, we conclude that a positively charged solid has a deficit of electrons, and a negatively charged solid has an excess of electrons, and that it is only the electrons which migrate in frictional charging. The migration of ions of both signs occurs in other electrical processes, particularly in liquids and gases, and in a certain restricted class of solids as well.

What would happen if glass were rubbed by fur, since both have a tendency to give up electrons? In such cases one substance has a greater tendency to lose electrons than the other, and charging still results. Here, the fur happens to lose electrons more easily, and so the glass is negatively charged.

11.6   Conductors and Nonconductors

Many substances have the property of allowing electrons to wander between the molecules with relative freedom. In metals, which exhibit this most strongly, there are a large number of "free" electrons in the body of the material which can move easily under the action of electrical forces. Other materials, because of a different arrangement of the atoms or of the electrons in the atoms have few or no free electrons. While there is no sharp division between substances in which free charges are present or absent, names are commonly given to these two extremes. Substances with many free electrons are called *conductors*, those with very few free electrons are *nonconductors* or *insulators*.

There is no material which either perfectly conducts or perfectly insulates. For solids, the metals are, in the main, good conductors; and the non-metals range from fair to good insulators. Some liquids are fair conductors due to the presence of free ions, while others with few ions are insulators. Most gases at ordinary pressures and temperatures are good insulators. The earth itself is a fair conductor because of ions which exist in moist soil. The human body is a fair conductor due to ions in the body fluids, the cells, and on the skin surface.

If a negatively charged rubber rod is touched to a piece of glass, say, very little charge will leave the rod because neither the rubber nor the glass conducts charge easily. If, however, the charged rod is wiped across the palm of a hand there will be little or no charge left on it, because the moisture on the surface of the hand conducts away the excess electrons to the body surface; eventually these electrons flow to the earth through the shoes, the floor, etc. This process of neutralizing a charged body by touching it to a conductor which is either directly or indirectly in contact with the earth is called *grounding* the charge. In grounding a negative body, its excess electrons are drained off into earth (Fig. 11.4); in grounding a positive body, electrons from the

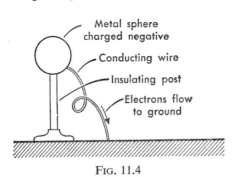

Metal sphere
charged negative

Conducting wire

Insulating post

Electrons flow
to ground

FIG. 11.4

earth flow up to fill the deficit. We can safely assume that the earth is big enough to absorb all the excess of electrons given it or to supply all the deficit required.

11.7   Induced Charge

Suppose a sphere made of copper is mounted on a glass rod and a positive charge is given to the sphere. (This could be done by repeatedly touching it with a glass rod that had been rubbed with silk, or by connecting it to an electrostatic machine which effectively does this automatically.) Since the sphere is a conductor, the deficit of electrons will be shared throughout

the sphere, but the glass insulating support will insulate the sphere from earth and prevent the deficit from being neutralized by the earth. Now suppose an uncharged metal sphere is brought near the first (Fig. 11.5). There will be an electrostatic attraction—Coulomb attraction—between sphere A and the free electrons in B. Since B is a conductor, these electrons will move under the force of

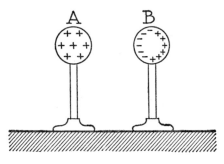

FIG. 11.5

attraction to the region nearest A, leaving a deficit at the distant side of B. Though B as a whole is still uncharged there has been a redistribution of its charges to give it two oppositely charged regions. Since the charges in these regions exist only by the influence of sphere A they are said to be *induced* charges. If A is removed, then B settles back to its original state of no separation of charge.

However, it is possible to leave sphere B with a net charge without ever touching it to A. This is done as follows. If, while A is maintaining a separation of charge on B, we *ground* the right side of B by touching it, the deficit of electrons will be supplied by the earth, but the excess on the left side of B will be trapped by the Coulomb force of A and will not flow to ground. If the ground is now removed, the left side of B is negative, the right side neutral, so that B possesses a net negative charge. Removing A allows the electrons making up the negative charge to redistribute themselves evenly over B. Hence we have charged B by *induction* without expending any of the charge on A. Of course it was the earth that actually supplied the excess of electrons. This whole process of induction is just reversed if A started with a negative charge. The electrons on B are pushed to the right side of B, there drained to earth when grounded, and the deficit maintained on the left face of B can now be shared throughout B. Observe that the charge on a body which is charged by induction is always opposite in sign to the charge which is held nearby.

11.8 The Electroscope

An *electroscope* is a device employed to show the presence of charge (Fig. 11.6); in its simplest form only qualitative information is obtained, but it is possible to construct one with sufficient care to allow precise quantitative measurement as well. A thin aluminum or gold strip is attached across its top to a conducting rod, which itself is brought out through an insulating collar

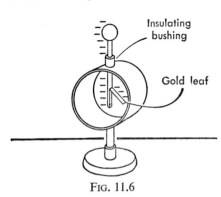

Insulating bushing

Gold leaf

in a glass-enclosed chamber. The rod is usually terminated in a knob or disk. If a charge is given to the rod, the leaf shares this charge and will stand away from the rod under the Coulomb force of repulsion. (Evidently, this occurs for either sign of charge.) As long as the rod and leaf are insulated from additional charging effects the separation of the leaf from the rod will remain fixed.

FIG. 11.6

Suppose an electroscope is charged by touching it with a charged hard-rubber rod. Its rod and leaf system now has an excess of electrons. If a negatively charged body is brought *near* such a charged electroscope, it will send even more electrons down into the leaf to cause even more divergence between leaf and rod; on the other hand a positively charged body brought near will induce a positive charge in the distant leaf and cause its partial collapse toward the rod. Thus a charged electroscope can be used to detect the presence of charge and to determine its sign as well.

An electroscope can be charged both by conduction and by induction. This latter process is identical with that used to charge the sphere B of Fig. 11.5: A charged rod is brought near the electroscope, the induced charge is grounded by touching the top plate of the rod, the ground then removed, and finally the inducing charge removed; the charge which was being held by the inducing charge now distributes itself throughout the rod-leaf system, and the electroscope leaf stands away from the rod.

PROBLEMS

1. A charge of $+40$ esu is placed 10 cm from a charge of -90 esu. What is the force between them? What is its direction on the $+40$ esu charge?

Ans. 36 dynes.

2. A charge of 3×10^9 esu is placed 10 meters from a like charge. What is the force of repulsion? *Ans.* 9×10^{12} dynes.

3. A charge of 6×10^3 esu is 1 meter from a 3-gm pith ball that carries a charge of 300 esu. What is the initial acceleration of the pith ball? *Ans.* 60 cm/sec².

4. Three charged spheres, A, B, and C, lie in a row. A is charged with -5000 esu, B with -1000 esu, and C with -2000 esu. The distance between A and B is 2 meters, between B and C is 1 meter. Find the force on the middle charge. What direction is the force? *Ans.* 75 dynes.

5. On one corner of a square that has 10-cm sides is placed a charge of $+400$ esu; on the opposite corner is a charge of $+300$ esu. Find the total force on a $+10$ esu charge placed at a third corner of the square. *Ans.* 50 dynes.

6. An electroscope is charged by induction with a glass rod that has been rubbed with silk. An unknown charge is brought near the electroscope and the leaves are found to converge. What is the sign of the unknown charge?

Suggested Reading

BRAGG, SIR WILLIAM, "Electricity," New York, The Macmillan Co., 1936.
Popular lectures on electrical phenomena.

MAGIE, W. F., "Source Book in Physics," New York, McGraw-Hill Book Co., 1935.
Page 408, Coulomb's original experiments on the law of force between electric charges.

Electric Field and Potential Difference

12.1 Electrostatic Field

In describing the interaction of electric charges it is not possible to say that a charge exerts a force at one certain point in space and nowhere else, as we can say of a stretched spring, for example. Instead we realize that the electrical charge will exert a force throughout all the space surrounding it. The same situation occurs with gravitational force; it does not act only on a mass placed at a certain longitude and latitude, but acts on all masses placed anywhere in its neighborhood. Actually, this neighborhood extends to infinity, but practically the force at a great distance is negligible because of the inverse square nature of the force law. To indicate this regional action of gravitational and electrostatic forces the concept of *field of force*, or more briefly, the *field*, has been introduced. The field is all space in which a force is felt. Though little use was made of the concept of field in the discussion of gravitational force, it becomes of much greater utility in electrostatics.

We define a field in electrostatics as follows: *An electrostatic field of force is any region in which a charge would experience a force.* Observe that nothing is said about the source of this field; our criterion is simple—if a test charge put at a given point in space experiences a force acting on it then by definition there is a field at that point.

The *intensity* or *strength* of an electrostatic field is a quantitative measure of the field. In words, it is defined as the force acting on a *positive* charge divided by the magnitude of this charge. The symbol for electric field strength is **E**. So

$$\mathbf{E} = \frac{\mathbf{F}}{q'} \qquad\qquad 12.1\,]$$

Field strength is a vector, and a positive charge q' (the prime is used to indicate it is a *test* charge) is arbitrarily stipulated to establish the sense of the vector. The unit of field strength is a dyne per esu of charge. For one very common

138

case we can calculate **E** quite easily with the aid of Coulomb's law. This is
the case of the field due to a point
charge or a uniformly charged sphere
(uniform spherical charge distribu-
tions can always be treated as
though the charge were concentrated at the center of the sphere).
Suppose we have a sphere with a
charge q (Fig. 12.1) and ask what
strength the field has at point A, a distance s away. By definition, **E** is the
force on some test charge q' that we place at A, divided by q'. So, placing q'
at point A, we can calculate this force from Coulomb's law,

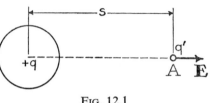

FIG. 12.1

$$F = \frac{qq'}{s^2}$$

then

$$E = \frac{F}{q'} = \frac{q}{s^2} \quad \text{(field due to a point charge)}$$

The direction of E depends on the sign of the spherical charge producing the
field; if it is positive then E is away from the field producing charge; if negative, E is toward it, since these are the directions of the forces on q'.

If the charge producing the field is neither a point charge nor a spherically
distributed charge then E must be evaluated by a summing up of the fields of
all the individual charges of which it is composed. This summing usually involves calculus.

12.2   Lines of Electrostatic Force

By calculating the value of E for each point in space about a charge it is
possible, of course, to get a complete description of the field due to that charge.
This tedious process can be summarized by introducing the concept of lines
of force. *A line of force is a line in space which at every point is directed along
the electric field.* In our imagination we place a test charge (test charges must
always be positive, by agreement) at any point in space and let it move
slightly, tracing out a short segment of path under the action of the electric
force; the process is repeated at the end of each segment to obtain a connected series of segments of a line, whose direction at any point is the direction of the force on the test charge. Evidently we can trace out an infinite
number of such lines, depending on where we start. These lines of force
represent the field in a graphic manner.

A map of the field due to an isolated point charge is given in Fig. 12.2. The lines of force are radial and go out to infinity if the charge is truly isolated from everything else. The field between two unlike point charges is shown in Fig. 12.4, and that between like charges in Fig. 12.3. These two figures suggest a pictorial explanation for the direction of force between unlike and like charges; in the case of unlike charges the lines of force seem to bind the two charges together, apparently attempting to reduce the distance between them; on the other hand the lines of force between like charges seem to be pushing the charges farther apart. Note in Fig. 12.3 that there is a region between the charges which is devoid of lines of force; this is a region of zero field.

Though lines of force are only the hypothetical paths traced by a test charge, they are such a fruitful concept in electricity

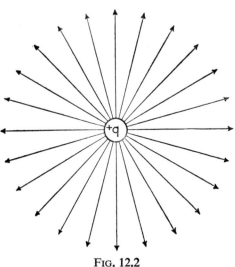

FIG. 12.2

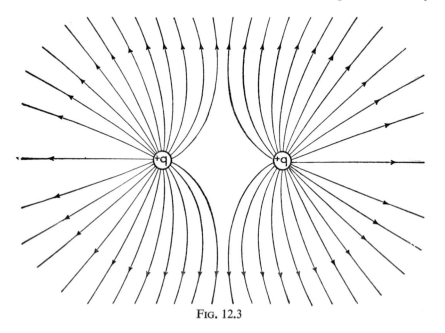

FIG. 12.3

that they usually become endowed with a sort of reality that leaves us with a picture of a charge bristling with tentacles which bend as a second charge is approached. One even talks about "cutting lines of force" as though it were a physical operation.

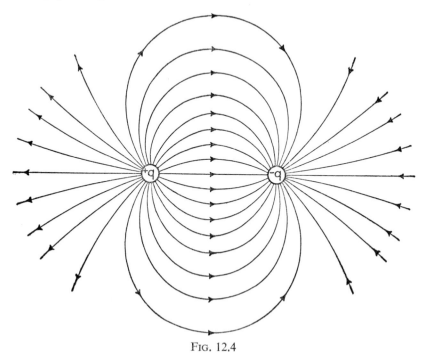

FIG. 12.4

The fields due to point charges or combinations of them are all *non-uniform* fields. The closer we come to the source of the field the stronger the field becomes ($E = q/s^2$). There exists a simple case of a *uniform* field: the field be-

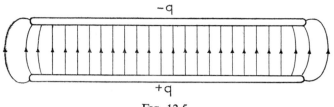

FIG. 12.5

tween two charged parallel sheets (Fig. 12.5). Except at the edges, the lines of force are straight, parallel lines, and the field has the same value at all points between the sheets. Such a field has served a very useful role in experiments in atomic physics and will be referred to frequently later.

12.3   Potential and Potential Difference

The first step of progress in understanding the electrodynamics of a particle has been completed. We are able to characterize qualitatively and quantitatively the forces due to charges at rest. Before going on to the study of charges in motion we had best consider the remaining problems in electrostatics, namely, the *energy* of a charge at rest. In dynamics a mass at rest possessed energy due to its position, which we termed potential energy. Actually, we should have termed it "potential energy difference" since it was always measured relative to some level. Thus the potential energy of a book on a desk relative to the floor was different from its energy relative to the ground level, and probably different relative to sea level, etc. The expression for gravitational potential energy, *mgh*, measured only the potential energy difference corresponding to a height *h* above some arbitrarily chosen plane.

The situation is exactly analogous in electricity. We can define what we mean by electrostatic potential difference, but we will have to be arbitrary in establishing a definition of absolute potential. (And we have no conveniences in electrostatics which correspond to floors, ground, sea level, etc.) We speak of electric potential as a characteristic of a point in space, whether that point is or is not occupied by matter. The definition of potential difference is, then, referred to two points in space: *The potential difference between two points in space is the amount of work done in moving a charge from one point to the other, divided by the charge.* Note that electrical potential difference is work per charge, not just work; it has units of ergs per esu of charge; or we may say that the potential difference between two points is the work done on a unit charge in moving it from one point to the other. As usual, the charge carried will be a positive test charge q'. If the two points are A and B (Fig. 12.6) then we can express the definition in symbols:

$$V_{AB} = \frac{W}{q'} \qquad [12.2]$$

where W is the work done, V_{AB} stands for the potential difference between A and B. It should be apparent that since work is the product of force and distance there must be an electric field in order for an electric potential difference to exist.

To define absolute potential we shall choose an arbitrary point of zero potential, namely a point at infinity, where infinity is some distance many times larger than the distances involved in the system we are viewing. This choice is reasonable, because at infinity there will be no force acting on a charge ($F = qq'/\infty^2 = 0$). Then the absolute potential at a point is the amount of work required to bring a charge from infinity to that point, divided by the charge.

$$V_A = \frac{W}{q'}$$

Since in the laboratory we do not normally deal with infinite distances, the potential difference between two points is a much more useful quantity. In fact, except in specific cases, we shall drop the subscript AB on V, writing just V, but always meaning potential difference.

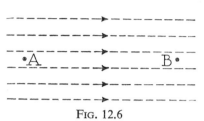

FIG. 12.6

The sign of V is established very simply and follows the same rule as for gravitational potential energy. If a positive charge gains kinetic energy in going from A to B then A is at the higher potential (the charge has gone downhill, as it were); if work must be done on the charge to take it from A to B then B must be at the higher potential. In either event the difference of potential is the work divided by the charge that is moved (work per unit charge).

The calculation of the gravitational potential energy for masses near the surface of the earth is an easy procedure because the gravitational field is uniform over the distance involved, hence the force (mg) is constant. This is not true for the case of the field due to a point charge; since the force varies with distance, there is no simple way to calculate the total work. Once again the methods of calculus supply the answer which we write down without proof: The absolute potential due to a charge q at a point a distance s' from q is

$$V_A = \frac{q}{s'} \qquad\qquad [\,12.3\,]$$

The potential difference between two points A and B at distances s' and s'' is obtained from the above expression:

$$V = V_A - V_B = \frac{q}{s'} - \frac{q}{s''} = q\left(\frac{1}{s'} - \frac{1}{s''}\right) \quad \text{(for a point charge field)}$$

For the uniform field case—the field between parallel charged sheets—we can calculate the potential difference easily. Here the force is constant, so the work is just $W = F \times d$ where d is the distance between plates. Then, by definition

$$E = \frac{F}{q'} \quad \text{so} \quad F = Eq' \quad \text{and} \quad W = Eq'd$$

giving

$$V = \frac{W}{q} = Ed \quad \text{(for uniform field)}$$

In practice, this expression is usually used to calculate the field E, since potential difference is much easier to measure than is the field.

12.4 Practical Units of Electrical Quantities

The three quantities so far introduced in this discussion of electricity are electric charge q, electric field strength E, and electric potential difference V; the units assigned them arose from the cgs units of the dynamical quantities of force, distance, and work, and the only name given to these electrical units was electrostatic units or esu. Thus the esu of potential difference is an erg per esu of charge. In the study of current electricity we will continue to build up this cgs system. However, there we will find that many cgs electric units are of inconvenient size for ordinary measurement. A second system known as the system of *practical units* has grown up; in this system specific names borrowed from the names of the early workers in electricity have been assigned to the electrical units. The relations between the size of the practical unit and its corresponding cgs unit are somewhat less arbitrary than they may appear here, but we will make no effort to justify them.

> *Charge q:* cgs unit: esu of charge
> Practical unit: *coulomb*
> Relation: 1 coulomb is 3×10^9 esu of charge
> *Potential difference V:* cgs unit: erg per esu of charge or simply esu of potential difference
> Practical unit: *volt*
> Relation: 1 volt is 1/300 esu of potential difference
> *Work W:* cgs unit: erg
> Practical unit: *joule*
> Relation: 1 joule is 10^7 ergs
> *Power P:* cgs unit: erg/sec
> Practical unit: joule/sec or *watt*
> Relation: 1 watt is 10^7 ergs/sec
> *Electric field strength E:* cgs unit: dyne per esu of charge, or simply esu of field strength
> Practical unit: none used in this text but may be defined as a volt per meter.

It is evident that the practical system of units is awkwardly related to the cgs system. We introduce practical units because of their widespread use in science and industry, but their use must be accompanied by a word of caution. They may be used only in those equations in which every quantity has been assigned a practical unit. Thus in Coulomb's law $F = qq'/s^2$, q and q' must be in cgs units for we use no practical unit for F or s. In the definition of potential difference, $V = W/q'$, all quantities may have practical units.

Example 1. A positive charge of 10^{-6} coulombs (a microcoulomb) is concentrated on a small sphere. Find the field intensity and the absolute potential at a point 100 cm away from the sphere.

GIVEN: $q = 10^{-6}$ coulombs; $s = 100$ cm
$E = ?$; $V = ?$

Solution: The field due to a point charge or spherical distribution is given by

$$E = \frac{q}{s^2}$$

Since this involves distance we must use cgs units.
$$q = 10^{-6} \text{ coulombs} = 10^{-6} \times 3 \times 10^9 \text{ esu} = 3 \times 10^3 \text{ esu}$$
So
$$E = \frac{3 \times 10^3}{(100)^2} = 0.3 \text{ esu of field}$$

The direction of E is the direction in which a positive test charge would move, namely, *away* from the charged sphere.   *Ans.*

The potential due to a spherical charge is

$$V = \frac{q}{s}$$

Again we can use only cgs units, though here the answer may be converted to practical units if we wish.

$$V = \frac{3 \times 10^3}{100} = 30 \text{ esu of potential}$$
$$= 30 \times 300 = 9000 \text{ volts}   Ans.$$

Potential is a scalar (work per charge), hence has no direction.

Example 2. Find the field and absolute potential at a point half way between two point charges that are 20 cm. apart, where one charge is a negative 50 esu, the other positive 100 esu (see Fig. 12.7).

GIVEN: $q_1 = -50$ esu; $q_2 = +100$ esu, separation $= 20$ cm
$E = ?$; $V = ?$ at the midpoint

Solution: The resultant field at the 10-cm point is the vector sum of the fields due to the two charges. Hence,

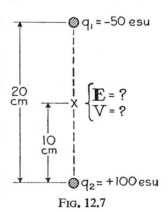

FIG. 12.7

$$E_1 = \frac{q_1}{s^2} = \frac{50}{10^2} = 0.5 \text{ esu toward } q_1$$

$$E_2 = \frac{q_2}{s^2} = \frac{100}{10^2} = 1.0 \text{ esu away from } q_2$$

Resultant:

$$\mathbf{E} = \mathbf{E_1} + \mathbf{E_2} = 1.0 + 0.5 = 1.5 \text{ esu toward } q_1 \qquad Ans.$$

Likewise, the total potential is the numerical sum of the potentials due to each charge taken separately.

$$V_1 = \frac{q_1}{s} = -\frac{50}{10} = -5 \text{ esu}$$

$$V_2 = \frac{q_2}{s} = +\frac{100}{10} = +10 \text{ esu}$$

Total

$$V = V_1 + V_2 = -5 + 10 = 5 \text{ esu} = 1500 \text{ volts} \qquad Ans.$$

Example 3. A difference of potential of 3000 volts exists between two parallel plates that are 2 cm apart. What is the field strength between the plates?

GIVEN: $V = 3000$ volts $= 10$ esu; $d = 2$ cm
$E = ?$

Solution: $V = Ed; 10 = E \times 2$
$E = 5$ esu of field strength   *Ans.*

Example 4. How much kinetic energy does a charge of 2 coulombs acquire in moving through a potential difference of 100 volts?

GIVEN: $q = 2$ coulombs; $V = 100$ volts
$W = ?$

Solution: $V = W/q; 100 = W/2$
$W = 200$ joules $= 2 \times 10^9$ ergs   *Ans.*

PROBLEMS

1. Find the electric field intensity at a point 20 cm from a $+6000$ esu point charge. What direction is the field?   *Ans.*   15 esu of field.

2. A charge of $+500$ esu is separated from a charge of -200 esu by 40 cm. Find the magnitude and direction of the field intensity at a point halfway between the two charges.   *Ans.*   1.75 esu of field.

3. Three positive charges of equal magnitude are placed at the corners of an equilateral triangle. Sketch their lines of force.

4. Find the field between two parallel plates that are separated by 1 cm and between which there is a difference of potential of 100 volts.   *Ans.*   1/3 esu of field.

5. At the corners of a square of 5-cm sides are charges of $+20$ esu, -50 esu, $+30$ esu. Find the potential at the fourth corner of the square (the corner opposite the -50 esu).   *Ans.* $+2.9$ esu of potential.

6.   At the corners of a square 10 cm on a side are placed equal charges of $+100$ esu. What is the potential difference between corners? What is the potential at the center of the square?   *Ans.*   0 esu; 56.5 esu of potential.

7.   How much work is done in moving 10 coulombs through a potential difference of 50 volts?   *Ans.*   500 joules.

Suggested Reading

"A Treasury of Science," Harper & Brothers, New York, 1946.
   Benjamin Franklin's discoveries in electrostatics.

BRAGG, SIR WILLIAM, "Electricity," New York, The Macmillan Co., 1936.
   Chapter I of these popular lectures on electrical phenomena.

Electric Currents

13.1   Requirements for an Electric Current

In the discussions in the preceding two chapters we concerned ourselves only with charges at rest, making no inquiry into the processes in which charge flowed from one body to another. The next several chapters will be devoted to this latter aspect of electricity. Our procedure will be straightforward: We shall ask what conditions are necessary for an electric charge to flow and what are the effects produced by such a flowing charge. We shall make these inquiries from the point of view of atomic physics, a viewpoint which will of necessity debar much of interest in engineering electricity.

If we consider the first of the two questions posed—what conditions are necessary for an electric charge to flow—we find that our knowledge of static electricity provides some useful suggestions. If two points in space (which may or may not be occupied by charged bodies) are at different potentials, then energy will be given to a positive charge moving from the point of higher potential to the point of lower potential, that is, the positive charge receives energy if it moves "down potential." The region through which the differences in potential exist is, of course, one in which an electric field also exists. The force exerted by the electric field is the source of the charge's motion. Hence, *for a charge to move there must be a potential difference between points along its path of motion.*

In addition to the existence of a potential difference, an electric current clearly requires charges which are able to move through their surroundings. As we have seen in §11.6, materials can be divided into two classes: conductors and nonconductors. The conductors are those materials in which charges exist which are able to move through the medium. Actually there are far too many molecules in solids and liquids to allow unimpeded motion of any single charge. Frequent collisions between the accelerated free electrons and the molecules of the conductor prevent any appreciable motion of any single

148

electron. However, since free electrons in the conductor find themselves in the field set up by the potential difference across the conductor, they all are set in motion in a very brief time, and the energy is propagated rapidly. This type of conductor is best exemplified by the *metals*, and to a lesser extent by liquids and gases under certain conditions.

In a vacuum a charge can move with complete freedom, gaining energy as it goes. However, a vacuum has no supply of charges in itself, so that for conduction, charges must be supplied from outside; one does not speak of a vacuum as a conductor although there is conduction through the vacuum.

13.2   Electric Current

Before elaborating on the two requirements for a flowing charge it will be convenient to define a quantity with which to measure the flow. We define *current* as the amount of charge flowing past a point per unit time. The symbol for current is *I;* thus

$$I = \frac{q}{t}$$

The cgs unit of current is one esu of charge per second; the practical unit is 1 coulomb per second, which is called an *ampere* (amp). Thus 1 amp is one coulomb per second flowing past a point. There are 3×10^9 esu of current in 1 amp. Current is analagous to flowing water; we speak of a conductor carrying a current of 5 amp (5 coulombs/sec) just as a pipe may carry 5 gal/sec of water.

A word of explanation should be said about the conventional direction of current, *I.* Since the definition of electric field, *E*, employed a positive test charge, then the positive charge will flow down potential, that is, from + to −; it is this direction of flow of charge which is adopted for the current. Actually, in metallic conductors positive charge does not migrate; instead, electrons move up potential because of their negative charge. Hence, we speak of current moving from the point of higher potential (+) to one of lower potential (−), but remind ourselves that in metals the actual motion is a flow of electrons in the opposite direction.

To restate our conclusions of the last section: To obtain a current we must have available a difference of potential between two points which are connected by a conductor. How is a difference of potential obtained, and how is it maintained?

13.3   Sources of Potential Difference

There are several devices known today which, though they develop a relatively small amount of potential difference, possess the ability to maintain that potential difference over an extended period while supplying current. Of these devices there are two that are important: the *voltaic cell*, which converts chemical energy into electrical energy; and the *electric generator*, which converts dynamical energy into electrical energy.

A specific term is applied to the potential difference that such a source can maintain. It is the *electromotive force* of the source (abbreviated emf). The electromotive force of any source is defined as the maximum potential difference maintained by the source. Observe that the term is slightly misnamed—it is not a force, but is a potential difference (work per charge); its units are just those of potential difference, the esu of potential difference or, in the practical system, the volt. We shall now turn to the question of what constitutes a voltaic cell and how it generates an emf.

13.4   The Voltaic Cell

The fact that chemical energy can be converted into energy of moving electric charges was discovered by Galvani in 1786 and extended and developed by Volta. There are many kinds of cells known today, ranging from the familiar "dry" cell used with doorbells to the "storage cell" found in an automobile. To avoid becoming involved in the complex chemistry of these more common devices we will limit this discussion to the action of a simple prototype cell, the copper-zinc-acid cell (Fig. 13.1).

If a copper plate and a zinc plate are suspended in a weak acid solution it is found that both the copper and the zinc tend to dissolve slowly into the solution. Two significant phenomena occur. When a copper atom leaves the copper plate and enters the liquid it does so as a positive ion, leaving two electrons behind on the plate; therefore for each copper atom going into solution the copper plate has an excess of two negative charges, the solution has an excess of two positive charges, namely, the copper ion. Thus the copper plate is at a lower potential than the liquid surrounding it. Exactly the same action occurs at the zinc plate, which also becomes

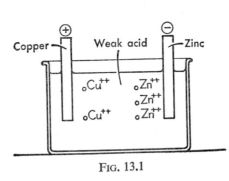

FIG. 13.1

negative relative to the solution around it. However, zinc goes into solution more readily than copper, and therefore the zinc plate becomes more negative than the copper plate. Hence, the copper plate is at a higher potential relative to the liquid than is the zinc plate—there is a potential difference between the terminals of the cell. Since most solids tend to go into solution to some degree in weak acids, the requirements for a voltaic cell are simply two dis- similar solids placed in a weak acid solution. The copper and zinc of the above cell are called *electrodes*, the one at the higher potential (Cu) designated as positive, the lower potential (Zn) negative. The weak acid solution is termed an *electrolyte*. The emf of a Cu-Zn cell is about 1 volt.

The complete chemical action of even this simple cell is considerably more complicated than we have indicated. Specifically, a feature disturbing to the electrical usefulness of the cell is the tendency for hydrogen gas, released from the electrolyte, to adhere to the copper electrode, partially forming a hydro- gen-zinc cell instead of the copper-zinc cell desired. In more complicated cells means are introduced to counteract all such effects which tend to reduce the emf of the cell. Neglecting these extraneous influences we can now see how a cell can maintain a potential difference. When the electrodes are first dropped into the electrolyte, Cu and Zn ions go into solution until the large negative charge acquired by each electrode tends to prevent additional positive ions from departing. Equilibrium is thus established and the electrodes have then their maximum potential dif- ference. Now if the electrodes are connected externally with a conduc- tor, the excess electrons on the Zn plate will flow into the conductor and the Cu plate will acquire ad- ditional electrons from the conduc- tor, that is, a current flows (Fig. 13.2). However, the zinc plate is now somewhat less negative than

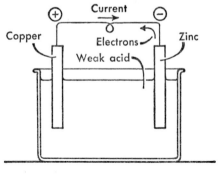

FIG. 13.2

formerly, hence more zinc atoms will go into solution; likewise the copper plate is more negative so fewer Cu atoms will go into solution. Though each electrode has changed its potential relative to the liquid, there still exists a potential difference between them, and current will continue to flow as long as there is zinc left.

To complete the picture we must consider what goes on within the electro- lyte, again oversimplifying the chemistry somewhat. The large sheath of positive zinc ions tends to expand more and more into the cell in spite of the smaller sheath of copper ions; this has the effect of an actual transport of positive charge across the cell, corresponding to the flow of electrons in the conductor outside of the cell. It is to be noted that in contrast to the motion of charge in metallic conductors, positive charge does move in liquid conductors. Because of the large opposition to this motion by the molecules of the liquid the rate of travel of any single ion is very slow, but the net effect is a steady advance of charge through the cell. It is evident that energy must be supplied to move this positive charge within the cell as well as to move the electrons in the external conductor; this will be referred to again.

13.5   Cells in Series

If the conductor connected to the positive and negative terminals of the Cu-Zn cell had been a perfect conductor there would have been a completely unimpeded flow of electrons which would quickly have exhausted the cell, and the two cell terminals would no longer have a potential difference. (We say that the cell is "short-circuited.") By the very meaning of a perfect conductor there can never be any permanent potential difference between the ends of such a conductor. Though there are no perfect conductors avail-

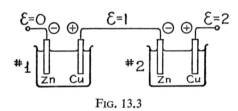

FIG. 13.3

able in the laboratory, a thick copper or silver wire is a good approximation. Hence, connecting two points with such a wire immediately removes any difference of potential between these two points. This offers the interesting possibility of connecting the negative terminal of one cell to the positive terminal of a second cell with a copper or silver wire (Fig. 13.3). There can be no chemical action between the connected points because there is not electrolyte between them. Since the copper plate of cell 1 is 1 volt of potential above the zinc plate of cell 1 and the chemical action of cell 2 makes its copper electrode 1 volt above its zinc plate, the positive electrode of cell 2 must be 2 *volts* above the negative plate of cell 1. The combination has an emf equaling the sum of the individual emf's. The cells are said to be connected in *series;* if we use the symbol ε (E is retained for electric field) for emf we can write

$$\text{In series: } \varepsilon = \varepsilon_1 + \varepsilon_2$$

It is evident that the current which moves through one cell must also move through the second cell, for otherwise there would be a piling up of charge somewhere, which is contrary to our idea of the action of a cell. Adding many cells in series—a battery—is the method of obtaining large potential differences. The common portable radio battery possesses thirty 1.5-volt cells in series to give 45 volts of emf.

13.6 Electrolysis—Avogadro's Number

The voltaic cell is a means of converting chemical energy (resulting from the chemical interaction of the electrodes and the solution) to electrical energy. The direction of this conversion can be reversed and electrical energy can be converted into chemical energy. This process is of particular significance in atomic physics since it is the accepted method of measuring Avogadro's number.

Suppose into a slightly acid solution of copper sulfate, $CuSO_4$, are placed two *like* electrodes of copper (Fig. 13.4). Quite evidently this does not make a voltaic cell, for there can be no potential difference between *like* electrodes. If, however, we connect the electrodes to an external source of potential difference—a battery—an appreciable transport of copper from the positive electrode to the negative electrode will be observed. This transfer of material

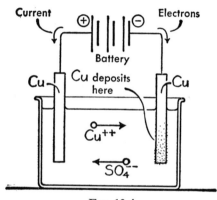

FIG. 13.4

through the electrolyte from one electrode to the other under the action of a potential difference is called *electrolysis*. Again oversimplifying the chemical complexities we can explain electrolysis as follows. The copper sulfate molecule in the slightly acid solution displays a tendency to break into two component ions, one composed of the copper atom less two of its electrons, the other of the residual molecule, SO_4, which retained the two electrons lost by the copper. These ions may be represented as Cu^{++} and $(SO_4)^{--}$. Under the action of the impressed electric field these ions will migrate, the Cu^{++} going to the negative electrode, the $(SO_4)^{--}$ to the positive electrode—the normal Coulomb attraction of unlike charges. At the negative electrode the Cu^{++} takes on the two electrons it had lacked and is deposited on the electrode. At the positive electrode the $(SO_4)^{--}$ delivers its two extra electrons, meanwhile combining with a copper atom from the electrode to return into solution as $CuSO_4$. Thus copper atoms are removed from the positive electrode, and copper atoms are deposited on the negative electrode. It is to be noted that the quantity of $CuSO_4$ in solution remains unaltered. This process of electrolyzing copper onto the negative electrode can be repeated with many other metals if suitable electrolytes are chosen. Most inexpensive plated metal-ware has been electroplated in this manner.

From this experiment a significant result can be obtained. We can evaluate Avogadro's number (§9.6)—a typical example of the indirect methods employed to obtain atomic information. To do so we must borrow the results of an experiment to be discussed in Chapter 17, which determines the charge of an electron to be 16×10^{-20} coulombs (4.8×10^{-10} esu). As each copper atom deposits on the negative electrode it takes away two electrons; these are supplied by the external battery which ultimately regains them from the electrons given up at the positive electrode. Now if the electrolysis process is allowed to continue long enough to produce just 1 gram-atom of copper (63.6 gm), the number of electrons supplied at the negative electrode is just twice the number of atoms in the gram-atom of copper, that is, twice Avogadro's number. It is much easier to measure current and time than it is to measure charge. From the definition of current

$$I = \frac{q}{t} \quad \text{so} \quad q = It$$

If this charge q is divided by the charge on the electron the result is the number of electrons taken by the copper, or twice Avogadro's number.

Example.   63.6 gm of copper were deposited by electrolysis when a current of 10 amp passed through the solution for 5 hr and 21 min. Calculate Avogadro's number.

GIVEN: Mass of Cu = 63.6 gm = 1 gm-atom
$I = 10$ amp; $t = 5$ hr, 21 min = 19260 sec
$N = ?$

Solution: The total charge delivered to the negative electrode is
$q = It = 10 \times 19{,}260 = 192{,}600$ coulombs
Since the charge on each electron is 16×10^{-20} coulombs the total number of electrons given to the electrode is $192{,}600/16 \times 10^{-20} = 12{,}040 \times 10^{20} = 12.04 \times 10^{23}$. Two electrons were supplied to each copper atom. Therefore, the number of copper atoms in 1 gm-atom = Avogadro's number = 6.02×10^{23}.

13.7   The Conduction of Electricity in Metals

When a difference of potential is applied between two points on a metal conductor the large numbers of relatively free electrons in the conductor experience a force. If there were no opposition to their motions these electrons would accelerate and gain kinetic energy. However, in the presence of the vast number of molecules composing the conductor, elastic collisions between electrons and molecules result, and there is a sort of electron-molecule equilibrium mixture having many of the properties of a gas. The electron current is simply a slow drift of electrons in the field set up by the potential difference; because of frequent collisions the average kinetic energy of the electrons is the same all along the conductor. It must be noted carefully that though the actual electron motion through the conductor is slow the *energy* is propagated rapidly—the forward motion of the electrons starts quickly, since all the free electrons in the conductor will find themselves in the same field. If we open a valve in a water pipe we get a flow of water promptly, though minutes or hours may be needed for a molecule of water to travel from the pump to the valve.

The above description of current flow applies equally to electrical conduction in liquids if we add the proviso that here we are dealing with the motion of positive and negative ions instead of (or sometimes in addition to) electrons.

13.8 Electrical Resistance

In anything less than a "perfect" conductor there is opposition to the flow of current. It is essential to have a quantitative measure of this opposition. If for a given conductor the potential difference V across its ends is increased our picture of metallic conduction would suggest that the opposition to current flow should be overcome more readily, and the current should increase. (If we increased the pump pressure we would expect a greater flow of water.) Therefore, a reasonable measure of this opposition would be the potential difference required per unit current. This ratio is defined as the *resistance R* of the conductor. In symbols the definition is

$$R = \frac{V}{I}$$

Its practical unit is a volt per ampere and is called an *ohm:* One ohm is $\frac{1}{9} \times 10^{-11}$ esu of resistance. Since the resistance to flow of current depends on the molecular properties of the conductor, we should expect from the mechanism of conduction that R would depend on several factors: (a) The resistances of conductors depend on the material. Even the pure metallic elements vary by a factor of more than fifty. (b) The resistance of a given conductor depends in direct proportion on its length. (c) The resistance of a given conductor depends on the cross-sectional area (inverse proportion). (d) The resistance of metallic conductors increases with temperature. However, the resistance of a given conductor held at constant temperature does not change. This means that tripling the potential difference across the conductor must triple the current or halving one must halve the other, etc. This fact was first observed by Georg Ohm, and is called *Ohm's law*. This law is valid only for metallic conductors and does not apply to liquids or gases.

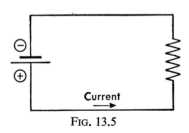

Current

FIG. 13.5

Though all conductors possess resistance, that of thick copper wires is sufficiently small to allow its neglect when used in connecting wires. On the other hand, iron, nickel, and many alloys in the form of long, thin wires (usually wrapped on small forms) are employed deliberately to supply very appreciable resistance. To designate schematically those conductors which have appreciable resistance a saw-toothed symbol is used: ‒ᴡᴡ‒. Connecting wires of negligible resistance are represented by straight lines. In this same scheme the symbol for a battery or cell is two parallel lines, one short, one long, where the long line represents the positive terminal of the battery: ‒⊣⊢‒. Thus, the schematic drawing for a simple circuit containing a battery, connecting wires, and a resistance is as shown in Fig. 13.5.

13.9 Electric Energy

Because there is resistance to the flow of charge through a conductor, energy is required to maintain the current. Since on the average the moving electrons gain no kinetic energy from the electric field due to their collisions with molecules in the conductor, the energy spent on the current simply increases the kinetic energy of the molecules, that is, the conductor is heated by the current. The amount of work to cause current to flow can be calculated readily. From the definition of potential difference

$$V = \frac{W}{q} \quad \text{so} \quad W = Vq$$

But

$$I = \frac{q}{t} \quad \text{so} \quad W = VIt$$

Hence, the work done is the product of the potential difference across the conductor, the current in the conductor, and the time for which the current flows. In the practical system of units if V is in volts, I in amperes, t in seconds, then

W must be in joules. This expression for energy can be put in terms of the resistance of the conductor:

$$R = \frac{V}{I} \quad \text{so} \quad W = VIt = (RI)It$$

or

$$W = I^2Rt$$

This energy always appears as heat in the conductor.

The *power* expended follows at once from its definition:

$$P = \frac{W}{t} = \frac{VIt}{t} = VI \quad \text{watts (joules/sec)}$$

or

$$P = \frac{W}{t} = \frac{I^2Rt}{t} = I^2R \quad \text{watts}$$

By definition:

$$1 \text{ watt} = 1 \text{ joule/sec}$$

hence

$$1 \text{ watt-sec} = 1 \text{ joule}$$

It is common practice in the electrical industry to use watt-seconds in place of joules for electric energy. The two are equivalent. Energy consumption on a large scale is measured in terms of kilowatt-hours; evidently

$$1 \text{ kw-hr} = 1000 \text{ watt-hr} = 1000 \times 3600 \text{ watt-sec}$$
$$= 3.6 \times 10^6 \text{ watt-sec} = 3.6 \times 10^6 \text{ joules}$$

13.10 Energy of a Voltaic Cell

It was pointed out in §13.4 that a voltaic cell not only spends energy to maintain an external current, but must also supply energy to transport charge within its electrolyte from one electrode to the other. This internal conduction encounters a resistance which is called the *internal resistance* of the cell. A symbol r is used to designate internal resistance. When a current I is supplied by the cell, the potential difference required to drive this current through the internal resistance is called the *internal potential drop*, Ir, of the cell. Thus the electromotive force must supply two potential differences (Fig. 13.6), the external V and the internal Ir:

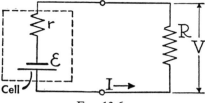

FIG. 13.6

$$\mathcal{E} = V + Ir$$
$$= IR + Ir$$

where R is all the external circuit resistance. The energy the cell must supply is

$$W = I^2Rt + I^2rt$$

Of course, the internal work spent, I^2rt, produces heat within the cell and is not available to the external circuit. To keep this diverted energy as small as possible requires the internal resistance r to be as small as possible. As a cell ages its internal resistance increases because of the chemical changes that occur, and therefore the cell becomes less useful. The potential difference V available to the external circuit is often called the terminal potential difference and is always less than the emf of the cell by the amount of the internal potential drop Ir.

13.11   Circuit Problems

Example 1.   A 2-volt cell has an internal resistance of 0.1 ohms (Fig. 13.7). How much current can it supply to an external circuit containing a 0.3-ohm resistance?

GIVEN: $\mathcal{E} = 2$ volts; $r = 0.1$ ohms; $R = 0.3$ ohms
$\qquad I = ?$
Solution: $\mathcal{E} = V + Ir = IR + Ir$
$\qquad\qquad 2 = I \times 0.3 + I \times 0.1 = 0.4I$
$\qquad\qquad I = 5$ amp   *Ans.*

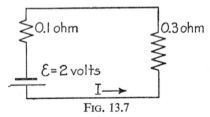

FIG. 13.7

Because of its internal resistance the cell has an internal drop of $Ir = 5 \times 0.1 = 0.5$ volts; though the cell has an emf of 2 volts its terminal potential difference is only $2 - 0.5 = 1.5$ volts. We can calculate the distribution of electrical power expended by the cell:

External $P = I^2R = 5^2 \times 0.3 = 7.5$ watts
Internal $P = I^2r = 5^2 \times 0.1 = 2.5$ watts
$\qquad$ Total $P = 10$ watts

also

$\qquad$ Total $P = \mathcal{E}I = 2 \times 5 = 10$ watts

One-fourth of the power generated by the battery is being wasted internally.

Example 2.   What current does a 100-watt lamp draw when connected into the ordinary 110-volt house circuit? What is the resistance of the lamp?

GIVEN: $P = 100$ watts; $V = 100$ volts
$\qquad I = ?\ R = ?$
Solution: $P = VI;\ 100 = 110I$
$\qquad\qquad I = 0.9$ amp   *Ans.*
$$R = \frac{V}{I} = \frac{110}{0.9} = 121 \text{ ohms} \qquad Ans.$$

Example 3. Assuming the electron charge is 16×10^{-20} coulombs how many electrons pass through the filament in the lamp of Example 2 in 10 min?

GIVEN: $I = 0.9$ amp; electron $= 16 \times 10^{-20}$ coulombs
No. of electrons $= ?$; $t = 10$ min $= 60 \times 10$ sec

Solution: $I = q/t$; $q = It = 0.9 \times 10 \times 60$
$$= 540 \text{ coulombs}$$
$$\text{No. of electrons} = \frac{540}{16 \times 10^{-20}}$$
$$= 33.7 \times 10^{20} \text{ electrons!} \qquad Ans.$$

Put differently, for every second that a 100-watt lamp burns roughly six-million-million-million electrons flow through the wire. The electron is indeed a small charge!

PROBLEMS

1. A certain light bulb draws a 2 amp current. How much charge flows through the filament per second? How many electrons flow per second?
$\qquad$ *Ans.* 2 coulombs/sec or 125×10^{17} electrons/sec.

2. How much copper is deposited in a copper electrolytic cell when a 5-amp current flows for 2 hr? $\qquad$ *Ans.* 11.9 gm.

3. In a silver electrolysis cell it was found that a current of 3 amp flowing for 4 hr and 20 min deposited 52.3 gm of silver. Knowing that silver is monovalent (loses or gains only one electron) find its atomic mass. $\qquad$ *Ans.* 107.9

4. A certain light bulb draws 0.4 amp when 30 volts is connected across it. However, with 100 volts across it the light bulb draws 1 amp. Find the resistance in each case and account for its change.

5. How much current does a 600-watt electric toaster draw when connected across a 110-volt line? What is its resistance? $\qquad$ *Ans.* 5.45 amp; 20.1 ohms.

6. A current of 10 amp flows through a 50-ohm resistor for 1 hr. How much energy is converted into heat? How much power is required?
$\qquad$ *Ans.* 18×10^6 joules or 5 kw-hr; 5 kw.

7. How much energy has an electron (charge 16×10^{-20} coulombs) after moving freely through a difference of potential of 1 volt? $\qquad$ *Ans.* 16×10^{-13} ergs.

8. A battery of cells has a total emf of 20 volts, a total internal resistance of 2 ohms. How much current flows when a 10-ohm resistor is connected across the battery? What is the terminal potential difference of the battery? The internal potential drop?
$\qquad$ *Ans.* 1.67 amp; 16.7 volts; 3.3 volts.

Suggested Reading

MAGIE, W. F., "Source Book in Physics," New York, McGraw-Hill Book Co., 1935.
Page 427, the first electric battery (Volta, 1800). Page 465, Ohm's discovery of the law of metallic conduction (1826). Page 492, Faraday's discovery of the laws of electrolysis.

The Magnetic Field

14.1   Interaction of Two Currents

The preceding chapter discussed the requirements for producing and conducting an electric current. It is now appropriate to consider the effects (other than the heat generated in a conductor) produced by currents. The development of electricity, possibly more than of any other branch of physics, is studded with "discoveries," many of them accidental, others the result of planned experiments. To maintain a logical development of the subject we shall forego all historical sequence, and borrow from the twentieth, nineteenth, and eighteenth centuries as we see fit. Thus we shall avoid relating the many misconceptions held about electricity, and instead will phrase our discussion in terms of the picture as it is thought to be true today.

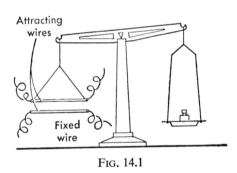

FIG. 14.1

A few relatively simple experiments will reveal one of the most significant characteristics of a current, its magnetic field. Suppose we suspend horizontally from the arm of a sensitive balance a straight wire in which a current is flowing; parallel to the wire and a little below it we mount a second straight wire, also carrying a current (Fig. 14.1). The connectors to the upper wire should be flexible and adjusted so as not to interfere with its motion. Now if the currents in the two wires are in the same direction we find that the wires attract one another—demonstrated by the tipping of the balance; if the currents are flowing in opposite directions the wires repel one another. *Two electric currents will interact*. The experiment can be repeated in a vacuum, and the result is the same. If we try to destroy the interacting force by interposing thin strips of material between the wires we would find little or no effect until we tried an iron strip; in the presence of the iron the interacting force is reduced almost to zero. If we change the value of the current in the wires the force changes, increasing with increasing current. If we stop the current in either wire the force disappears.

At first thought one might conclude that we have here some manifestation of electrostatic attraction and repulsion. There are two considerations that will quickly eliminate this possibility. In the first place a current does not increase the charge in a conductor, for as many electrons enter the positive terminal of a battery as leave the negative terminal. The current is just the motion of electrons already present, and the wire has no more charge than if the battery were disconnected. Therefore, we are not dealing with charged wires. In any case the interacting force can be made either attractive or repulsive by proper choice of the directions of the currents, whereas the electrostatic interaction of like charges is one of repulsion. It seems evident that we are not dealing with electrostatic fields.

If we look at the second result of the experiment—of the ordinary materials only iron is effective in altering the interaction—we are led into a new line of thought. It is common experience that two pieces of iron when magnetized will attract or repel each other, depending on how they are oriented. In fact, it has been known since the thirteenth century that the ordinary steel compass needle points north and south because it is being attracted by the earth acting as a large bar magnet which itself is lined up north and south. Consequently, let us replace one of our two wires by a small compass needle to learn if there is any relation between the interaction of magnets and the interaction of currents. When this simple operation is performed we find that there is an interaction—*the compass needle takes a position at right angles to the current-carrying wire.*

14.2   Magnetic Field About a Current

Of the two ends of a compass needle (or any bar magnet) one always points to the geographic north, the other always points south. To distinguish them, the end pointing north is called a *north magnetic pole*, the end pointing south is called a *south magnetic pole*. With this in mind we define the magnetic field. The region in which a magnet experiences a force is defined as a *magnetic field;* the *direction* of a magnetic field is the direction of the force on a *north* magnetic pole. (This definition is analogous to that for an electric field, E, and its force on a positive charge.) The symbol for magnetic field strength is H. Further, we define a *magnetic line of force* as a line directed at every point in space along the direction of the force on a north pole. The lining up of the compass needle along the magnetic field is illustrated in Fig. 14.2. We see that the forces on the north and south poles of the needle are parallel but oppositely directed. So long as the needle makes an angle with H these

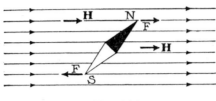

FIG. 14.2

two forces tend to rotate it until it is parallel to H. In this position the magnetic forces produce only a tension in the needle. Note that a line from S to N in the needle points along the direction of H when the needle is lined up with the field.

With the aid of this information let us plot the magnetic lines of force about a current. To do so requires only a small compass needle; its north pole will always point along the line of force. The result is shown in Fig. 14.3, revealing two important characteristics:

1. Magnetic lines of force are concentric circles lying in a plane perpendicular to the current.

2. The direction of the magnetic field is clockwise when the current recedes from the observer, counterclockwise when the current is approaching the observer.

This latter observation can be remembered more easily with the aid of the *right-hand thumb rule:* If the thumb of the right hand points in the direction of the current the fingers curl in the direction of the magnetic field.

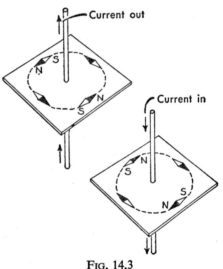

FIG. 14.3

14.3   Magnetic and Electric Fields

It is essential always to keep a clear distinction in mind between H and E (see Fig. 14.4). The electric field E is produced by every charge, whether at rest or in motion; if the charge is a point charge (or a small conducting sphere) the electric lines of force point in or out radially in all directions from the charge: out from a positive charge, in to a negative charge. The magnetic field *H* is produced by a charge *only if the charge is in motion;* its lines of force are concentric circles lying in a plane perpendicular to the direction of motion; their direction is established by the direction of force on the north pole of a magnet. Magnetic fields are associated with currents, electric fields with charges either stationary or in motion. We have made, and will make, no effort to explain the cause of these fields, anymore than we explained the nature of the charge itself; in fact, one can take the viewpoint that these fields completely describe the charge, and only the concept of the fields is fundamental—an electric charge is anything which exhibits such field properties. Whichever way we choose to settle this problem, we are confronted with the conclusion that there are two basic fields associated with electric charge. Their significance will be stressed throughout much of the remainder of this book.

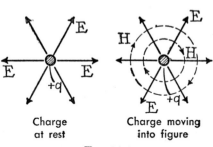

Charge at rest   Charge moving into figure

FIG. 14.4

14.4 Current Loops—The Solenoid

If the conductor that is carrying a current is bent into a circle we find that the magnetic field possesses a new symmetry (Fig. 14.5). Applying the right-hand rule shows that all the lines of force enter the center of the loop from one side of the plane of the loop, and all of them leave it on the other side. The bending of the wire into a loop produces a large field at its center since all parts of the wire aid in producing the field. Now a simple experiment will show that if two compass needles or bar magnets are brought near one another the north pole of one is attracted to the south pole of the other. Thus the face of the current loop toward which the north pole of a magnet is attracted is acting like the south pole of a second magnet, and since the test magnet points away from the opposite face of the loop, this face acts like a north pole. Consequently, a current in the form of a loop acts, at its center, like a short bar magnet (Fig. 14.6); the face of the coil into which the lines of force *enter* is a south pole (the N pole of a test magnet would point toward it); the face of the coil from which the lines of force *leave* is a north pole (the S pole of a test magnet would point toward it). Quite evidently if the direction of the current in the loop is reversed the direction of the lines of force is reversed.

Forming the current-carrying wire into a loop produces a large magnetic field at its center. This suggests the idea of arranging several such loops to in-

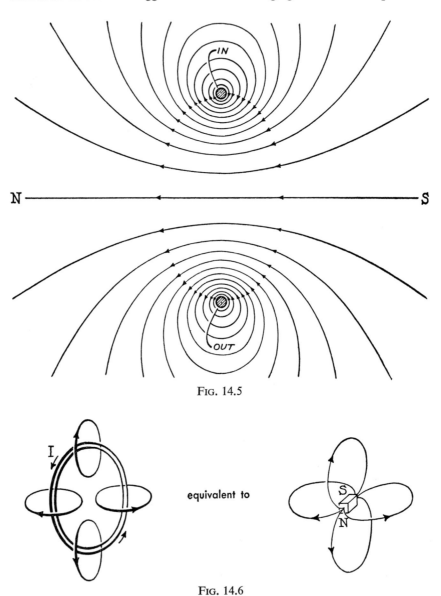

Fig. 14.5

equivalent to

Fig. 14.6

crease H still further. A long wire can be wound into a coil geometrically similar to the loop but containing several turns of wire (Fig. 14.7). Evidently each turn acts like a single loop and each carries the same current, so that the magnetic field at the center is equal to the number of turns multiplied by the field of a single turn. In another arrangement the wire is wrapped with a number of turns side-by-side on a cylindrical form. Such a coil is called a *solenoid* (Fig. 14.8). Since the current in each turn of the solenoid is parallel to that in the other turns, each adds to the magnetic field which now fills the whole inside of the solenoid. As before, the end of the solenoid into which the lines of force enter is a south pole, the end from which they leave is a north pole. Such a coil is the equivalent of the ordinary bar magnet. If two such coils (carrying current, of course) are brought end to end they will interact just as two bar magnets interact.

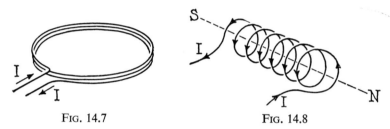

FIG. 14.7 FIG. 14.8

Magnetic lines of force around currents are always observed to be continuous. The designation of one face of a loop or a solenoid as a north or south pole is merely a means of labeling a region of concentrated field possessing a given direction (out if a north pole, in if a south pole). The continuity of lines of force demands that a current loop have two poles, since there will always be two positions from which to view the loop. The situation is also true for iron magnets—it is impossible to have a single magnetic pole. To repeat, magnetic poles are designations of points of view of the field, and there must always be two such points; they are labels, rather than physical entities. This fact is emphasized to avoid the common error of visualizing magnetic poles as the companions of electric charges; on the contrary we must think of only charges as having fundamental significance—it is their motions in certain paths that create these regions of concentrated magnetic field which we label as magnetic poles.

14.5 Iron Magnets

We have defined the magnetic field as a region of influence due to moving charges. We were aided in describing such fields by the use of compass needles and bar magnets, and in fact, the effect of iron on the interaction of currents gave us the first hint into the nature of magnetic fields. Then what can be said of a bar magnet itself, which possesses a magnetic field without the aid of any external source of current? The complete theory of such ferromagnetism, that is, the magnetism of iron, is far too complex for a full presentation in this text. However, a qualitative explanation will be advanced.

Two significant facts about iron magnets are suggestive. First, of the elements in the periodic table only three exhibit permanent magnetism: iron, cobalt and nickel, with iron showing the greatest effect. Secondly, any permanent magnet can be demagnetized, that is, can lose its magnetic properties, by sufficient jarring or heating. This latter strongly suggests that magnetism is intimately associated with the atoms or molecules of the material. The concept of an atom which was presented in §11.5 contained negative electrons circulating about a positive nucleus. Let us consider one such circulating electron (Fig. 14.9). Since it is a moving charge it constitutes a current, though of course it is an exceedingly small current. But a current moving in a loop produces a magnetic field similar to that of a short bar magnet. If several electrons in the atom move in parallel orbits and rotate in the same direction, these elementary magnets will aid one another to produce a stronger atomic magnet. There is still another possibility for producing an elementary magnet. There is good evidence in atomic physics that each electron associated with an atom is spinning on its own axis while rotating at the same time about the nucleus, just as the earth spins on its axis while rotating about the sun. The spinning of the electron charge produces a magnetic field (Fig. 14.9) whose poles are along the axis of spin. (Remember that a negative charge moving in one direction is the same as a current moving in the opposite direction. The polarity indicated in Fig. 14.9 would be reversed for a positive charge.) If the elementary magnets, produced by the motions of electrons in their orbits plus their spinning motion, are partially or completely lined up a strong atomic magnet will result. Curiously enough this occurs with only the three elements named, iron, cobalt, and nickel, although certain alloys can be made that share this property. In the body of an iron bar the iron atomic magnets tend to group themselves in clusters, the atoms lining up to give each cluster a strong magnetic field. However, without the application of an external field, the fields of the clusters are oriented at random (Fig. 14.10). The normal molecular kinetic

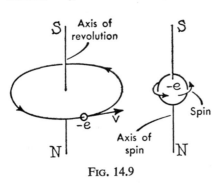

FIG. 14.9

motion within the iron tends to maintain this randomness. This is the picture of an unmagnetized bar of iron.

Let us now suppose that such a bar of ordinary iron is slipped inside a solenoid. The magnetic field produced by the current in the solenoid will tend to line up the iron atom clusters, with their north poles tending to point along the field. If the field is sufficiently strong this line-up may be complete (Fig. 14.10), and the iron is said to be magnetically saturated. When the current stops flowing, or the iron is removed from the field, two situations may occur, depending on whether the iron is "hard" or "soft." If the bar is of hard steel the clusters retain most of their alignment and the bar is a permanent magnet.

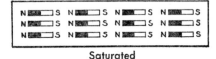

Unmagnetized   Saturated

FIG. 14.10

However, if it is jarred sufficiently, the clusters can be disaligned and the magnetism destroyed. Or if the temperature is raised sufficiently kinetic agitation produces the same effect. Ultimately even at ordinary room temperature the magnetism disappears, but this may require years to produce a noticeable effect. In pure iron—"soft iron"—most of the clusters are disaligned immediately on removal from the solenoid. Certain grades of iron and steel are magnetized and demagnetized readily, others are magnetized less easily but retain their magnetism. The earth itself is magnetized forming an equivalent bar magnet with ends near the geographic north and south poles.

This picture of permanent magnetism is consistent with our evidence that magnetism is just a property of electric currents; a permanent magnet relies on its own electron currents and requires external assistance only to aid the lining up of its magnetic clusters. The poles of the magnet are just those regions where the lines of force seem concentrated when viewed from outside the magnet.

14.6 Electromagnets

If a piece of soft iron is used as a core around which a solenoid is formed, the magnetic field due to the current in the solenoid will magnetize the iron. The resultant magnetic field will be the sum of that due to the current and that due to the magnetized iron; since the latter is usually large compared to the former, this procedure very considerably increases the usefulness of the coil as a magnet. Such an iron-core solenoid is called an *electromagnet*. Soft iron is used because of its tendency to lose its magnetism when the current magnetic field is removed. The strength of an electromagnet can thus be controlled at will by controlling the current in the coil.

If the iron core of an electromagnet is bent around so that its two poles face each other (Fig. 14.11), a strong and reasonably uniform magnetic field exists

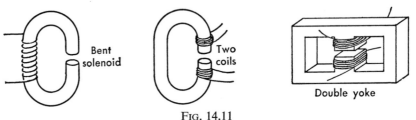

Bent solenoid

Two coils

Double yoke

FIG. 14.11

in the region between the poles. The current-carrying coil may extend over the whole length of iron, but it is usually more convenient to have the coil shorter than the core, or even to use two coils connected so that their magnetic fields have the same direction. The iron core is usually termed the *yoke*. Occasionally two iron yokes connect the poles, as illustrated in the third example in Fig. 14.11; the additional iron makes possible large magnetic fields distributed over relatively large areas. The types of electromagnets illustrated in Fig. 14.11 are widely used as sources of magnetic fields in experiments in atomic physics.

14.7   Force on a Current in a Magnetic Field

So far we have deliberately avoided a quantitative definition of H; a definition analogous to electric field intensity E (force per charge) is difficult because there is not available a single test magnetic pole. Nor have we determined quantitatively the interaction force between magnets. We can accomplish both aims by considering the interaction of a magnetic field (caused by some distant electromagnet, or a permanent magnet, or even the earth's magnetic field) and a current in this field (see Fig. 14.12). The relation between the interaction force, the magnetic field and the current is not derivable from any principles so far established in our discussion of electricity. It is basically empirical, arising from a relation between current and its magnetic field, first experimentally observed by Ampère in 1820; a series of arguments and confirming experiments then leads to the force law. To follow this procedure would take us too far afield in this discussion; we shall content ourselves with its statement as an experimentally observed law.

If a current is at right angles to a magnetic field, the force of interaction is the product of the length of the current in the magnetic field, the current, and the intensity of the magnetic field.

Or in symbols (the symbol $\frown$ is explained in 14.9):

$$F = L\overset{\frown}{IH} \quad \text{(force on a current)}$$

where L is the length of current in and at right angles to the magnetic field.
With the aid of the force law we can now define magnetic field intensity:

The unit magnetic field is that field in which a current of one esu flowing in a conductor one centimeter long (and at right-angles to the field) experiences a force of one dyne.

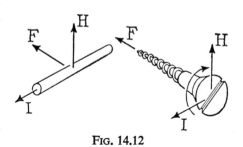

FIG. 14.12

Like the electric field strength E, we give no name to this unit, simply referring to it as the esu of magnetic field. Observe that the presence of the dynamical quantities F and L forbids the use of the practical unit of current. The esu of magnetic field is exceedingly large, and for laboratory purposes another unit, called an *oersted* is used:

$$1 \text{ oersted is } \frac{1}{3 \times 10^{10}} \text{ esu of magnetic field}$$

However, the oersted is not a member of the practical system of units and is mentioned here only because of its common use. Ordinary permanent magnets produce field strengths of some hundreds or thousands of oersteds; several thousand oersteds is an intense magnetic field.

14.8   Force on a Charge Moving a Magnetic Field

Though ordinary electric currents represent billions of charges passing any point per second, a single charge in motion also constitutes a current. This fact was referred to in discussing the theory of permanent magnets. However, the term "length of current" (L) is now the length of path in the magnetic field that the charge traverses. With this in mind we can now re-form the force law to apply to a single moving charge.

By the definition of current a charge q in motion is a current $I = q/t$. Hence

$$F = L\overset{\frown}{IH} = \frac{LqH}{t}$$

However, L/t is the distance traveled by the charge in the magnetic field divided by the time to cover this distance, in other words, the velocity v of the charge.

$$\frac{L}{t} = v$$

and therefore

$$F = qv\overset{\frown}{H} \quad \text{(force on a moving charge)}$$

This expression will be frequently useful in understanding and evaluating many atomic experiments.

14.9 Direction of the Force on a Current in a Magnetic Field

The magnitude of F is given by $F = LIH$, which is basically an empirical formula. To complete the description of F, its direction must be established, and to do so we must also resort to experimental observation. Two currents flowing in the same direction attract one another, while if in opposite directions they repel (§14.1). To generalize from this fact requires a certain amount of analysis of the vector directions involved in the problem.

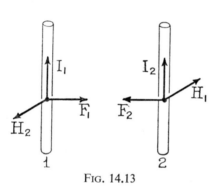

FIG. 14.13

Figure 14.13 represents two parallel wires carrying currents in the same direction. Experiment has determined that two such currents attract one another, and therefore the directions of F_1 and F_2, the force on wire 1 and wire 2, are determined. The magnetic field in which current 1 finds itself is due to the field H_2 of current 2, just as the field at I_2 is the field H_1 of current 1. The right-hand thumb rule indicates that the field due to I_2 consists of concentric circles which in the immediate region of I_1 have the direction labeled H_2 in Fig. 14.13; in the same way, the direction of H_1 in the immediate region of I_2 is established. These vector relationships can be generalized in the *right-hand screw rule*:

If a right-hand screw is rotated from *I* to *H* the motion of the screw has the same direction as *F*.

To designate this operation we have written the force law as $F = L\overset{\frown}{IH}$ where $\overset{\frown}{IH}$ means "rotate *I* into *H*"; a right-hand screw is always assumed. (Note that the thumb and fingers of the *right* hand will serve just as well as a screw—rotating the fingers from *I* to *H* leaves the thumb pointing along *F*.) Figure 14.12 demonstrates the right-hand screw rule, and the student should assure himself that it gives the correct directions of *F* in Fig. 14.13.

It should be observed carefully that the interaction between currents is actually an interaction between one current and the magnetic field of the other current. Furthermore, the direction of the force on a current is at right angles to *both* the current and the magnetic field superimposed on the current.

14.10   Force on an Unconstrained Moving Charge

A situation frequently met with in atomic physics is a single charge moving in a vacuum through a fixed magnetic field. Suppose the charge is a positive ion of mass m, moving with a velocity v, and let no electric fields be present. The force is

$$F = qvH$$

The direction of F is found by rotating a right-hand screw (or the fingers of the right hand) from v to H. In Fig. 14.14 v is to the right, H is upward: ; hence rotating v into H gives F pointing out of the plane of the paper. Since the charge is not constrained by any solid conductor it will be deflected out of the plane of the paper by this force. Repeating this directional analysis for every point along the path of the charge, we find that as long as the charge is in the magnetic field there is always a force at right angles to its motion. Such a force on a moving mass is a centripetal force (see §3.7) causing the mass to move in an arc of a circle. Equating the expression for a centripetal force to its value in this case we have

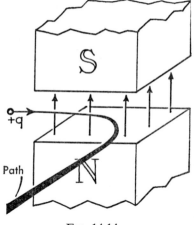

FIG. 14.14

$$\frac{mv^2}{r} = qvH$$

or

$$mv = qHr$$

where r is the radius of the circular path. Measurement of q, H, and r allows the determination of the particle momentum, mv. The bending of charged particles by magnetic fields is a standard technique in atomic and nuclear physics for the measurement of particle momenta.

14.11   The Galvanometer

The force on a conductor in a magnetic field is directly proportional to the conductor current, provided that its length and the field remain constant. This fact is exploited as a means of measuring current by an instrument called a *galvanometer*.

Suppose a rectangular coil (Fig. 14.15) is suspended between the poles of a permanent magnet, and current is led in through the top suspension and out through the bottom wire. Fig. 14.15a is a top view of the coil; applying the

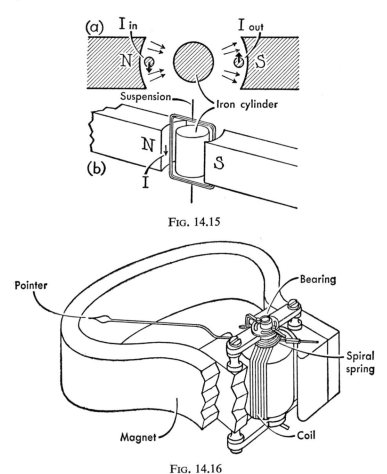

Fig. 14.15

Fig. 14.16

screw rule to each side of the coil we find that there will be oppositely directed forces on the two sides of the coil, producing a counterclockwise rotation when viewed from above. This twist acts against a Hooke's law force of the suspension attached to the top of the coil; for a given force producing rotation an equilibrium position proportional to this force—and hence proportional to the current—will be reached. Thus the angle of deflection is

proportional to the current. To maintain this proportionality for large deflections the magnetic field must always be at right angles to the sides of the
coil. This is accomplished by mounting a fixed iron cylinder inside of, but free
from, the coil. A pointer on the coil, or a light beam reflected from a mirror
attached to the coil, measures the angle of rotation. A coil of many turns is
employed to increase the rotational force for a given current. With careful design galvanometers can be constructed to measure very small currents. Many
turns of small, light-weight wire on a coil carefully suspended by a fine gold
wire or ribbon will permit detection of currents as small as 10^{-10} amp. A
common laboratory galvanometer is made portable by using a coil mounted
on jeweled bearings (Fig. 14.16). Such an instrument, even though designed
for rough usage, can measure 10^{-6} amp. The resistance of galvanometer coils
varies from a few ohms to a few thousand ohms.

14.12   Ammeters and Voltmeters

If a galvanometer designed to deflect full scale for 10^{-6} amp, say, receives a current appreciably greater than this, it can be readily ruined. The
bearing or suspension system may
be permanently destroyed by the
excessive deflection, and the coil
wire may be melted by the I^2Rt
heat. To obtain an instrument capable of reading amperes instead
of microamperes the galvanometer

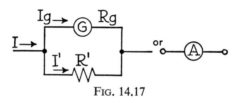

FIG. 14.17

is modified by placing in parallel with it a very low resistance (Fig. 14.17)
often called a "shunt" resistance. This modified galvanometer is then termed
an *ammeter*. The purpose of the resistance is to by-pass the major part of the
current; however since the fraction of the total current in the galvanometer
is dependent only on the shunt and galvanometer resistances, the galvanometer reading will always be proportional to the total current in the circuit.
A galvanometer or an ammeter is used to measure the flow of current, hence
must be connected directly into the current circuit. If the potential difference
across the meter is negligible compared with other potential differences in the
circuit, the meter will have a neg-
ligible disturbing effect on the circuit. Since $V = IR$, this requires
that the ammeter resistance be as
small as possible. This is the measure of a good ammeter.

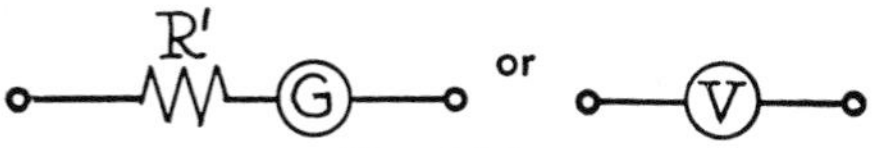

FIG. 14.18

A *voltmeter* is a galvanometer with a *high* resistance in series (Fig. 14.18) and is used to measure the potential difference between two points in a circuit. Hence it is always placed *across* this portion of the circuit. The galvanometer deflection is proportional to the potential difference V. The purpose of the high series resistance R' is to limit the current through the galvanometer. A good voltmeter possesses a high internal resistance in order to draw the minimum amount of current from the circuit, since the voltmeter current changes the measured potential difference from that which existed before the voltmeter was connected.

PROBLEMS

1. A wire 40 cm long and carrying a current of 20 amp is placed in and at right angles to a magnetic field. The resulting force on the wire is 800,000 dynes. What is the intensity of the magnetic field? (Watch your units!)
      Ans. 3.3×10^{-7} esu or 10^4 oersteds.

2. An electron ($q = 4.8 \times 10^{-10}$ esu) experiences a force of 0.01 microdyne in a field of 10^{-8} esu (300 oersteds). Find the speed of the electron.
      Ans. 2.08×10^9 cm/sec.

3. A certain horseshoe magnet is mounted in a vertical plane with its north pole uppermost. A current is passed through a horizontal wire placed between the poles of the magnet. Draw a diagram of this situation, assume a direction of flow of the current, and determine the direction of the force on the wire.

4. A positive ion moving in a horizontal plane from east to west enters a magnetic field and is observed to be deflected downward out of its horizontal plane. What must be the direction of the magnetic field?

5. A beam of electrons moving along the horizontal is aimed just to miss a south pole of a bar magnet which lies in a plane at right angles to the path of the electrons. What is the direction of the force on the electrons?

6. The mass of the electron of Problem 2 is 9.1×10^{-28} gm. What is its radius of curvature in the magnetic field of that problem?   *Ans.*   3.94 mm.

7. An ion of mass 2×10^{-23} gm and charge 4.8×10^{-10} esu is found to be bent in a radius of curvature of 1 m by a magnetic field of 5×10^{-7} esu. Find the velocity and kinetic energy of the ion.   *Ans.* 1.2×10^9 cm/sec; 14.4 microergs.

Suggested Reading

MAGIE, W. F., "Source Book in Physics," New York, McGraw-Hill Book Co., 1935.
      Page 436, Oersted's discovery of the magnetic field of a current (1820). Page 447, Ampèr'es formulation of the interaction of currents.

MOULTON, F. R., and SCHIFFERES, J. J., "The Autobiography of Science," New York, Doubleday Doran and Co., 1945.
      Excerpts from Gilbert's "On Magnetism and Magnetic Bodies," the first great work on science published in England (1600). Interesting.

Induced Electromotive Force

15.1 Motion of a Conductor in a Magnetic Field

The basic phenomenon of the preceding chapter was the force which a moving charge experiences in a magnetic field. As applied to a current in a wire this force is described as the interaction of the external magnetic field with the moving electrons in the wire which derive their motion from an electric field along the wire (an applied electromotive force). The converse phenomenon, the production of electric fields and current flow by the motion of wires or magnets, is the subject of the present chapter. Historically, these so-called induced currents were discovered more-or-less accidentally by Faraday and independently by Henry; the phenomenon was presented as new and distinct from the subject we have discussed in Chapter 14. Even to-day, current induction is frequently so separated. However, it could have been predicted as a result of deductive arguments from the known forces on moving charges in a magnetic field. We shall adopt this procedure.

A current-carrying wire in a magnetic field experiences a force. If the motion of the current or its conductor is to be prevented, an external equal and opposite force must be applied. Now suppose we have a conductor in which no current is flowing; in fact, it need not be part of a circuit, but simply a wire. We apply an external force, allowing the conductor to move perpendicularly to a magnetic field, and ask if there will be a reaction force on the conductor. In effect we have simply reversed our viewpoint. We can use the same reasoning developed in the preceding chapter; the difference, however, lies in the fact that the electrons in the conductor are not moving along the wire under an applied electromotive force, but are moving because of the motion of the wire. Let us assume that the magnetic field is in the plane of the paper and is horizontal (Fig. 15.1), while the wire is vertical and moving down into the plane of the figure. Since in moving the wire we are moving the electrons in the wire, there are minute currents all along the path of the wire, and each current is directed out of the plane of the paper (since negative electrons are moving into that plane). Each of these moving charges interacts with the magnetic field, and we determine the direction of force by applying the right-hand screw rule; I rotated into H gives an upward force on each electron. Since the electrons are reasonably free to move in the wire there will be a flow of electrons to the upper end of the wire, just as if an electric field were present. The top end of the wire becomes negative; the bottom end becomes positive. As the electrons move to the upper end they will interact with the magnetic field to produce the reaction force directed outward from the plane of the figure—the force which we originally sought. Between the two ends of the conductor there is now a potential difference; if connected into an external circuit, current would flow as long as the conductor is in motion relative to the magnetic field.

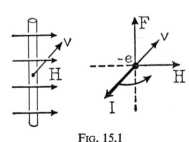

FIG. 15.1

The phenomenon of generating a current by the motion of a conductor through a magnetic field is called *electromagnetic induction;* since the conductor is now a source of potential difference it is said to have an *induced electromotive force,* and the current that flows is an *induced current.* If there is no external circuit connected to the conductor, then electrons within the wire will flow to one end until the electric field set up by this accumulation of electrons cancels the electric field produced by the motion. Thereafter, there is no net force causing current to flow, no interaction with the magnetic field, and hence no opposition to the applied force. However, if the current is allowed to flow in an external circuit there will always be an opposing force; the applied work is required to keep the current flowing in the external circuit.

It is probably unnecessary to state that this deductive prediction is completely confirmed by experiment. The most prevalent source of potential difference, the electric generator, operates on this principle.

15.2   Direction of Induced Current—Lenz's Law

The argument just completed determined the direction of the induced current to be such that its interaction with the magnetic field opposed the applied force. This rule for the direction of current flow is known as *Lenz's law.* However, by considering work and the conservation of energy we can gain further insight into this principle, for we shall see that the induction must oppose the external force if energy is to be conserved.

Consider the work done on a conductor moving with constant velocity through a magnetic field. The induced current generates heat in the conductor, and this heat energy must come from the work done in moving the conductor. But the work to supply this heat energy can be done only against a force opposing the motion (work = force × distance). Hence to conserve energy the force of interaction must oppose the applied force, which is just the statement of Lenz's law.

15.3   Induction by Changing Magnetic Fields

All induced emf's are not the result of conductors moving in magnetic fields. They are also produced, indeed quite frequently, by magnetic fields

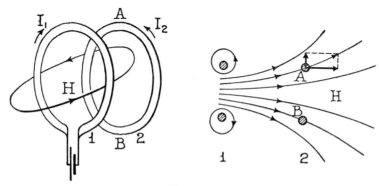

FIG. 15.2

which change in magnitude or direction while the conductor itself remains fixed. That a change of field with time produces an electromotive force along a conductor in this field can be shown most easily by analyzing the fields and currents in two coils placed parallel and near to one another.

Consider two loops of wire whose planes are parallel (Fig. 15.2). Let a current flow in loop 1, and let loop 2 be approaching loop 1. Thus the magnetic field through loop 2 due to the current in loop 1 increases with time. As the result, a current is induced in loop 2 in such a direction that its field opposes the approach. To find the direction of this current let us consider the magnetic field due to loop 1 at point A in Fig. 15.2. Since it makes an angle with the direction of motion of coil 2 we divide H into components that are parallel and perpendicular to the motion; applying the right-hand screw rule to the perpendicular (vertical) component determines that to have a force on coil 2 opposing its motion, that is, a force to the right in Fig. 15.2, the current at A must be down into the plane of the paper. The interaction of this current with the horizontal component of H produces a stretching force on the coil that plays no role in Lenz's law. In every such analysis of Lenz's law it is found that only the component of H perpendicular to the motion is effective in producing an induced current. If we repeat the above reasoning at point B, the bottom of coil 2, we find that the induced current is directed outward from the plane of the paper. In the same manner we could have considered the effect of the magnetic field due to the induced current in loop 2 on the current in loop 1; we would have found the reaction force on coil 1 (the usual action-reaction pair). The result of this whole argument is that a *changing* magnetic field through a loop of wire induces a current, and hence an electromotive force, along the wire.

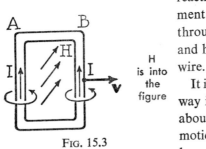

H is into the figure

FIG. 15.3

It is clear from the above example that the way in which the changing field is brought about is immaterial. It may be due to the motion of loop 2, or a changing current in loop 1, or any combination of these two. In general then, a change in field through a loop induces an electromotive force along the conductor. This emf is present for any closed curve, whether it is a conducting loop or not. Of course, only in the latter case does an induced current flow.

There is one aspect of the phenomenon of electromagnetic induction that deserves emphasis. An electron in a conductor experiences a force when in the presence of a changing magnetic field, exactly as it experiences a force under the action of an electric field along the conductor, so that we can consider that the changing magnetic field has generated an electric field. Thus there is a certain symmetry, wherein a changing magnetic field causes a charge to move, and a moving charge produces a magnetic field. Symmetry also exists between observers. Consider the example of Fig. 15.2. An observer on loop 2 sees a changing magnetic field and its resultant electric field, all due to motion of loop 2; likewise an observer on loop 1 sees, in addition to the electric field impressed by an external battery, a changing magnetic field and its resultant electric field due to loop 2. This symmetrical action of motional electricity is expressed in the adjective "electromagnetic"; for example, we have already referred to light and radio waves as examples of electromagnetic waves. In emphasizing these symmetrical relations it should be remembered, however, that a charge at rest relative to an observer has no magnetic field, only an electric field.

15.4 Induced Currents in Coils

As illustrations of induction we will consider several examples. These will concern coils, closed loops of one or more turns of conducting wire. Initially we shall consider the circumstances under which a coil can be moved so that *no* current is induced.

Example 1. Suppose a rectangular coil is moving perpendicularly to a *uniform* magnetic field. Figure 15.3 indicates this situation, where the uniform field is directed into the plane of the figure and the coil is moving to the right and lies in the plane of the figure. Let us determine the direction of the induced current in the two sides *A* and *B* of the coil (the top and bottom sides have no induced emf). To oppose the motion to the right a force to the left must arise from the induced current; therefore the current *I* must flow upward in the side *A* of the coil (right-hand screw rule). Side *B* must likewise have an opposing force to the left, and hence the induced current is likewise upward in this side. Since the fixed field is uniform the induced emf's in each conductor have the same magnitude, but each accumulates electrons at the bottom of the coil (remember, electrons move oppositely to *I*), after which no circulating current flows, even though an emf exists. This result is due to the fact that the coil is moving across a *uniform* field and the field through the coil is not changing. If the field were non-uniform then it would be weaker at *B*, say, and the two induced emf's could not completely oppose one another, resulting in a current flow around the coil.

Example 2. If instead of laterally displacing the coil of Fig. 15.3 we rotate it about an axis that is perpendicular to the field (Fig. 15.4a), we discover the interesting result that the induced current alternates in direction as the coil goes through one complete rotation. Just at the instant that the coil occupies the positions shown in Fig. 15.4b and 4d the conductors *A* and *B* are moving parallel, not at right angles,

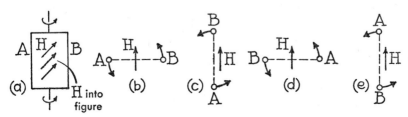

Fig. 15.4

to the field; therefore at these instants there can be no induced current. However, as the counterclockwise motion continues, both *A* and *B* have a component of their motion which is perpendicular to *H*; in the positions in Fig. 15.4c and 15.4e the entire motion of *A* and *B* is perpendicular to the field, and here we would expect the greatest induced emf. By applying the right-hand screw rule to find the direction of current whose interaction with *H* would oppose the counterclockwise motion we find that from position in Fig. 15.4b to position 15.4d the current in *A* must be out of the plane of the paper, and at the same time the current in *B* must be into the plane of the paper. This current in the coil ceases at position in Fig. 15.4d because *A* and *B* are moving parallel to *H*. During the remaining half of the revolution (Fig. 15.4d to 15.4b) the current in *A* is into the paper, the current in *B* is out. The current flow in one revolution is plotted in Fig. 15.5. Each half revolution the current reverses direction. It is called an *alternating current* (AC). In contrast, a current whose direction remains unchanged is called a *direct current* (DC).

Example 3. The reasoning employed to determine the direction of induced current may be illustrated by still another example. Suppose a bar magnet or electromagnet is moved toward a coil along its axis (Fig. 15.6a). Since the lines of force

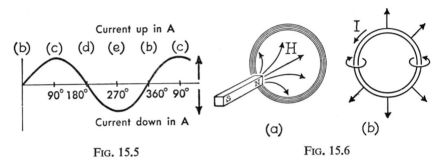

Current up in A

(b) (c) (d) (e) (b) (c)

90° 180°   270°   360° 90°

Current down in A

Fig. 15.5

(a)

(b)

Fig. 15.6

curve out from a magnetic pole there will be a component of *H* which cuts across the coil perpendicularly. If the N pole of the magnet is nearer the coil this component of the field is directed outward, away from the approaching pole (Fig. 15.6). To prevent the approach of the bar magnet there must be a force on the coil that attempts to move it away from the magnet (and thereby prevent the motion of the magnet relative to the coil); such a force on the coil must be down into the plane of the paper. Rotating *I* into *H* to obtain this direction of *F* demands that *I* be counterclockwise as viewed from the magnet side. If the motion of the magnet is reversed, the coil must now attempt to follow the receding field to prevent a relative motion, and the current reverses.

15.5   Two Fixed Coils—The Transformer

As we shall see, a magnetic field without any actual displacement of its source can induce a current in a fixed conductor. Suppose a coil is connected to a battery through a switch and then placed near, and parallel to, a second coil (Fig. 15.7). This is similar to the arrangement by which Faraday discovered induced currents. The coil into which current is introduced from an external source is called the *primary* coil, and the one in which current is induced is the *secondary* coil. The combination is known as a *transformer*. At the instant the switch is closed, current starts to build up in the primary coil, and the magnetic field accompanying this current increases; when the current reaches its final value its field becomes constant. During the interval that the current is building up, the secondary coil finds itself in a region of changing magnetic field, and a current will be induced; its direction is deduced by the same argument employed with the coils of Fig. 15.2. Thus the secondary current, I_s, must flow counterclockwise if the primary current, I_p, is clockwise (Fig. 15.7). When I_p becomes steady I_s reduces to zero. If the switch is opened, the whole process just reverses owing to the apparently receding field of the decreasing primary current. If the battery and

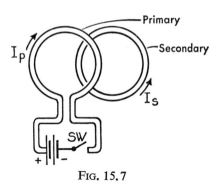

FIG. 15.7

switch are replaced by a source of alternating current, then the flow of induced current in the secondary is continuous and likewise alternating (Fig. 15.8). Note carefully that the requirement for an induced emf in the secondary is a *changing* current in the primary; a transformer produces no secondary current if steady DC flows in the primary.

To increase the amount of field linking the primary and secondary coils, an

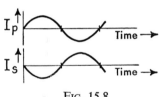

FIG. 15.8

iron core (see §14.6) made common to both is used (Fig. 15.9). This iron normally is in the form of a yoke on which the coils may be wound separately (Fig. 15.9a) or on top of one another (Fig. 15.9b); occasionally a single iron bar is used (Fig. 15.9c).

The utility of the transformer lies in its ability to transform an emf from one value to another. It is observed that not only does the emf in a coil depend on the number of turns in the coil, but also that the ratio of emf's in two coils arranged as a transformer is equal to the ratio of coil turns. Or

$$\frac{\text{emf in secondary}}{\text{emf in primary}} = \frac{\text{Number of turns in secondary}}{\text{Number of turns in primary}}$$

$$\frac{\mathcal{E}_s}{\mathcal{E}_p} = \frac{n_s}{n_p}$$

This relation is strictly true only for a perfect transformer, one in which all the field of one coil links completely the second coil, but is a good approximation for ordinary transformers. If the secondary has more turns than the primary then $\mathcal{E}_s$ is larger then $\mathcal{E}_p$, and we have a "step-up" transformer. The reverse of this is "step-down" transformer. Since commercial transformers are nearly 100% efficient, that is, deliver nearly 100% of the energy they receive, we can, to a good approximation, write

$$\text{Power into primary} = \text{Power out of secondary}$$

or

$$\mathcal{E}_p I_p = \mathcal{E}_s I_s$$

Therefore

$$\frac{I_s}{I_p} = \frac{\mathcal{E}_p}{\mathcal{E}_s} = \frac{n_p}{n_s}$$

Thus, if n_s is greater than n_p the emf is stepped up, but the current is reduced. Therefore a step-down transformer (the name always refers to $\mathcal{E}$, not I) is used

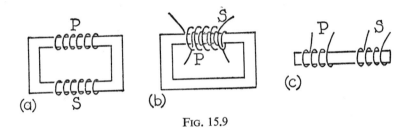

(a)   (b)   (c)

FIG. 15.9

to increase current. Bear in mind that the emf's and currents being discussed are AC; there is no transformer action with DC.

Finally, a word might be said about the reason for the widespread use of AC, though the subject is somewhat removed from atomic physics. To transfer electrical power over many miles of distance requires conductors which, because of their length, will have an appreciable resistance. Current flowing through these conductors produces heat, I^2Rt, and the greater the amount of current, the greater the amount of energy dissipated, and the less the power delivered to the consumer. Therefore, it is desirable to transfer power at low currents; since $P = \mathcal{E}I$, this demands a high $\mathcal{E}$. A step-up transformer at the generator end of the line increases $\mathcal{E}$ from the generator voltage (often a few hundred volts) to as much as several hundred thousand volts; at the receiving end a step-down transformer reduces this to the ordinary 110 v or 220 v used in homes and industries. Thus AC is prevalent because with the aid of transformers it can be transmitted more economically than DC.

15.6   The Electric Generator

In the discussion of ways in which a conductor can move through a magnetic field (§15.4) we are tacitly describing electric generators. Specifically, when a coil is rotated about an axis perpendicular to the magnetic field an alternating emf results. This is the standard method in the design of genera-tors. The only problem left to be clarified is the means by which such a rotating coil can be con-nected to an external circuit. There are two methods; one employs *slip rings* and supplies alternating cur-rent; the other has a *commutator ring* and delivers direct current.

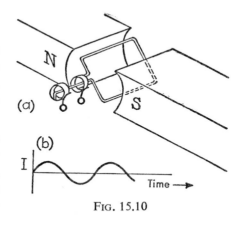

AC Generator.   One end of the coil is brought out to one copper ring, the other coil wire to a second ring, both mounted along the axis of rotation (Fig. 15.10). The pair of slip rings form an electrical con-

Fig. 15.10

tact with fixed "brushes," one for each ring. The brushes are usually of graphite and are shaped to fit smoothly at the regions of contact with the rings; the brushes form the terminals of the generator. The output emf and current has the form shown in Fig. 15.10. The frequency of the AC depends on the rate of rotation of the coil; usually several coils are employed, each one producing an alternation of emf in one revolution. In this country most AC has a 60-cycle/sec alternation rate, that is the emf goes through a complete cycle in $\frac{1}{60}$ of a second. Observe that the heating effect of the current, I^2Rt, depends on the *square* of current, hence is independent of its direction of flow. Alternating current produces the same heating as direct current; hence electric irons, toasters, heaters, light bulbs, etc. all operate equally well on AC or DC (provided they contain no electromechanical devices such as relays, current regulators, and the like).

DC Generator.   To obtain direct current from a rotating coil a single ring is split in half, and the two halves are separated by an insulator (Fig. 15.11). Each segment of the ring, known as a commutator ring, is attached to a coil end. Brushes are placed in contact with opposite sides of the ring. At the in-stant when the current in one side of the coil is changing direction, its contact with a given brush is broken and remade with the opposite brush. Thus at each brush current always flows in the same direction. Though the use of a commutator ring produces direct current, it is not a steady current, as the graph in Fig. 15.11 indicates. To reduce this variation several coils are used and each coil is connected to a pair of segments of the commutator ring; the brushes are placed so that each coil is generating its maximum current at the instant it connects with the brushes. This produces a series of maxima, one for each coil, so that the current does not fall to zero but varies slightly about a fixed value. There are additional devices to remove the greater part of even this variation, giving DC almost as constant as that delivered by a battery.

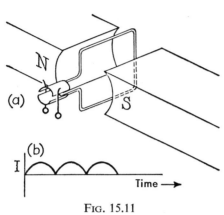

Fig. 15.11

15.7   DC Motors

As a final word to this chapter mention should be made of electric motors. A generator requires an external agent (a water turbine, steam turbine, diesel motor, etc.) to perform dynamical work in rotating the coil system; this work is converted by the generator into electrical energy. A motor is just the inverse of this: Electrical energy is supplied, and the motor converts it to mechanical energy of rotation. The galvanometer (§14.11) is the prototype of the motor—current supplied to a conductor in a magnetic field produces a force at right angles to the conductor and the field. As with the generator, the only problem is one of delivering a current from a fixed circuit to a continuously rotating coil. The solution to this problem for the DC motor is identical to that for the DC generator, namely, the use of the commutator ring. Fundamentally, the DC generator if delivered current will become a DC motor. (There are engineering design considerations that make this dual use impractical, however.) The current is delivered to the coil just as the plane of the coil is parallel to the magnetic field, for in this position the length of the coil is completely perpendicular to H, and the force is maximum. The description of AC motors is rather more technical than that of DC motors. Since it adds no new physical ideas we shall omit it here.

PROBLEMS

(Diagrams and lucid arguments should accompany problems on induced emf's.)

1.   A wire lying in a horizontal plane and pointing north-south is dropped through a magnetic field which is also in a horizontal plane but directed from east to west. Find the direction of induced current in the wire. Which end of the wire is positive?

2.   The axles on a freight car moving north pass over a magnetic field directed vertically upward. Find the direction of the emf induced in the axles.

3.   A coil of wire is loosely wrapped around the south pole of a bar magnet. The magnet is rapidly pulled away from the coil. What is the direction of the induced current viewed from the magnet side of the coil?

4.   Between the pole pieces of an electromagnet of the type shown in Fig. 14.11 is placed a loop of wire whose plane is parallel to the faces of the poles. Assume the current in the magnet coils is in such a direction that the top pole is N, the bottom S. Find the direction of the induced current in the loop as viewed from above when the current in the magnet coil is turned on.

5.   The primary of a transformer draws 3 amp at 50 volts. What is the secondary voltage, current, and power if the transformer turn ratio, i.e., secondary-to-primary, is 6 to 1?   *Ans.*   300 volts; 0.5 amp; 150 watts.

6.   A certain power station generates 100 kw at 200 volts. This power must be then transmitted through a power line having a total resistance of 4 ohms. Calculate the transmission efficiency, that is, the ratio of the power delivered to the power generated, if a transformer is used between generator and line whose turn ratio is (*a*) 5 to 1; (*b*) 50 to 1.   *Ans.*   (*a*) 60%; (*b*) 99.6%.

Suggested Reading

DAMPIER, SIR WILLIAM, "A History of Science," New York, The Macmillan Co., 1946.
     Pages 241–45, historical account of electromagnetic induction.

MAGIE, W. F., "Source Book in Physics," New York, McGraw-Hill Book Co., 1935.
     Pages 473–83 give part of Faraday's researches on induced currents. Pages 511–13 contain Lenz's statement of the law which bears his name. Pages 513–19 give a partial account of Henry's work on induction.

MOULTON, F. R., and SCHIFFERES, J. J., "The Autobiography of Science," New York, Doubleday Doran and Co., 1945.
     Quotations from the publications of Faraday and Henry on induced electromotive force.

CHAPTER 16

Thermionic Emission and Some Electronics

16.1 The Escape of Electrons from Metals

We have already discussed the role of the free electrons in metallic conduction. We shall now call upon this free electron picture again, this time in explaining the phenomenon of thermionic emission. In metallic conduction we have envisioned the free electrons as acting very much as the molecules of a gas. In collisions with the metal atoms they form an assembly with a distribution of velocities. The "temperature" of the electrons is governed by that of the metal as a whole. So long as there is no electric field in the body of the metal (no applied field) there will be no preferential direction of electron motion, only random motions at very high speeds; the great majority of the electron speeds will be in the range near the speed that is characteristic of the metal temperature. If an electric field is applied to the metal, there is added to each of the random velocities a small velocity directed along the field, so that there is a drift, a current, along the wire. In electron-atom collisions the kinetic energy of this drift speed is shared with the atoms, and the temperature of the metal rises (I^2Rt heat).

In this résumé of electron conduction it is significant to note that the electrons have freedom so long as they stay *inside* the metal, that under ordinary conditions no electrons are observed to be emitted from the metal surface. Under what influences might an electron escape through the surface of the metal? One such influence is a very great external electric field applied at right angles to the surface; however, for appreciable electron emission, fields as great as a million volts per centimeter are necessary. Another mechanism is photoelectric emission caused by light falling on the surface (this will be discussed in Chapter 21). The most common method of obtaining electron emission is by heating the metal to a high temperature. This process is called *thermionic emission*. (It would be more appropriately named thermoelectronic emission, since electrons rather than ions are emitted.)

It is evident that there must be a restraining force preventing the departure of an electron from the conductor, and energy must be supplied to overcome this force. The nature of the force can be fully understood only with a detailed study of the crystal structure of metals, which we must forego. However, one contribution to this force can be made clear. A conductor is uncharged; to remove an electron must require work, because a negative charge (the electron) is being separated from a positive charge (the conductor minus an electron), and to overcome such a force of attraction work must be done. The amount of work to remove a unit charge, in other words the potential difference between a point just inside and a point just outside the metal, has been measured for many conductors, and is of the order of a few volts. This we will call the *thermionic potential difference;* the corresponding work can be called the *thermionic work*, W_t. An electron near the surface of a conductor, if possessing this energy W_t, is able to escape the conductor. At room temperature only a negligible number of electrons in the high velocity tail of the distribution curve have kinetic energy as great as W_t. The effect of heating the metal is to increase the population of electrons with energies greater than W_t, and at very high temperatures currents of several milliamperes (10^{-3} amp) are emitted from a short length of wire. We quite literally "boil-off" electrons! This phenomenon was first discovered by Edison in 1883 while experimenting with incandescent lamps, but it was not seriously investigated until the present century.

The temperatures required for appreciable thermionic emission from pure metals are of the order of 2000°C, so that only metals with high melting points are suitable. (It has been found possible to make metallic compounds which have high emission at lower temperatures.)

16.2 Space Charge

To obtain the high temperatures necessary for thermionic emission the simplest method is to pass a current through a wire (the heat is I^2Rt). The electrons which escape from the heated wire accumulate in the region about it (Fig. 16.1); this cloud of electrons is called a *space charge*. Equilibrium is established when as many electrons are driven back into the wire by the electrostatic repulsion of the space charge as are emitted by the wire. An electron with just sufficient thermal energy to overcome the thermionic work, that is, its K.E. $= W_t$, will just

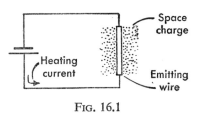

FIG. 16.1

escape; one with greater energy than W_t will have a balance of kinetic energy, which can drive it part way through the space charge. Thus the volume of space charge is a cylinder concentric with the wire and of a radius depending on the temperature of the wire. (Every electric light bulb has such a space charge, but no use is made of it.)

16.3 Effect of an External Electric Field—The Plate

Suppose that an external field is established in the region of space charge. This is usually done by surrounding the wire and its space charge with

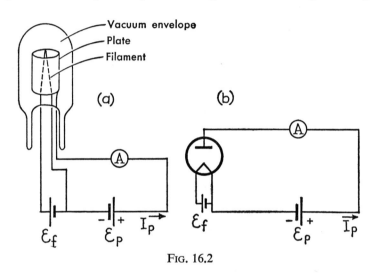

FIG. 16.2

a metal cylinder (Fig. 16.2a). If the space between the wire and cylinder is highly evacuated (to allow unimpeded flow of the electrons) and if a potential difference is placed between the cylinder and wire, then the electrons will move in the field when the cylinder is at a higher potential than the wire. This electron current traveling through the vacuum can be read on a current measuring meter (usually a milliammeter) in the external circuit. As shown in Fig. 16.2a, the emitting wire is doubled back on itself to obtain increased emission and permit both ends to come out of the base of the tube. It is called the *filament*. The cylinder surrounding it is called the *plate*. The combination when placed in an evacuated tube is called a *diode*. (Under certain circumstances the tube may contain gas, rather than a vacuum. To cover this possibility the general term of *electron tube* is preferred to the more common term "vacuum tube.") To complete this terminology, we note that the study of electron tubes and their associated circuits is called *electronics*. In electronics it is conventional to draw electron tubes schematically as in Fig. 16.2b rather than pictorially, as in Fig. 16.2a.

If the plate is made positive relative to the filament some of the electrons in the space charge will move through the vacuum to the plate; the reduction of space charge thus produced will allow more electrons to evaporate from the filament. We now see two possibilities: (1) The space charge may remain about constant in magnitude, with the replenishing process balancing the current flow. (2) The space charge may disappear if the applied electric field is sufficiently high to remove more electrons than can be supplied by the fila-

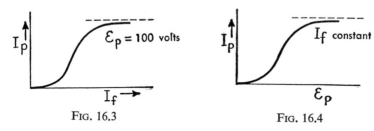

FIG. 16.3   FIG. 16.4

ment. To illustrate these limiting conditions let us consider the following experiment: with the plate voltage $\mathcal{E}_p$ held constant (100 volts, say), let us plot the electron current to the plate I_p as the filament current I_f (and thus the filament temperature) is increased. The result is shown in Fig. 16.3. For very low filament current the temperature of the wire is too low for appreciable electron emission. As the filament becomes hotter more electrons are emitted, and the electron current increases. Finally the curve levels off when the filament is hot enough to establish an equilibrium space charge. In the lower part of the curve the space charge is zero or small. As the curve starts to level off the space charge grows. Finally, at the leveled-off position the plate current is said to be "space-charge limited."

A second experiment will further illustrate the action of space charge. This time, let us keep the filament current constant and vary the potential difference between plate and filament. The plot of the plate current against the plate voltage is shown in Fig. 16.4. With zero plate voltage there is no field to remove electrons from the space charge; hence, there is little or no plate current. As the field is increased current flows, but the filament is able to replenish the space charge; this is the case from $\mathcal{E}_p = 0$ up to the point where the curve begins to bend over. From this point on, the filament emission is unable to keep up with the drain from the space charge; finally the field is so high that the space charge ceases to exist. Further increase of the field (plate voltage) will cause no more current, and the curve levels off; the plate current is said to be "temperature limited." Most electron tubes are normally used with a saturated space charge, that is, in the region below the bend in the curve of Fig. 16.4. For such tubes the plate current is usually of the order of milli-amperes, though some large tubes are designed for plate currents of several amperes.

16.4   The Diode as a Rectifier

The most common application of the diode is as a *rectifier*, that is, as a means of converting alternating current into direct current. In fact, this was the earliest use of electron tubes. If an alternating potential difference is placed between the plate and filament, plate current will flow when the plate is above the potential of the filament, but will not flow when the plate is negative relative to the filament. The diode acts like a valve (the British call them "valves" instead of electron tubes), passing current in only one direction. A circuit using a diode as a rectifier is shown in Fig. 16.5. Here the AC to be rectified comes from the secondary of a transformer (a common, though not an essential, arrange-ment). When the plate is + rela-tive to the filament, current flows

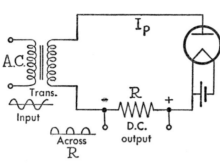

Fig. 16.5

in the diode from plate to filament, that is, electrons flow from filament to plate. The resistance R is introduced in order to obtain a DC voltage, $V = IR$; since current always flows from high to low potentials the right end of R (Fig. 16.5) must be at a higher potential (+) than the left end (−). During the half of the cycle when the plate of the diode is negative relative to the filament no current flows. Hence across R there is a direct-current voltage, even though it is not steady. The effect of the diode is to eliminate the lower half of the AC curve. Electrical "filters" (which we shall not discuss) may be used to smooth out the variations.

The use of a diode as a rectifier conveniently eliminates the need for batter-ies in the many situations where alternating current is available. For example, in a radio set several hundred volts at a few tens of milliamperes are required. A bank of batteries for this purpose is heavy, bulky, and expensive. It may be replaced by a rectifier with a transformer that steps up household 115 volts

AC to 300 or 400 volts, which is then rectified; after filtering out the fluctuations, this becomes a very adequate substitute for the batteries.

16.5 The Triode Electron Tube

In 1906 Lee DeForest added a third electrode to the electron tube, an invention which has had great impact on industry and society through the applications it made possible. This electrode is called a *grid*, and consists of a wire mesh placed between the plate and the filament. An electron tube containing a filament, plate, and grid is called a *triode*. Without a doubt the most significant of the many uses of triodes is as an *amplifier*, a device taking a small varying voltage at low power and converting it to a similar but larger voltage variation at higher power. (The ordinary transformer is not an amplifier since its output can have

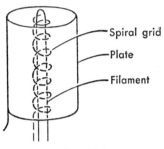

FIG. 16.6

no more power than its input.) Of course, this added power is supplied at the expense of the batteries or other power supplies that operate the electron tube.

First let us see what effect the grid can have on the most important feature of an electron tube, its space charge. The unique feature of the grid lies in its position in the space charge (Fig. 16.6). As we have pointed out, the space charge is the major determining factor in the flow of current; any slight change in the electric field in its neighborhood will have a large effect on the amount of space charge and hence the amount of plate current. The role of the grid is to make such slight field variations in the space charge, which it can do because of its strategic position.

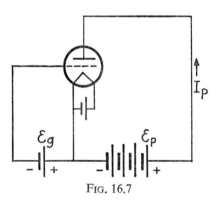

FIG. 16.7

The basic triode circuit is that shown in Fig. 16.7. Observe that battery ε_g gives a potential difference between grid and filament. (We shall refer all potentials in an electron tube to its filament. This then is a common connecting point for a terminal of each battery.) If ε_g makes the grid sufficiently negative, no electrons will get to the plate in spite of its positive voltage; in the region of space charge the field due to the grid has canceled the field due to the plate. If now the grid is made less negative, there will be a net attractive field and current will flow to the plate (though not to the grid because it is negative). Finally, flow of space charge current to the plate will be considerably aided if the grid becomes positive. However, in this case, even though the open mesh of the grid presents very little intercepting area, the grid will

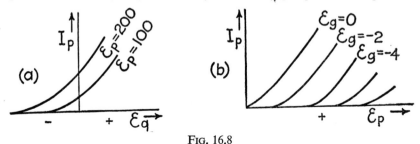

Fɪɢ. 16.8

collect electrons, and a grid current will flow. Usually, the grid is operated slightly negative (a few volts) to avoid this grid current.

This discussion can be summed up with two curves, known as "characteristic curves" of a triode. They are shown in Fig. 16.8. As with the diode, the dependent variable is the plate current. In Fig. 16.8a each curve is taken with a constant plate voltage; in Fig. 16.8b the grid voltage is held constant for all points on any one curve. Notice in Fig. 16.8b, and also in Fig. 16.4, that the ratio of plate voltage to plate current is not constant, that is, the resistance of the electron tube is variable in contrast to the resistance of a metallic conductor. Thus Ohm's law (see §13.8) is not valid for an electron tube.

16.6   The Triode as an Amplifier

The definition of an amplifier given at the beginning of the preceding section is in terms of a voltage variation. This might be simple AC: ⌇⌇⌇; or a complex AC: ⌇⌇⌇⌇; or it could be a DC variation: ⌇ (These latter are usually called voltage "pulses.") The first might come from a very weak AC generator, such as a coil rotating in the earth's magnetic field; the second kind might well represent the voltage variation from a microphone or telephone on which sound waves are impressed; the third type is common in nuclear physics, and might represent the response of a Geiger counter to an atomic or nuclear particle. All such voltage variations are grouped under the word *signal;* the first two are AC signals, the third is pulse signal. The role of the amplifier is to increase the amplitude of such signals.

The triode is able to amplify since a small variation of grid potential causes a large variation in plate current, due to the strategic placing of the grid in the region of space charge. A common amplifier circuit is shown in Fig. 16.9. The grid is made a few volts negative to prevent the flow of grid current during the positive peaks of the signal. The plate is usually two or three hundred volts

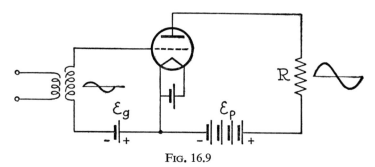

FIG. 16.9

positive. A transformer is used to introduce the signal. This alternating voltage makes the grid swing successively less negative and more negative, and the current through R is correspondingly large and small, causing the potential difference across R ($V = IR$) to rise and fall with the signal in the grid. We define as a measure of the amplifier performance its *voltage amplification A* as follows:

$$\text{Voltage amplification} = \frac{\text{Voltage variation across R}}{\text{Voltage variation of the grid}}$$

Example. When a 2-volt AC signal (the amplitude of the signal) is impressed on a grid whose DC potential is −3 volts, the plate current is found to vary from 3 milliamp to 7 milliamp when there is a 10,000-ohm resistance in the plate circuit. Find the voltage amplification of the tube.

GIVEN: Signal = 2 volts; $\mathcal{E}_g$ = −3 volts
I_1 = 3 milliamp; I_2 = 7 milliamp; R = 10,000 ohms
A = ?

Solution: The 2-volt signal swings the grid potential from $-3 + 2 = -1$ volt to $-3 - 2 = -5$ volts, and this causes the plate current to vary from I_2 to I_1. The voltage across R varies from I_2R to I_1R, that is, from
$I_2R = 0.007 \times 10,000 = 70$ volts to $I_1R = 0.003 \times 10,000 = 30$ volts
therefore

$$A = \frac{70 - 30}{5 - 1} = 10 \quad Ans.$$

In the example above we have not calculated the power gain. So long as a negligible grid current flows there is little power expended in the grid circuit, and the power gain is large (in the above example, it might be several hundred thousand). The example indicates the utility of an amplifier—a 2-volt signal was increased to a 10×2 or 20-volt signal. Amplifiers can be used in cascade with the output of one fed into the input of the second; the overall amplification is the product of the amplification of each stage. Thus a radio signal picked up by an antenna may be 10 microvolts (10^{-5} volts); by using five such amplifiers in the above example, this will be built-up to a 1-volt signal, enough to actuate an earphone. Today electron tubes are available which will produce a voltage amplification of several hundred; only two or three such tubes would then be needed for the amplification of the antenna signal.

16.7   Comments

We have presented only the simplest aspects of electronics. The subject has grown tremendously in technical importance, and many industrial processes today are intimately dependent on the electron tube. No reminder is needed of its place in telephone, radio, and television communication. But in addition to its engineering applications the electron tube is responsible for a host of devices in use in physics research. Geiger counters, ionization chambers, cathode-ray oscilloscopes, audio, radio, and ultra-high frequency oscillators, voltage regulators, power supplies—to name a very few—all include electron tube circuits. It is doubtful if we would have much of our present day knowledge of atomic and nuclear physics had we been deprived of the triode electron tube.

Yet the technical and the applied aspect of thermionic emission is of no greater importance than the fundamental knowledge of the nature of electrons that is offered. To understand the mechanism of thermionic emission we called upon three fundamental pictures of matter: the action of the electron in a metal, the kinetic theory of matter, and the concept of space charge. (It is interesting to note that no one of these in its original form applied to thermionic emission.) Furthermore, we are now presented with the possibility of isolating a current of electrons free from all other matter, to be investigated apart from the usual extraneous disturbances. It is inevitable that a clearer understanding should emerge, illuminating not only the properties of the electron itself, but also the nature of the atom from which it comes. We shall try to follow the progress of this understanding in the ensuing chapters.

PROBLEMS

1.   A diode rectifying circuit contains a 20,000-ohm resistor. The average rectified current is 2 milliamp. What is the average rectified output voltage?

Ans.   40 volts.

2.   At the grid of a triode amplifier is introduced an AC 1.5-volt (amplitude) signal The grid is biased at −4 volts. The plate circuit contains a 20,000-ohm resistance, and the plate current is found to vary from 1.4 milliamp to 4.6 milliamp. Find the voltage amplification of the tube.   *Ans.*   21.3

3.   An amplifier that has a 10,000-ohm resistance in the plate circuit is found to have a voltage amplification of 15. When the grid voltage is −3 volts, and in the absence of signal, the plate current is 8 milliamp. What is the variation of plate current when a 2-volt (amplitude) signal is introduced on the grid?

Ans.   5 to 11 milliamp.

4.   The signal received on a radio antenna is 5 microvolts. How many stages of amplification are needed to increase this signal to 10 volts or more if each stage has a voltage amplification of 50?   *Ans.*   4 stages.

Suggested Reading

McArthur, E. D., "Electronics and Electron Tubes," Schenectady, New York, General Electric Co., 1933.
  Pages 6–22, simply expressed elements of electron tube engineering by an authority.

Stokley, James, "Electrons in Action," New York, McGraw-Hill Book Co., 1946.
  The role of the electron in current electricity, communication, television, radar, etc. For the layman.

PART THREE

Atomic and Nuclear Phenomena

CHAPTER 17

The Identification of the Electron

17.1 Microphysics versus Macrophysics

In our work with the dynamics of a particle having mass and the electrodynamics of a particle having charge we have made an assumption that has not always been explicitly stated, namely, the "laws" of nature governing the motions and forces of an aggregate of particles apply equally well to the fundamental particles individually. For example, the derivation of the kinetic theory of gases began with the motion of a single molecule. By an averaging device, the mean-square velocity, attention was shifted from one molecule to the aggregate of molecules, and the theory that resulted was in terms of a hypothetical average molecule. It gave us no specific information about any individual molecule. To take another example, the force between two electrical currents is evidently the result of the interaction between all the charges in one current and the magnetic field due to all the charges in the second, and we assume that an isolated electron would experience the same force as it does in conjunction with the millions of other electrons in the current. This allowed us to calculate the force on a single charge ($F = qvH$).

Physical studies of matter in the aggregate—bulk matter which we might be able to see or touch—is *macrophysics* (macro = large). The study of the ultimate particles of matter, considered as entities, is *microphysics* (micro = small). Invariably, microphysical phenomena are beyond the range of our senses—we cannot see an atom or an electron; any information or conclusions about individual particles must be obtained completely by *inference*. The procedure employed to gain these inferences derives directly from the inductive method of science. A macrophysical observation is first made (and all observations must be macrophysical); a picture or *model* is then set up which will account for the macrophenomenon in terms of the action of each individual particle. The model is then called upon to explain other observations and to predict possible new ones. Its success rests directly on its ability to satisfy

199

these demands. Thus the molecular model of matter was useful to us not only in the kinetic theory of gases, where it explained the gas laws, but was also used in understanding electrical conduction and thermionic emission.

Since atomic and nuclear physics is completely in the realm of microphysics, we shall spend considerable effort in the construction of models, and we shall attempt to impose on these models the assumption that they obey the same physical laws as do large-scale bodies. We shall see that this attempt, which is essentially mechanical, often fails. To obtain the inferences that help construct the models will require careful analysis of experiments which are sometimes deviously remote from the immediate model. This process is not unlike that used by the astronomer, who must construct a model of the universe from tiny light signals observed on the earth. This process of forming models reveals the great value of inductive reasoning, for the worth of the model is directly measured by the experiments it explains. The deductive philosophers in ancient times established models (they spoke of the "music of the heavenly spheres"), but their correlation with experiment was usually negligible.

The careful student might well ask if these microphysical characteristics we infer are real. Might not the steps between observed evidence and deduced conclusions contain errors? And if there are errors would we ever be able to detect them? Hence, is there any *reality* to microphysics? These questions are valid and cogent. The philosopher of physics asks these and many others like them. The atom with its nucleus and electrons is too small to be seen; the smallest aggregate yet observed (with an electron microscope) contains several hundred thousand atoms. Yet this very statement implies that we know there are atoms—we are counting them! The fact of the matter, of course, is that we don't *know* there are atoms, much less do we *know* the internal structure of an atom. From a large body of indirect evidence we have constructed a model which includes molecules, atoms, electrons, nuclei. The model must be good enough to explain the observable evidence satisfactorily; if new phenomena are observed for which the model fails, then the model must be changed. The theories and models in macrophysics seem to us to be much less tentative.

The aim in the following chapters is to present the experiments which have contributed the indirect evidence for the nuclear atom and to present the arguments leading to the conclusions drawn from this evidence. It will be as important to study the inadequacies of the atomic model as to reveal its successes. That the latter outweight the former is the excuse for the detailed discussion that follows. The realm of microphysics will not yield realities directly, but its inductively constructed pictures can lead the experimenter to very real observable phenomena.

17.2 Conduction of Electricity in Gases

The evidence leading to the identification of the electron—and to the basic idea of the nature of electric charges presented in the previous chapters—arose from experiments on the electrical conduction in gases. It has been previously noted that gases are fairly good insulators. In fact, at atmospheric pressure approximately 30,000 volts are required to cause conduction across a 1-cm air gap between metal spheres. However, beginning in about 1850 the technique of obtaining a good vacuum was developed, and it was discovered that a gas becomes a much better conductor at reduced pressure. In Fig. 17.1 is shown a long glass tube connected to a pumping system. A metal disk is sealed into the tube at each end; such disks, between which a difference of potential may be placed, are called *electrodes*, the one given a positive potential is the *anode*, the negative one the *cathode*. When a difference of potential of several thousand volts is maintained between the

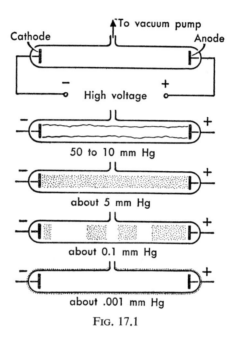

FIG. 17.1

two electrodes and the vacuum pump is started, a succession of phenomena is observed, as indicated in Fig. 17.1. Initially at atmospheric pressure (760 mm of mercury) there is no conduction. As the pressure is reduced to the region of 50 to 10 mm of mercury a series of thin, streamer-like discharges appear. These streamers increase in number until at about 5 mm they completely fill the space between the electrodes, giving the tube a glowing appearance. If the gas is air the discharge is purple, if neon it is orange-red, if argon it is blue, etc.—the color is characteristic of the gas. At this pressure the tube is simply the familiar neon sign, or rather, in this case it is a nitrogen sign.

Further reduction of pressure introduces further complexities in the appearance of the discharge. At about 0.1 mm pressure it has ceased to be uniform; the glowing regions alternate with regions of darkness. The most significant of these is the dark space around the cathode. Further reduction of pressure causes this dark space to grow until at a pressure of 0.001 mm of mercury it fills the tube—all nitrogen glow has disappeared. However, though there is now no light from the gas, the glass walls emit a dull greenish glow called fluorescence.

17.3 Mechanism of Gaseous Conduction

The discharge of electricity through a gas is a complicated phenomenon. We shall limit outselves to a discussion of its simpler aspects, and even in this it will be necessary to anticipate that which we are trying to explain in this section, namely, the structure of the atom (as we had to do in Chapter 11).

An atom consists of a positively charged nucleus surrounded by a cloud of negative electrons whose charges just neutralize the charge of the nucleus. If, by some mechanism, an electron is removed from the atom, the charge balance is upset, and the atom is now positively charged. Likewise, if an electron is added to the atom's normal quota, the result is a negatively charged atom. Because of this charge, such atoms will experience a force in an electric field ($F = Eq$) and will be accelerated. These charged atoms are the *ions* already mentioned in Chapter 11. The motion of an ion depends on the congestion in its surroundings. In most solids the ions are so hemmed in that there is no translational motion; in such materials the electrons do the moving if conduction occurs. However, in a gas, the atoms and molecules have a great deal more freedom of motion, leading us to expect that both positive and negative ions will move, some of them ultimately reaching the electrodes. Since by definition a current consists of a flow of charges, there is electrical conduction in the gas.

Under ordinary conditions there are always a few ions in any sample of gas. These primary ions are produced by radioactive contamination in the surroundings and by the cosmic rays in much the same manner in which ions themselves multiply to form a gas discharge, that is, by collisions between the high-speed cosmic and radioactive particles and the gas molecules. In such collisions an electron may be torn away from the neutral molecule by the force of the impact, leaving a positive ion and a free electron. True, the ion and an electron promptly recombine to form a neutral molecule, but at any instant there are, nevertheless, a few primary ions in the gas.

If an electric field is impressed on the gas the free electrons and the ions set free by the primary ionization processes will be rapidly accelerated and become high-speed projectiles capable of knocking out other electrons from the atoms in their path. Most of this secondary ionization is produced by the accelerated electrons, since they have a better chance of moving far enough to acquire the requisite energy for further ionization. The positive ions have shorter paths between collisions and seldom gain sufficient energy for ionization since in each collision they lose some of their kinetic energy.

At atmospheric pressure, unless the electric field is very intense, the possible ionizing agents, the free electrons and the primary ions, recombine to form neutral atoms before they get well started in their motions. However, as the pressure is reduced, the probability of collision becomes smaller, and a streamer-like path of ionization is formed. This path is visible because of the light which is emitted by recombining ions and from the many atoms along the path which are hit only hard enough to displace their electrons but not to remove them. (This radiation of light will be studied later.) Further decrease of pressure allows conduction along any path through the tube; hence the tube is filled with light (the neon sign pressure region). We will pass by the complications that set in at pressures of a few tenths of a millimeter, since they contribute little to our efforts to identify the electron. But the region of pressure in which the visible discharge disappears is significant. At this very low pressure there are only a few millionths of the original number of atoms or molecules, and an ion may travel the entire distance between electrodes without undergoing collision. An electron starting close to the cathode will attain a very high velocity by the time it reaches the anode. Since collisions in the gas are rare there is too little radiation of light to make the gas visible. The fluorescence of the glass walls is due to the direct bombardment of electrons and to the absorption of x rays which are formed when the electrons hit the anode, phenomena that will be discussed in a later chapter.

17.4 Cathode Rays

Assuming the correctness of the foregoing explanation of conduction in a gas, the significance of the last argument becomes apparent. At exceedingly low pressures a gas discharge tube presents us with a stream of very high-speed electrons, free of their parent atoms. Such streams were observed before knowledge of the electron existed; since they came from the region of the cathode they were called *cathode rays*. Note, however, they are not rays in the sense of waves, but rather are high-speed particles. We have seen in the preceding chapter that there is today a much simpler method of obtaining electrons, namely, thermionic emission from a hot filament. A modern *cathode-ray tube* (Fig. 17.2) employs a heated filament placed in a highly evacuated tube. If the anode is constructed with a small hole in it a pencil of cathode rays passes through the hole and will cause fluorescence at the point of contact with the screen at the end of the tube. Since glass fluoresces only feebly, this screen is usually covered with a brightly fluorescing salt such as zinc sulfide.

17.5 Cathode-Ray Oscilloscope

The modern cathode-ray tube used in oscilloscopes and television receivers makes use of a beam of cathode rays striking a fluorescent screen. In

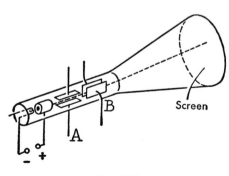

FIG. 17.2

the commonest oscilloscope tube, a narrow electron beam is formed and passed through two pairs of plates, as indicated in Fig. 17.2. If a difference in potential is impressed on the pair of plates A, the beam of electrons will be slightly deviated toward the positive plate (away from the negative) and undergoes a deflection in the vertical direction. Likewise, a voltage on the pair of plates B will cause a horizontal deflection. If a voltage which is uniformly increasing in time is placed on B, the beam will move across the screen horizontally at a uniform rate; removal of this voltage allows the beam to return to its original position. This horizontal "sweeping" voltage would then be of the form shown in Fig. 17.3a. Now, if at the same time as the beam is being swept horizontally a

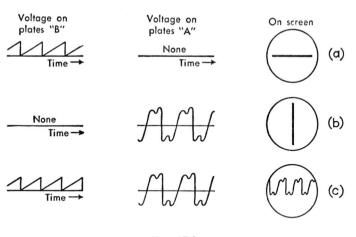

FIG. 17.3

varying voltage is put on the plates A (Fig. 17.3b), the resulting vertical motion of the beam will be swept across the screen, as it were, "unfolding" the shape of the variation of the voltage on the A plates. Hence we get a picture of this variation on the screen as in Fig. 17.3c. If the sweeping voltage on *B* is made to repeat itself in synchronism with the cycle of the voltage on *A*, the picture repeats itself over and over, and forms a stationary pattern on the screen. Such a cathode-ray tube and its associated electrical circuits is called a *cathode-ray oscilloscope;* it allows us to "see" the rapid variations of an electrical signal.

In a television picture tube two sweep voltages are used to form a set of several hundred closely spaced horizontal lines. An additional electrode similar to the grid in a triode controls the electron beam current, making each point on each line either bright or dark in response to the video signal from the television transmitter. The aggregate of such spots of light and darkness forms the picture.

17.6 Measurement of e/m of the Electron—J. J. Thomson's Experiment

We now encounter the first of the many experiments whose interpretation contributes directly to the picture of microphysics. In this experiment a beam of cathode rays is deflected by electric and magnetic fields. This is possible since it is known that they are negative charges in motion. (They are attracted to the positive electrode.) We have seen in Chapter 14 that a charged particle in motion will experience a force in a plane perpendicular to a magnetic field. Hence it should be possible to bend cathode rays either by electrostatic fields or by magnetic fields, or by both. The Thomson apparatus in Fig. 17.4 has the magnetic field crossed with the electric field. Due to the magnetic field (*H*) alone, the electric field being zero, the beam is deflected vertically upward (it must be remembered we are dealing with a *negative* particle). The force on a moving charge (*q*) in a magnetic field is given by (see §14.8) $F_H = qv\overset{\frown}{H}$. The charge on the electron assumes such importance in physics that it is given a separate symbol *e*. So for an electron

$$F_H = ev\overset{\frown}{H}$$

Due to the electrostatic field (*E*) alone, the magnetic field being zero, the negatively charged cathode rays are deflected vertically downward. The force on the charge *e* is given by the definition of electric field *E* and is

$$F_E = Ee$$

If these two forces are made equal (by adjusting *E*, say) the net force is zero on the charged particle, and it will be undeflected. Under this condition.

$$evH = Ee$$

or

$$v = \frac{E}{H}$$

It is evident that we can balance the two forces for all the particles with a given E and H *only* if all the particles have the same velocity v. Put differently, if when we try to adjust E so that no deflection results we get a sharply focused beam, then we can conclude that all the particles must have the same velocity. This was the case actually observed, indicating that virtually all the cathode rays start their career at (or very near) the cathode of the discharge tube, since they all have acquired the same velocity. Of course, this result could have been guaranteed by replacing the gas tube with a filament source of electrons, but such a source was not available at the time this experiment was first performed.

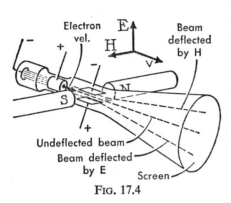

Fig. 17.4

The second part of the experiment involves making $E = 0$. When this is done, there is a deflection upward due to H; the particle is bent out of its straight path. This force must be a *centripetal force* (see §14.10), and the particle moves along the arc of a circle during the time it is in the magnetic field (see Fig. 14.14). If the mass of the particle is designated by m then

$$F_H = \frac{mv^2}{r}$$

Since this force is caused by the charged particle's motion in a magnetic field we can write

$$F_H = evH = \frac{mv^2}{r}$$

or

$$\frac{e}{m} = \frac{v}{Hr}$$

By measuring the deflection of the beam, r can be determined from simple geometrical considerations. We have already seen from the first part of the experiment that $v = E/H$. Thus, substituting this for v we have

$$\frac{e}{m} = \frac{E}{H^2 r}$$

Since all the quantities on the right-hand side are measurable, the value of the charge-to-mass ratio of the cathode-ray particle can be determined. It is found to be

$$\frac{e}{m} = 17.6 \times 10^7 \text{ coulombs/gm} = 5.27 \times 10^{17} \text{ esu/gm}$$

This experiment was conceived and performed by J. J. Thomson in 1897. Though he was unable to determine either the charge or mass separately, he had succeeded in showing that cathode rays consist of particles having a definite charge-to-mass ratio which is the same for all cathode rays. The particles were called electrons (a name already suggested by Stoney), and Thomson is given full credit for their identification.

17.7   Measurement of e—Millikan's Oil-Drop Experiment

It is evident from the Thomson experiment that a separate measurement of either e or m is required if both e and m are to be known. Many experimenters worked on this problem, but the most successful was R. A. Millikan, who started his measurements in 1906 and repeated and improved them in the following years.

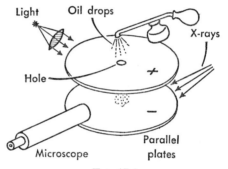

Millikan's apparatus is illustrated by the diagram of Fig. 17.5. Oil drops are sprayed above a pair of plates between which a difference of potential of a few hundred volts can be maintained. A hole in the center of the top plate allows a few drops to enter the air space between the plates. These drops are illuminated by a light source and viewed by a microscope equipped with a calibrated scale in its eyepiece. A beam of x rays produces ions between the plates, and some of these ions will attach themselves to the oil drops. With no electric field the drops fall in the gravitational field. Because of the large frictional force of the air, which opposes the gravitational force, the drops do not accelerate uniformly, but very quickly reach a *terminal velocity*, falling at a constant speed thereafter. This terminal velocity depends on the size and mass of the drops and is proportional to the applied force (*mg* in this case). If the density of the oil is known, it is possible to calculate the mass of the drop from a measurement of the terminal velocity.

FIG. 17.5

If a potential difference is impressed on the plates, the upper one positive, say, those drops which acquire negative ions will move upward due to electrostatic attraction. Here the net upward force on the drop of charge q is

$$F = Eq - mg$$

in the electric field E. By again measuring the terminal velocity, the force Eq can be found and since E is known the charge q on the drop is found. Of course, Millikan did not assume that an oil drop had collected just one electronic charge; it might have several electron charges, and it might change its number of charges from time to time. In fact, by intermittently exposing the region between the plates to x rays, he could vary the charge on any single drop, noting this by observing the sudden variations in the upward terminal velocity of the drop. By holding a single drop in the field of view of the microscope, letting it fall, pulling it upwards, letting it fall, etc., but never permitting it to hit either of the plates, Millikan obtained data of the following kind:

$$q = \ \ 32 \times 10^{-20} \text{ coulombs}$$
$$q = \ \ 80 \times 10^{-20}$$
$$q = \ \ 64 \times 10^{-20}$$
$$q = 112 \times 10^{-20}$$
$$q = \ \ 48 \times 10^{-20}$$

The important feature of these data lies in the fact that they all have a common multiple:

$$(32 \times 10^{-20})/2 = 16 \times 10^{-20}$$
$$(80 \times 10^{-20})/5 = 16 \times 10^{-20}$$
$$(64 \times 10^{-20})/4 = 16 \times 10^{-20}$$
$$(112 \times 10^{-20})/7 = 16 \times 10^{-20}$$
$$(48 \times 10^{-20})/3 = 16 \times 10^{-20}$$

Never did he find a value of q which was not a multiple of 16×10^{-20} coulombs. The inescapable conclusion is that 16×10^{-20} coulombs must be the unit charge which the oil drop picked up and lost, and it was concluded that this was the charge of the electron. So

$$e = 16.0 \times 10^{-20} \text{ coulombs}$$

or, in the esu system,

$$e = 4.80 \times 10^{-10} \text{ esu}$$

Millikan's experiment offered excellent proof that the charge of the electron is constant, the same value for all electrons. Repeated experiments have never yielded a sub-multiple of this value. Hence the electron charge appears to be the "atom" of electricity, of which all other charges are simply multiples. Furthermore, when positively charged drops were measured the same value for the unit charge was found. This bears out our assumption that a positive ion is an atom or molecule lacking one or more electrons, a negative ion an atom or molecule with an excess of electrons.

As we have seen in §13.6, Avogadro's number can be determined by combining the results of electrolytic experiments with Millikan's measurement of the electronic charge. This illustrates only one of the important subsidiary results of the knowledge of e.

17.8   The Mass of the Electron

It is now possible to go back to the results of the J. J. Thomson experiment to determine the mass of the electron. From that experiment

$$\frac{e}{m} = 17.6 \times 10^7 \text{ coulombs/gm}$$

Millikan's results:

$$e = 16.0 \times 10^{-20} \text{ coulombs}$$

Therefore,

$$m = 9.11 \times 10^{-28} \text{ gm}$$

This is the lightest particle yet found in nature.

We will see in Chapter 20 that the relativity principle shows that a particle moving with a velocity near that of light undergoes a pronounced increase in mass. Hence the above value for the electron must be designated the *rest mass* of the electron. Just how fast an electron may be moving without appreciably changing its mass is determined by a calculation in relativity theory.

17.9   Calculation of Electron Velocities

When electrons are accelerated through a difference of potential V the work done on the charge is just

$$W = Ve$$

which is equal to the kinetic energy acquired by the electron. If the potential differences are less than a few thousand volts, the relativistic mass increase is negligible, and

$$Ve = \tfrac{1}{2}mv^2$$

where m is the electron's rest mass. Thus by knowing Ve and m the electron velocity may be determined.

Example. Suppose an electron starts at rest at the cathode and moves through a potential difference of 1000 volts. How much energy does it receive and what is its final velocity as it strikes the anode?

$$\text{Energy} = \tfrac{1}{2}\, mv^2 = Ve = 1000 \text{ volts} \times 16 \times 10^{-20} \text{ coulombs}$$
$$= 16 \times 10^{-17} \text{ joules} \quad \text{(practical units)}$$
$$= 16 \times 10^{-10} \text{ ergs} \quad \text{(cgs units)}$$

This very small amount of energy produces a very large electron velocity, for

$$\frac{mv^2}{2} = 16 \times 10^{-10} \text{ ergs}$$

$$9.1 \times 10^{-28} \times \frac{v^2}{2} = 16 \times 10^{-10}$$

$$v^2 = 3.52 \times 10^{18}$$
$$v = 1.88 \times 10^9 \text{ cm/sec}$$
$$= 11,700 \text{ mi/sec}$$

Such an electron could travel a mile in a completely evacuated space in eighty-five millionths of a second!

17.10   The Electron Volt as an Energy Unit

Since most methods of obtaining energetic particles in the laboratory employ acceleration between electrodes having a potential difference, a new unit measuring this particle energy in terms of potential difference is in common use in atomic and nuclear physics. It is the *electron volt*, or for higher energies, the million electron volt. The abbreviations for these units are ev and Mev (occasionally Kev—thousand electron volt is used also). The electron volt is defined as the energy gained by a particle having a charge of 16×10^{-20} coulombs falling through a difference of potential of 1 volt. This is related to the fundamental unit of energy very simply:

$$W = Ve = (1 \text{ volt}) \times (16 \times 10^{-20} \text{ coulombs})$$
$$1 \text{ ev} = 16 \times 10^{-20} \text{ joules}$$
$$= 16 \times 10^{-13} \text{ ergs}$$

Thus in the preceding problem the electron in falling through 1000 volts of potential difference gains 1000 ev of energy or $16 \times 10^{-13} \times 1000 = 16 \times 10^{-10}$ ergs. Since a positive ion, if singly ionized, has the same charge as the electron, it would acquire the same energy for the same potential difference. Note, however, that its velocity would be very much less, because its mass is much greater than that of the electron. If an ion, either positive or negative, is doubly ionized, its energy in electron volts is twice the voltage accelerating it. In subsequent chapters, particularly in nuclear physics, we will frequently measure energies in electron volts.

PROBLEMS

1. What is the force on an electron moving between parallel plates whose separation is 0.2 cm and on which there is a potential difference of 6000 volts. (Hint: See §12.3.   *Ans.* 0.05 microdyne

2. A magnetic field of 3×10^{-9} esu is crossed by an electric field between parallel plates of 0.1 cm separation. What potential difference must be between the plates to cause an electron of velocity 5×10^9 cm/sec to remain undeflected?
Ans. 1.5 esu or 450 volts.

3. When the electric field of Problem 2 is made zero, what is the radius of curvature of the electron path in the magnetic field?   *Ans.* 3.16 cm.

4. From its rate of fall an oil drop between plates of 5 mm separation was found to have a mass of 2.26×10^{-10} gm; with a potential difference on the plates of 3000 volts the drop was observed to be balanced exactly. What is the charge on the drop?
Ans. 23e.

5. How much energy is gained by an electron falling through a potential difference of 750 volts? What is its velocity?   *Ans.* 12×10^{-10} ergs; 1.63×10^9 cm/sec.

6. How many ergs in 35 ev? In 150 Kev? In 5 Mev?
Ans. 5.6×10^{-11}; 2.4×10^{-7}; 8×10^{-6} ergs.

Suggested Reading

BORN, MAX, "The Restless Universe," London, Blackie & Son, 1935.
Chapter II on electrons and ions. Excellent reading.

DAMPIER, SIR WILLIAM, "A History of Science," New York, The Macmillan Co., 1946.
Pages 384–89, historical description of electron's discovery and properties.

MILLIKAN, R. A., "Electrons (+ and —)," Chicago, University of Chicago Press, 1947.
Chapters III, IV, and V describe early work on determining charge on the electron. Readable and authoritative.

STRANATHAN, J. D., "The Particles of Modern Physics," Philadelphia, The Blakiston Co., 1942.
Chapter 4, complete account of e/m measurements on cathode rays.

The Discovery of Isotopes

18.1   The Positive Ray Experiment—J. J. Thomson

In a gas discharge tube there are both positive ions and electrons. We have already seen that the electron beam (cathode ray) can be fruitfully studied. Experiments with beams of positive ions were equally rewarding, and in the hands of J. J. Thomson, in 1907, they revealed a significant fact about the masses of atoms—that the atoms of a given chemical element might be of several masses.

As early as 1886 Goldstein observed a luminous beam of positive ions emerging from a hole in a discharge-tube cathode. These beams were called *positive rays*, and a similar arrangement has been used to obtain them in later experiments. The experiment of J. J. Thomson was designed to study the characteristics of these "rays," specifically their charge-to-mass ratio. To do this, it might seem necessary only to repeat the e/m experiment, this time, how-ever, on the opposite end of the discharge tube. At once a difficulty is en-countered with the crossed E and H technique used in the e/m experiment. It is impossible to balance E and H to produce zero deflection for all the positive rays. Since in the e/m experiment success in obtaining a zero deflection balance was considered good evidence that all cathode rays in the tube had the same velocity, we would conclude that all positive rays do *not* have the same velocity. This is not surprising. The ions are formed in the gas, and an ion starting near the anode will have greater velocity upon reaching the cathode than one starting from a point halfway along the tube. For this reason we cannot use the crossed E and H method since we are unable to fill one of the two conditions of that experiment, namely, the balance for zero deflection.

The solution of this difficulty was supplied by Thomson by the use of *parallel E* and *H*. The method has come to be known as the "positive ray parabola" method. Figure 18.1 indicates the spatial arrangement of the fields. The magnetic field will cause the positive ion to move toward the right (the $+x$ direction); the electric field moves it at the same time vertically upward (the $+y$ direction). A slow ion will have a large x and y deflection, a fast ion a smaller deflection. It can be shown, however (see below), that all ions having the same charge-to-mass ratio, regardless of their velocities, will fall along

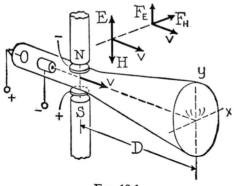

FIG. 18.1

the same curve. The mathematical form of this curve is that of a parabola, hence the name of the method. Any single parabola represents ions of the same charge-to-mass ratio.

18.2 Theory of the Positive Ray Parabolas

Let us assume that we are dealing with a single ion of mass m, charge e, and velocity v, and that the electric and magnetic fields are uniform over the path length L. The electric force is equal to

$$F_E = eE$$

and is directed along $+y$ (Fig. 18.1), giving a uniform acceleration

$$a = \frac{F_E}{m} = \frac{eE}{m}$$

in that direction. This is analogous to the falling motion of a horizontally fired projectile where the gravitational field in the projectile case is here replaced by a uniform electric field (see §5.8). Hence the particle rises a distance

$$y = \tfrac{1}{2}at^2 = \tfrac{1}{2}\frac{eE}{m}t^2$$

$$= \tfrac{1}{2}\frac{eE}{m}\frac{L^2}{v^2} \qquad\qquad [18.1]$$

in a time $t = L/v$.

The magnetic force is evH and is directed perpendicularly to the electron path, or

$$F_H = evH = \frac{mv^2}{R}$$

From Fig. 18.2

$$R^2 = (R - x)^2 + L^2$$

or

$$R = \frac{L^2}{2x} \quad \text{(approximately)}$$

so that

$$x = \frac{L^2}{2R} = \frac{HeL^2}{2mv}$$

and

$$x^2 = \frac{H^2e^2L^4}{4m^2v^2} \qquad\qquad [\,18.2\,]$$

Dividing Eq. 18.2 by Eq. 18.1 and solving for x^2, we get

$$x^2 = \left(\frac{H^2eL^2}{2mE}\right)y$$

All the terms inside the parentheses are constants, and this is the equation of a parabola giving the deflections x and y of the beam as it emerges from the E and H fields. All quantities except e/m are constants of the apparatus and can be measured. Hence by determining x and y Thomson could calculate e/m for various kinds of ions. A typical set of parabolas is shown in Fig. 18.3.

For each of the traces in Fig. 18.3 the ions striking at various points have the same e/m and differ only in velocity, fast ones hitting near the center and slow ones farther out along the parabola. To obtain both branches of the parabola the direction of H is reversed during the experiment. By introducing various gases into the discharge, e/m can be measured for various ions.

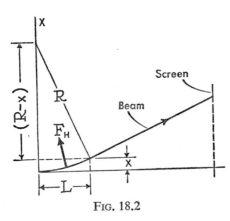

FIG. 18.2

18.3   The Discovery of Isotopes

In one experiment Thomson used pure neon as the gas in the discharge tube. Like all so-called pure gases, however, it contained slight traces of other gases—oxygen in this case. Consequently, he expected to find an e/m parabola for Ne^+, probably a faint curve for O^+, and possibly Ne^{++} and O_2^+. These he observed, but in addition there was a faint parabola which was not expected.

It lay quite near the expected neon parabola. By measuring the positions of the main neon curve and its neighbor relative to the oxygen curve, it was possible to determine the masses of the ions responsible for the curves. Following the well-established custom of the chemists of arbitrarily giving 16 mass units to the oxygen atom, the two neon curves were found

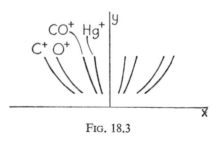

FIG. 18.3

to represent masses of 22 units (the weaker curve) and 20. The atomic mass found by the chemists for neon was 20.2 on the same scale, so it was reasonable to assume that the mass 20 curve was due to neon. The possibility that the weaker curve of mass 22 was an impurity had to be ruled out as unlikely because there is no other element having a mass close to 22, and any molecule having 22 as its molecular mass should also show curves due to its constituent atoms. (For example, when CO_2 was in the discharge tube, curves for CO_2^+, C^+, O_2^+, O^+ were all found.) Neither was it possible to attribute the 22 curve to neon of mass 20 but having slightly smaller charge, since the oil drop experiment (and many others) had shown unambiguously that charges were always found as multiples of e; $0.9e$ or any other fraction did not exist. After the careful elimination of such possibilities Thomson concluded that the mass 22 curve had to be neon also. It appeared that all the atoms of neon, though chemically identical, did not have identical masses; one out of every ten (the intensity ratio of the curves) is about 10% heavier than the other nine. Atoms of the same element but having different masses are called *isotopes*. The word derives from two Greek words meaning "same place," that is, such atoms occupy the same place in the periodic table. Thomson succeeded in showing that neon has two isotopes, neon 20 and neon 22. (In point of fact, it possesses three—neon 21 was observed later; its very low abundance makes it difficult to observe.)

18.4   The Mass Spectrograph

Since the apparatus used by Thomson to demonstrate the existence of isotopes performs a separation of the masses of the ions, it is correctly called a *mass spectrograph*, i.e., a device which separates the different atomic masses, forming a mass "spectrum," just as a diffraction grating forms a wave-length spectrum. In the hands of Aston, Dempster, Bainbridge, and many others the mass spectrograph has been developed into an instrument of high precision; in its present form the fields are usually crossed but arranged in sequence rather than in superposition in order to gain "velocity selection." Their precision is indicated by the mass number 22.0086 which is the measured mass of the neon 22 isotope. The significance of these accurate masses will become evident later when we study nuclear reactions. It is still customary to refer to an isotopic mass by its nearest whole number (the maximum deviation from a whole number yet found is only 0.8%). Thus we speak of neon 22, not of neon 22.0086, etc.

In addition to yielding accurate mass values the mass spectrograph reveals the relative abundances of isotopes by measuring the relative intensities of their traces on the photographic plate. Many interesting features of the isotopic composition of the elements have been learned. Hydrogen, the lightest of all elements, possesses two isotopes, of which 99.98% is hydrogen 1 and 0.02% is hydrogen 2. Hydrogen 2 combined with oxygen gives so-called "heavy water." In going through a table of isotopes we find, curiously enough, that fluorine, sodium, aluminum, phosphorus, iodine, and several other elements have only a single isotope; the others have two or more. Tin, with 10 isotopes, has the greatest number. (The elements beyond lead are in a special category which will concern us later; they have to be exempted from most of this discussion.) Thus a sample of tin contains atoms of mass numbers 112 up through 124, with 113 and 123 missing; the ordinary chemical atomic mass, 118.7, is an average of these values weighted in accord with the abundance of each isotope. Furthermore, every sample of tin yet analyzed has had the same relative abundance of its isotopes. In fact, mass spectrographic data show that the relative abundances of the isotopes of nearly all the elements found in nature are fixed and unchanging. The original causes which determined these abundances are not fully understood.

18.5 Physical versus Chemical Atomic Mass

By careful determinations of the weights of substances which combine to form molecules, the chemist has obtained the relative atomic masses of all the elements. He found that if atomic oxygen was assigned 16 units then many of the lighter elements would have approximately whole-number atomic masses. Thus the atomic mass of hydrogen was 1.008, helium 4.002, carbon 12.01, nitrogen 12.008, fluorine 19.000, etc. On the strength of this Prout had proposed in 1813 that all atoms were built up out of hydrogen atoms; as we shall see later this shrewd guess is partially correct. However, the Prout hypothesis offered no help in explaining fractional atomic masses, such as chlorine with 35.5, copper with 63.6, and many others.

The discovery of the existence of isotopes has necessitated a more careful scrutiny of the meaning of atomic masses. The chemist, dealing with large numbers of atoms of an element, obtains an *average* atomic mass relative to naturally appearing oxygen as 16. Such an average determination is called the *chemical atomic mass*. On the other hand, the physicist, making measurements with the mass spectrograph, separates the different isotopic components, and by observing the amount of bending in electric and magnetic fields obtains the mass of each of these components. These are known as *isotopic masses*. Knowing the isotopic masses we should be able to predict the chemical mass. For example, chlorine has two isotopes: Cl 35 (actually 34.979) which is 75.4% abundant, and Cl 37 (36.978) which is 24.6% abundant; therefore

$$\text{Chemical mass} = 35 \times .75 + 37 \times .25 = 35.5$$

A second distinction between chemical and isotopic masses arose in 1929 when Giauque and Johnston discovered that the standard of reference, oxygen, itself was a mixture of isotopes! It consists of 99.76% oxygen 16, 0.04% oxygen 17, and 0.20% oxygen 18. It is this mixture which has the chemical mass of 16.000 by definition. It is obvious that such a mixture will not serve as a reference for isotopic masses. Therefore, all *isotopic masses* are based on the isotope oxygen 16, with the unit mass then being $\frac{1}{16}$ the mass of oxygen 16. Hence, prediction of average (chemical) atomic masses using isotopic masses will not quite agree with the measured average masses of the chemists. The discrepancy is important only in the most accurate determinations; it amounts to one part in 4000. In a study of the physical properties of the atom such as we are engaged upon in this book, it is natural to refer all atomic masses to the isotopic scale, that is, our unit atomic mass will be $\frac{1}{16}$ the mass of the isotope oxygen 16.

18.6 Mass of the Unit Atom

The most precise measurement of Avogadro's number has determined the mass of the "unit atom" to be: $(1.66035 \pm 0.00031) \times 10^{-24}$ gm. We will have occasion to use this figure frequently, but with fewer significant figures. Writing mu as the symbol for the atomic mass unit, we will approximate the value as

$$1 \text{ mu} = 1.66 \times 10^{-24} \text{ gm}$$

Such an atom has an atomic mass of 1, by definition. Using the symbol A for the isotopic mass number of any element, its actual mass in grams is

Mass of isotope of mass number $A = A \times 1.66 \times 10^{-24}$ gm

Thus, for the isotope chlorine 35 the mass is

$$1.66 \times 10^{-24} \times 35 \text{ gm} = 58.1 \times 10^{-24} \text{ gm}.$$

There exists in nature no element of unit atomic mass; the nearest to it is the isotope hydrogen 1. Its atomic mass number (compared to oxygen 16 in the mass spectrograph) has been found to be 1.008130; hence its mass is

$$1.660 \times 10^{-24} \times 1.008 = 1.673 \times 10^{-24} \text{ gm}$$

It is instructive to compare this with the smallest mass yet found in nature, that of the electron. The most accurate determination of the electron mass is

Mass of electron $= 9.1066 \times 10^{-28}$ gm

If we form the ratio between the mass of the hydrogen atom and the mass of the electron we get

$$\frac{1.673 \times 10^{-24}}{9.107 \times 10^{-28}} = 1837$$

Hence the lightest atom, hydrogen 1, is 1837 times heavier than the electron. Since the mass spectrograph measures the mass of an ion, the small correction of the missing electron mass must be made in determining atomic masses. Isotopic masses are always quoted for neutral atoms.

18.7 The Periodic Table of the Elements

The great advantage gained by arranging the elements in a specific order was demonstrated by many chemists, beginning with the work of Meyer, Newlands, Mendeleeff and others in the decade following 1860. In all, 92 elements have been found on earth. Though it has been possible recently for the physicist to produce a few more than this (element 94, plutonium, is a noted example) the natural elements form the basis of the world as we know it. The most common array of the elements is the periodic table, one form of which is given at the back of the book. The elements in each column of the table possess chemical similarities. In the early tables the elements progressed in order of increasing atomic mass. The criterion used today is one of nuclear charge, that is, the elements in the table are arranged in the order of increasing nuclear charge. The position, and hence the nuclear charge, of an atom is its *atomic number*. Thus, hydrogen is number one, neon number 10, etc. down to uranium number 92. Since an atom has two significant designations, its atomic number and its isotopic mass, it is useful to employ a notation that will indicate both. At the upper right corner of the chemical symbol for the element is placed the isotopic mass; at the lower left corner is the atomic number. Thus the isotopes are designated:

Hydrogen	$_1H^1$ and $_1H^2$
Nitrogen	$_7N^{14}$ and $_7N^{15}$
Oxygen	$_8O^{16}$, $_8O^{17}$, and $_8O^{18}$
Uranium	$_{92}U^{234}$, $_{92}U^{235}$, and $_{92}U^{238}$

The evidence for the nuclear atom with its central + charge balanced by the charge of its surrounding negative electrons came slowly but convincingly from several lines of research. Its chief support was the success of the Bohr model of the atom (Chapter 23) in which the nuclear atom was a basic assumption. However, there were other confirming observations. No amount of mass spectrographic research has ever revealed an ion of atomic hydrogen that is lacking two electrons; we conclude that hydrogen has only one electron to lose. Likewise, helium has been found singly or doubly ionized but never triply ionized. Lithium ions have shown a maximum possible charge of three. It becomes exceedingly difficult to "strip" other atoms of more than two or three electrons, but it has been done in a few cases: carbon, $_6C^{12}$, has been made into the ion C++++++ (now usually written C⁶⁺). All such evidence indicates that the atom has only a certain number of electrons, and since normally atoms are electrically neutral, the nucleus of the atom must have a positive charge equaling this number.

We can use the concept of atomic number (nuclear charge) to re-define isotopes: *Isotopes are atoms having the same atomic number but different atomic masses.* Thus $_{10}Ne^{20}$ and $_{10}Ne^{22}$ each have 10 positive charges on the nucleus, but one has a mass of two units more than the other. As suggested before, there are a few elements that are "mono-isotopic," that is, all he atoms of that element have the same mass. For example, all the atoms of fluorine, $_9F^{19}$ have masses of 19 units.

18.8   The Separation of Isotopes

Because the isotopes of an element are chemically identical, there is no simple chemical method for isolating one of the isotopes of an element. Of course, the apparatus which led to their discovery, the mass spectrograph, does perform a very satisfactory separation. The difficulty lies in the very small amounts separated; after many hours of operation the ordinary laboratory variety of spectrograph yields only a few millionths of a gram of separated isotopes. During World War II gigantic spectrographs were constructed to increase this yield, although this process is difficult and expensive. In addition to mass spectrographs many other methods have been tried, most of them designed to give only a partial separation, i.e., enrichment of one particular isotope of the element. Invariably all methods must depend on the mass difference itself, and, except for the hydrogen isotopes where the difference is 100%, it is small (10% for Ne^{20}, Ne^{22}; 8% for C^{12}, C^{13}, etc). These separation methods are too involved for complete discussion here, but the basic principles of the design of the more common ones will be indicated.

1. The rate of certain chemical reactions depends to some degree on the masses of the atoms or molecules; thus a heavy isotope will react at a slightly different rate than a light one; this method has been particularily successful in enriching the N^{15} and C^{13} isotopes which are now available commercially.

2. Two isotopic atoms at the same temperature, i.e., having the same kinetic energy, will have slightly different thermal velocities because of their mass difference. Hence, in the gaseous state the one having the lighter mass and greater velocity will diffuse through a porous solid, such as unglazed porcelain, more readily than the slower one; if the lighter ones are swept away immediately after diffusion, to prevent them diffusing back again, there will result a partial separation. In a variation on this method the porous solid is replaced by some more of the same kind of gas (this is called "self-diffusion"). Temperature differences have also been used to effect a separation. These diffusion methods have proved fairly successful for the lighter elements.

3. A centrifuge filled with a gas hurls the heavy atoms farther out from the center than the light ones. Hence, a very high-speed centrifuge can be used as a sort of cream separator, where the lighter isotope is the cream, the heavier is the milk. The high speeds required (of the order of 1000 revolutions per second) to cause an appreciable separation introduces enough mechanical trouble to make the method difficult.

4. The method that works extremely well for the hydrogen isotopes, because of their large mass difference (100%), involves the electrolysis of water. The molecules containing two H^1 atoms electrolyze more rapidly than those few molecules having two H^2 atoms. The residue of an electrolytic bath slowly becomes enriched with "heavy" water. By such means the 0.02% normal abundance of H^2 has been increased to more than 99%!

A word is in order to suggest why separated isotopes are desired. Their use in studying nuclear reactions and especially in nuclear fission will be considered in detail later on. They have also become a very powerful tool in all branches of science as *tracer* agents. A sample of carbon enriched in C^{13}, for instance, would be treated by a growing organism just the same as any ordinary carbon, since the two forms are chemically identical; however, the carbon 13 is always identifiable physically, and its progress in the presence of ordinary carbon can be watched. Its rate of dissemination throughout the organism can be found by periodically tapping any section and analyzing the carbon to find if it has gained in one isotope (a mass-spectrograph chore). The samples of enriched isotopes are often referred to as "tagged" atoms—they can be spotted regardless of the company they keep. We shall see later that there is another, and more easily handled, form of tagged atoms, the radioactive atom. These two forms of tracer agents have served and are continuing to serve a very effective role in scientific research.

PROBLEMS

1. Measurements made on a set of positive ray parabolas showed that for a certain fixed value of x (see Fig. 18.1) the y for each parabola had the following value: $y_1 = 3.50$ mm, $y_2 = 4.00$ mm; $y_3 = 4.75$ mm. If the parabola of y_2 is known to be due to O^{16}, find the masses of ions producing the other two parabolas (assuming singly charged ions). Identify the elements.   *Ans.*   14.0, 19.0.

2. Knowing the isotopic abundance of magnesium (see Table D), calculate the chemical atomic mass of magnesium.   *Ans.*   24.36 mu.

3. Using the accurate masses and abundances of the oxygen isotopes (Table D), calculate the physical atomic mass of ordinary oxygen.   *Ans.*   16.00440 mu.

4. List the four possible isotopic forms of lithium chloride (LiCl).

5. Find the approximate mass in grams of each of the uranium isotopes (see Table E).   *Ans.* 3.88×10^{-22}; 3.90×10^{-22}; 3.95×10^{-22} gm.

6. A certain atom has a mass of 8.466×10^{-23} gm. What is its mass number?   *Ans.*   51.

Suggested Reading

ASTON, F. W., "Mass-Spectra and Isotopes," New York, Longmans, Green & Co., 1933.
    Chapters III–V give an authoritative and readable account of positive ray analysis by an authority on the subject.

DAMPIER, SIR WILLIAM, "A History of Physics," New York, The Macmillan Co., 1946.
    Pages 389–91, discovery of isotopes.

MAGIE, W. F., "Source Book in Physics," New York, McGraw-Hill Book Co., 1935.
    Pages 576–78, Goldstein on positive rays. Pages 597–600, Wien's early experiments on the deflection of positive rays.

Light Waves and the Electromagnetic Theory of Light

19.1 Light and Modern Physics

The historical period in which the electron and positive rays were discovered marks the beginnings of atomic physics, or what is called the modern period in physics. These discoveries gave some significant hints of the ultimate constitution of matter, and much of the remainder of this book will be devoted to the further development of this atomic picture. Yet it should be noted carefully that the Thomson experiments rested solidly on the physical principles then known; no *new* basic laws were introduced, no deviation from accepted dynamics and electrodynamics was necessary. Only a shift of emphasis from the aggregate to the elemental, from the macroscopic to the microscopic, was required. The masses and charges of atomic and subatomic entities and their interaction forces and motions could be handled with the well-established laws of classical physics.

If this were the content of modern physics, simply a reduction of physical phenomena to basic models, it would hardly capture the imagination today or ever lead to anything fundamentally new. Such is not the case. The particles are of considerable importance, to be sure, and their mechanical and electrical properties are indispensable, but contemporary physics shows that some of the fundamental laws of physics on the atomic scale are not the old laws in microscopic dress, but something quite different. Specifically, *relativity theory* and *quantum theory* have arisen in the present century to supply new and more complete insight into the nature of the physical world.

Curiously, both of these products of theoretical genius were precipitated by the same physical phenomenon—*light waves*. Relativity theory arose from the problem of the propagation of light, and quantum theory started with the question of the emission and absorption of light. To understand the necessity for revision of the classical theory of light and the role of these two theories in the problem we must review the ideas that were in good repute during the nineteenth century and the reasons for their inadequacy.

19.2   Maxwell's Electromagnetic Theory of Light

Let us for the moment ignore the detailed process of light emission and consider the nature of the light waves themselves.

It was seen in Chapter 10 that light will undergo constructive and destructive interference, thus confirming the *wave* nature of light. The fact that it can be polarized declares it to be a *transverse* wave. Further, we saw that any wave is characterized by three measurable quantities: its velocity (v), its frequency (ν) and its wave length (λ). Only two of these quantities, however, are independent, for the third is related to them by the simple expression

$$v = \lambda\nu$$

Of the many examples of waves (light waves, sound waves, water waves, seismic waves, etc.) only light waves and particle waves bear large significance in the study of atomic structure. The fundamental role in nature played by light has led to the practice of giving its velocity a separate symbol c. Hence when the wave under consideration is light, we will write

$$c = \lambda\nu$$

The velocity of light in air, or more properly in a vacuum (the two values differ only slightly), is a highly important "universal" constant, that is, it has the same value regardless of how one varies the experiment employed to measure it. (For example, the acceleration due to gravity, g, is not a universal constant—its value depends on the position of the observer relative to the center of the earth, on surrounding masses, etc.) Indeed, the constancy of the velocity of light is the keystone of the relativity theory. We find the quantity c showing up in many strange places, places where the propagation of light is not immediately involved at all.

Light has been referred to in our previous discussions as an *electromagnetic wave*. This concept was first advanced by Clerk Maxwell in the latter half of the nineteenth century, and with some modification it is the current picture. Although the details of this electromagnetic theory are too advanced to present in an elementary discussion of physics, the picture that results from the theory can be given. It declares that the emission of light is due to an accelerated charge (which we now know to be an electron). Every charge is surrounded by an electric field, represented by lines of force radiating outward from the charge, and a *moving* charge is also surrounded by a magnetic field, represented by magnetic lines of force forming concentric circles about the moving charge, perpendicular to the electric lines of force and to the path of motion. If the charge is oscillating, the electric and magnetic fields about the charge are likewise oscillating. Maxwell was able to show from the theory of such varying fields that the electric and magnetic lines of force at large distances from the charge are periodic in space and time; they are waves. The charge is said to be radiating electromagnetic waves; *it continues to do so as long as it is being accelerated.* Only that component of the electric field that is parallel to the acceleration of the moving electron enters into the radiation. Hence an electromagnetic wave (Fig. 19.1) is pictured as a combination of oscillating electric and magnetic fields that are perpendicular

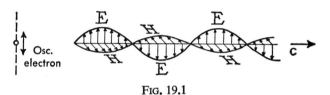

Fig. 19.1

to each other and also to the direction of propagation of the wave. Maxwell succeeded in showing that all such electromagnetic waves traveling in a vacuum have the same velocity, regardless of their wave length, regardless of their source. Visible light is such an electromagnetic wave; so are x rays. Maxwell's theory predicted the possibility of producing such waves of wave length many millions times *longer* than visible light, and in 1887 Hertz found a method of generating such long wave lengths; they were then known as Hertzian waves; they are now known as radio waves. Radio waves are identical with light except for their longer wave lengths; they may be a few hundred meters in length, whereas a visible light wave may be a half-millionth of a meter long. Likewise x rays are electromagnetic waves, differing from light only in that their wave lengths are shorter.

19.3   Measurement of the Velocity of Light

The extremely important place of the velocity of light in physics has led to its determination by many methods, dating from the seventeenth century to the present day. Most methods depend on the technique of measuring small time intervals, a few ten-thousandths of a second. Certainly the method outstanding in ingenuity was the one devised by Foucault and Fizeau in 1850 and modified for much greater accuracy by Michelson, culminating in 1926 in the experiment indicated schematically in Fig. 19.2. A source of light, an octagonal mirror that could be rotated, a viewing eyepiece, and other optical apparatus which is omitted in the figure were set up on the top of Mt. Wilson in California. On Mt. San Antonio 22 miles away was placed a large mirror for reflecting the light back to M. Suppose the octagonal mirror M were held fixed in the position shown in Fig. 19.2. Then the beam of light reflected by surface A will travel the 22 miles to the mirror M' and return to be reflected by surface C into the eyepiece. The observer will thus see an image of the light source. Now suppose the mirror M is rotated counterclockwise a slight amount and then again held fixed. The outgoing beam of light is now reflected at a different angle and may miss M' altogether; in any event, if

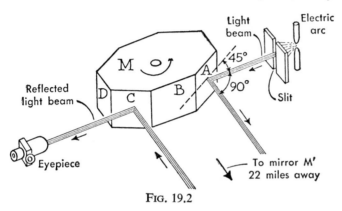

FIG. 19.2

M' is large enough to catch and reflect it, the surface C will not deflect it into the eyepiece. This situation is true until the sides B and D are moved exactly into the positions formerly held by A and C; then light will once again enter the eyepiece. Suppose the mirror M is now set in rapid rotation, and we choose an instant when light is reflected out to M' by side A. While this light travels the 44-mi path to M' and back again, side C will have moved out of the position in which the light beam is properly reflected into the eyepiece. However, if the mirror is rotating at just the right rate (about 32,000 rev/min), side D will have moved into the correct position while the light has gone out and back, and the observer will once again see an image of the source. By accurately measuring the speed of rotation of M and the distance between M and M' the velocity of light is determined. Correcting for the fact that light travels slightly slower in air than in a vacuum, Michelson obtained for the velocity 299,796 km/sec in a vacuum. In view of this result and later determinations, the best accepted value today is:

$$c = (2.99776 \pm 0.00004) \times 10^{10} \text{ cm/sec}$$

or about 186,300 mi/sec in a vacuum. For ordinary calculations the velocity of light in air or a vacuum may be taken as

$$c = 3 \times 10^{10} \text{ cm/sec}$$

It should be noted that the relativity theory shows that a moving mass can approach but never reach this velocity and, of course, it can never be exceeded. Electrons have been observed at some 99.9% of the velocity of light.

19.4 The Wave Lengths of Visible Light

The measurement of the wave length of light is far easier than determining its velocity. We have already seen (Chapter 10) that the action of a diffraction grating on light is to separate its component wave lengths, and this separation is called a spectrum. Such a grating when mounted with its proper optical and measuring system is known as a *grating spectrograph*. By measuring the grating spacing d and the angle of diffraction of the light in a given order n, the wave length λ can be calculated (see §10.9). Instead of observing visually, the spectroscopist usually uses a photographic plate. A good spectrograph is capable of measuring wave lengths to six or even seven significant figures. Because of the smallness of these wave lengths of light, a derived unit is commonly used, the *angstrom*, abbreviated Å. One angstrom is one one-hundred millionth of a centimeter. Or

$$1 \text{ Å} = 10^{-8} \text{ cm}$$

The physiological response to different wave lengths in the visible spectrum is *color*. We associate different colors with different wave lengths. The longest which we can see is red, the shortest violet. The correspondence between wave length and color is approximately as follows:

$$\lambda = 0.000075 \text{ cm} = 7500\text{Å}; \text{ deep red}$$
$$\lambda = 0.000060 \text{ cm} = 6000\text{Å}; \text{ yellow}$$
$$\lambda = 0.000052 \text{ cm} = 5200\text{Å}; \text{ green}$$
$$\lambda = 0.000045 \text{ cm} = 4500\text{Å}; \text{ blue}$$
$$\lambda = 0.000040 \text{ cm} = 4000\text{Å}; \text{ violet}$$

The eye is insensitive to light longer than about 7500 Å and shorter than 4000 Å. The region of long wave lengths beyond the visible is called the *infrared* or heat-radiation region; wave lengths shorter than 4000 Å are in the *ultraviolet* region, finally becoming short enough to be considered x rays. The latter are a few angstroms or less in wave lengths.

19.5   The Sources of Electromagnetic Waves

The source of radio waves is the oscillating current in an antenna which is set up by the electrical circuits in the radio transmitter. The individual electrons in the antenna are accelerated periodically and emit electromagnetic waves as a result of their acceleration. In recent years waves as short as a few millimeters in length have been produced in a controlled manner by oscillating circuits, thus overlapping the wave-length region associated with the far infrared region of the optical spectrum.

Beginning in the millimeter wave-length range and carrying through the visible spectral region and on to the region of a few hundred angstroms, the

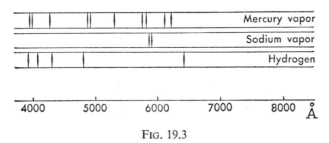

FIG. 19.3

sources of light are atoms and molecules. Various means exist for causing them to emit light.

One of the simplest sources of light is a piece of solid matter raised to a high temperature. This might be an iron sphere, for example, that has been heated to "red heat" or even "white heat"; or it could be a tungsten filament such as used in a light bulb, heated by the passage of a current. The spectrum of such a source is found to contain *all wave lengths* of visible light and is said to be a *continuous spectrum*. A photographic plate will indicate that much of the energy is in the infrared. Furthermore, if the temperature of the hot body is raised, the maximum energy region will move from the infrared into the visible region (our eyes would then judge the body "white hot"). This shift of maximum energy toward the shorter wave lengths with increasing temperature is an important phenomenon whose significance will be discussed in the next chapter.

Another common light source is the electrical discharge tube. Whereas a hot solid gives a continuous spectrum, an excited gas emits a *discrete spectrum*, that is, a spectrum having only certain wave lengths present. Figure 19.3 shows photograms of such spectra, emitted by hydrogen, mercury, and sodium. There are several noteworthy characteristics of these spectra. Let us assume that the discharge tube contains neon. Many spectral "lines" (images of the narrow slit placed in front of the neon source) each corresponding to a particular wave length are observed. This collection of wave lengths is unique with neon. Helium, for example, gives an entirely different set. *No two elements ever have the same spectrum.* The spectra of most elements contain a very large number of lines; a few are simpler. Sodium provides probably the least complicated of all visible spectra, since almost all its energy lies in two yellow lines which have nearly the same wave length: 5890 Å and 5896 Å. Such a source, having most of its energy in a very small wave-length band, is approximately *monochromatic* (one color), and a sodium light produced by introducing a little sodium metal or NaCl (table salt) into a gas flame is a very common laboratory source of nearly monochromatic light.

19.6   The Significance of Discrete Spectra

The existence of the unique and characteristic set of wave lengths of each element is a clue to atomic structure that demands careful consideration. Beginning with the kinetic theory of gases we have been accumulating evidence that macroscopic phenomena can often be explained in terms of atomic concepts. So far, however, the experiments performed or the theories assumed have told us only about the atom as a rigid structure—we have very few suggestions regarding the *internal* structure of the atom. True, we have been pretty well forced to agree that the electron came from the atom, but might it not be just a sort of chip of atomic matter?

The radiation of light by an atom in a gas strongly implies some sort of internal activity in the atom. The fact that each atom radiates an entirely unique set of wave lengths would lead us to conclude that if there is an internal structure, it must be different for each atom. The Maxwell theory of electromagnetic waves holds that a light wave is radiated by an accelerated charge. Fortunately, we already have evidence that there must be positive and negative charges in the atom, for it is possible to remove one or more negative charges, and there must be positive charges to balance these negative ones which have been removed. Therefore, do we not have all the agents at hand to explain the spectrum of an atom? Let us try to do so.

To generate light a charge must be accelerated (Maxwell). Suppose we assumed that this is the result of the positive and negative charge in the atom rushing toward each other under electrostatic attraction. But this is a collapsing atom; if atomic charge is like its macroscopic counterpart, the two charges should neutralize each other and coalesce. What mechanism would ever separate them? It would seem much better if we could contrive a scheme that involved acceleration without having one charge approaching the other. This is a kind of motion we know well—centripetal acceleration caused by motion in a circle. Suppose we allowed one charge to circle about the other, the centripetal force being just the electrostatic force of attraction. We shall have to assume that somehow one charge was set in motion about the other at the birth of all matter and has been rotating ever since, the centripetal force being due to electrostatic force. Two difficulties arise from this circulating charge picture. The first occurs when we realize we are not free of the threat of atomic collapse, for the Maxwell theory demands that the conservation of energy be obeyed—the energy radiated out as light must come at the expense of the moving charge; if it is thus slowed down, it will be pulled toward the central charge. Since the charge moving in the circular orbit is always accelerating (centripetal acceleration), it must always be radiating until it finally spirals into the nucleus. The time required for this catastrophe would be only a small fraction of a second. Anyway, regardless of collapse, why isn't a gas continuously self-luminous, since the moving charge is continuously accelerating? The second and even more disturbing difficulty lies in the fact that atoms exhibit *discrete* spectra, while our accelerating charge gives off a continuous range of energy as it spirals in. These two problems, the spiraling in of the charge and the continuous radiation that it must emit in so doing, were Goliaths to be overcome in forming a model of the atom. Their defeat required the bold measures taken by Niels Bohr in 1913 (Chapter 23).

19.7 Absorption Spectra

Before abandoning the discussion of spectra we should pose this question: A gas radiates characteristic wave lengths when it is made luminous. Will it also absorb such characteristic wave lengths? The question is a reasonable one when we consider that such "resonance" absorption is characteristic of all sources of sound waves. (A piano string will be set in "sympathetic" vibration if the frequency which it can produce is sounded near it.) The experi-

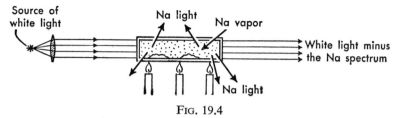

FIG. 19.4

ment to answer this question is easy to perform (Fig. 19.4). A cloud of sodium vapor is placed in the path of the light from a hot solid. Exactly the wave lengths (5890 Å and 5896 Å) which sodium would radiate if it were excited are missing from the otherwise continuous spectrum. These "black lines" are just as characteristic of the sodium atom as the bright lines in its emission spectrum. From this and similar experiments we can conclude: *All substances are capable of absorbing the same wave lengths that they can radiate.* The most important example of an absorption spectrum is that of the sun (Fig. 19.5). The hot interior radiates a continuous spectrum which is partially absorbed by the cooler layers of vapor in the sun's outer atmosphere. By comparing the absorption lines (often called "Fraunhofer lines" after their discoverer) with the spectra of known elements, the constitution of the vapor is unambiguously determined. In fact, there existed a family of lines in the solar spectrum that for many years remained unidentified. It was finally decided that its source must be an element not present on the earth, and it was named "helium"

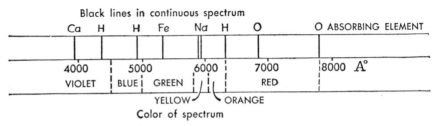

FIG. 19.5

(Greek helios—the sun). It was only later that helium was discovered in our atmosphere and in oil deposits. Thus the spectrograph was responsible for a highly important addition to the periodic table—found 93,000,000 miles away!

The constitution of most stars has now been determined by their spectra (some have emission, other absorption spectra). These spectra show that stellar matter consists of most, if not all, of the elements that we have on earth.

19.8 Electromagnetic Waves and the Ether

We have noted that the emission of light is not explicable on the electromagnetic theory, and we shall find that its explanation leads to the modern quantum theory. Similarly the propagation of light led to the theory of relativity. This latter development is bound up with the problem of the *ether.*

The ether was a hypothetical substance postulated in the nineteenth century to be the carrier or medium for light waves. Evidently the ether could have no mass or mechanical properties in the ordinary sense. Light travels from the stars to us, and yet the free motion of celestial bodies indicates that they move in an almost perfect vacuum. But since all other types of waves require a propagating medium, the ether was endowed with the ability to propagate light, and, it appears, no other observable properties at all. As a commentary on its unusual nature it has been defined half facetiously as the "noun of the verb, to undulate," or, "that which waves in empty space." As the theory of the ether was developed its role became more and more difficult. It must be perfectly "elastic" since it did not dissipate the light energy it transmitted, yet "stable" so that it did not collapse. But the ether's death stroke came in the question, is it moving?

If a ball is thrown into the wind its speed will be reduced, just as it will be increased if thrown with the wind. Now if the ether pervades all space we would presume it to be a calm sea through which the earth in its motion about the sun is rushing with a speed of some 3×10^6 cm/sec. Thus there should be an ether "wind" against the earth, and light moving in a direction parallel to the earth's motion would, to an earth observer, have a velocity of $(3 \times 10^{10}) - (3 \times 10^6)$ cm/sec, while light moving anti-parallel to the earth's motion will be carried along by the ether wind so that its velocity is increased to $(3 \times 10^{10}) + (3 \times 10^6)$ cm/sec. To make a direct determination of this velocity change due to ether "drift" is exceedingly difficult, but an ingenious though somewhat less direct method was devised using the *Michelson interferometer*.

19.9 Michelson—Morley Experiment

Without doubt this experiment, performed in 1881, ranks in the history of physics as the most famous piece of research which produced a negative result. Figure 19.6 shows a simplified diagram of the interferometer used in the experiment. S is a monochromatic light source. Mirror M_1 is lightly silvered on the front so that the incident light waves from the source are split into two beams, one going to M_2 and one to M_3. Mirrors M_2 and M_3 are silvered and reflect their beams back to M_1; ultimately part of each beam goes to the observer. Interference between these two beams will occur, giving a set of light and dark fringes. Suppose that the central fringe is bright and consider the effect of moving M_2 parallel to itself and away from M_1. The path lengths of the incident and reflected beams are thereby increased so that for each $\lambda/4$ motion of M_2 the total path length increases by $\lambda/2$, and a bright central fringe becomes a dark fringe. This alternation from bright to dark continues with each additional $\lambda/4$ of motion of M_2. We see that by calibrating the motion of M_2 one can measure the wave length of the light used, or, conversely, one can measure a given motion of M_2 in terms of the wave length of the light. The precision of such length measurements is very high; a trained observer can detect a pattern shift of $\frac{1}{20}$ of a wave length of light.

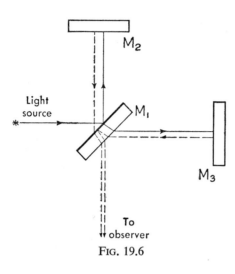

Suppose the distances M_1M_2 and M_1M_3 are adjusted to give a bright fringe (constructive interference) at exactly the center of the field of view of the observer. If now the entire interferometer (including observer) is *rotated* 90° the fringe should remain unmoved if the propagation of light is independent of direction. On the other hand, if light had a velocity along the ether wind different from that across it, the interchange of light paths should cause the fringe to move slightly, that is, either M_2 or M_3 would have to be moved to compensate for the change in velocity of the light. (It should be noted that the net effect of moving with and then against the ether wind is not zero, because the mirrors M_1 and M_3 also move while the light is traveling between them; likewise M_2 is moving laterally, and the light travels a diagonal path between M_1 and M_2; detailed analysis of these two effects shows that there still should be a resultant fringe shift due to the motion relative to the ether.)*

FIG. 19.6

This experiment was performed by Michelson and Morley, and repeated trials revealed *no fringe shift*. If by chance the ether were carried along with the earth, the negative result of the experiment might be explained. But other experiments on the annual change in direction of the light from distant stars indicated that the earth must move through the ether. In any case, it is difficult to believe that by chance the ether was moving with exactly our motion, changing just as our velocity changed as we traveled an elliptical orbit around the sun. Presumably the ether would remain fixed in an inertial system. The fatal moment had come for the ether—perhaps it didn't exist at all.

In the following chapter we shall see some of the consequences of the relativity theory, which postulates that the velocity of light is the same for all

* This calculation shows that the effect of the earth's motion is to increase the path M_1M_2 by a factor $[1 + (v^2/c^2)]$, and the path M_1M_3 by a factor $[1 + \frac{1}{2}(v^2/c^2)]$. Rotation of the apparatus interchanges these factors. (v is the velocity of the earth through the ether.)

observers whether moving or not. The successes of this theory are based on the denial that motion can be detected by measuring light velocities, so that the reason for the ether's existence has been removed. It has not been revived since the advent of the relativity theory.

PROBLEMS

1. The distance from the earth to the sun is 93,000,000 mi. By how much is a sunset delayed?   *Ans.*   500 sec. or 8.3 min.

2. The astronomer measures distances in units of light-years. How many miles is one light-year?   *Ans.* 5.85×10^{12} miles.

3. Galileo attempted to measure the velocity of light by timing the travel of light between observers stationed on two hills. If the hills were separated by 1 mi what is the time interval he would have had to measure?   *Ans.*   5.4 microsec.

4. How long does it take a radio wave to travel from New York to San Francisco, a distance of 2580 mi?   *Ans.*   0.014 sec.

5. Find the frequency of yellow light (6000 Å).   *Ans.* 5×10^{14} vibrations/sec.

6. An interferometer is forming interference fringes of monochromatic light of $\lambda = 5000$ Å. One of the interferometer mirrors is then moved exactly 1 mm. How many fringes cross the field of view during this motion?   *Ans.*   4000.

Suggested Reading

Hecht, Selig, "Explaining the Atom," New York, Viking Press, 1947.
   Chapters II, III, IV review the internal structure of the atom in readable fashion.
Magie, W. F., "Source Book in Physics," New York, McGraw-Hill Book Co., 1935.
   Pages 528–38, Maxwell's announcement of the electromagnetic theory of light.
Michelson, A. A., "Light Waves and Their Uses," Chicago, University of Chicago Press, 1930.
   Lecture VIII, the author's views on the ether and light propagation *before* the theory of relativity. Note the difficulties of reconciling the various experimental facts.
Moulton, F. R., and Schifferes, J. J., "The Autobiography of Science," New York, Doubleday Doran and Co., 1945.
   Huygens' writing on waves and ether (1690).

Aspects of the Theory of Relativity

20.1 Origins of the Theory

We have seen in the preceding chapter that the question of the propagation of light led to some very disturbing problems in connection with the measurement of light velocities by moving observers, and we have stated that the theory of relativity resolved these difficulties. But this is by no means the principal contribution of this theory which has its roots much deeper in the nature of the physical world. Indeed, the popular appeal of the theory could hardly be explained by such a single technical accomplishment.

The theory of relativity is difficult to catalog. The laws of propagation of light are important to the theory, yet it does not concern itself with the physical nature of light waves. It is not dynamics although it treats dynamical problems; nor is it specifically concerned with atomic and nuclear problems as might be imagined from its present day fame. Electrical and magnetic theories are only completely in accord with experiment when treated relativistically, but this is only an application of the theory. In short, the theory of relativity embraces all physics, but it is not a branch of physics. Unlike the subjects of our previous chapters it arose not as a result of a particular series of experiments but rather as a critical study of known physical laws and accepted principles. On the one hand it changed the most fundamental concepts in science, space and time. Yet its equations agree with ordinary dynamics and ordinary electrodynamics for the usual experimental conditions. Its interpretations are many, its predictions of new phenomena are few, but these few are of enormous importance to modern physics. The well-popularized mass-energy equivalence ($W = mc^2$) is one of them.

The disturbing paradox disclosed in the problem of light propagation at the close of the nineteenth century was really of wider scope than we have thus far indicated. It reached directly to inadequacies in the most fundamental physical concepts: those of space and time. These concepts, which had evolved in

234

Newton's dynamics, seemed to be inapplicable to the theory of electricity and magnetism which had just succeeded in explaining the nature of light waves. Both dynamics and electrodynamics rested on firm experimental bases, yet the two were incompatible in some fundamental way. This incompatibility arose from the necessity of assigning to electromagnetic radiation—light—an absolute motion.

It had long been recognized that dynamical motion involves displacements that are relative to some inertial (non-accelerated) system. True, there was a difficulty (generally ignored) in connection with establishing the identity of an inertial system, and some confusion was present even in the greatest works in dynamics. Newton, in his *Principia Mathematica* says that "absolute motion is the translation of a body from one absolute space to another absolute space," but he does not specify what he means by absolute space. However, the question of absolute motion was not troublesome in dynamics, for all the laws of motion had been established in what was defined as an inertial system, and in that and other inertial systems the motion of the system did not enter into the laws themselves. Thus a body falling to the surface of the earth was governed by a force $F = mg$ relative to the earth; it mattered not whether the body was being observed inside a uniformly moving train or from a platform at rest, for in either case the force was mg. (True, the trajectory of the motion differs, for if the body is dropped from the train, it is a horizontally fired projectile to the platform observer and a freely falling body to the traveling observer; but the law of motion is the same to both, which is all that is being proved.)

In contrast, a fundamental form of absolute motion arose in connection with electrodynamics. Maxwell had shown that electromagnetic radiation was the result of an accelerated electric charge, and from his theory was able to predict the velocity of the radiation to be $c = 3 \times 10^{10}$ cm/sec, a value satisfactorily confirmed by experiment. But this velocity depended only on the medium through which the waves traveled, and thus was a *constant* for any uniform medium, such as a vacuum, that is, the "ether." Constant relative to what? Constant relative to an inertial system was not a suitable answer since the velocity measured as c in one system would be different in another system. Thus, the ether was postulated as an "absolute" system for the wave motion. But the Michelson-Morley experiment showed that the velocity of light was the same whether the observer was moving with the light beam or not. Newtonian dynamics is at a complete loss to explain such a result. In fact, according to Newtonian dynamics the laws governing electromagnetic radiation must depend on the motion of the inertial system in which they are being investigated; and any other physical laws which were established with the aid of light measurements must likewise depend on the motion of the observer. An observer on a star would thus have quite a different set of laws of nature from those which we accept.

Various attempts were made to resolve this conflict between dynamics and electrodynamics, but none was very satisfying because each in turn introduced new complexities. Finally in 1905, Einstein showed that the theories were compatible if certain changes were made in the traditional ideas of space and time. His ideas are embodied in the *theory of special relativity*. To appreciate fully the departure made by this theory let us first examine the meaning of relative motion in Newtonian dynamics.

20.2   Galilean Transformation Between Inertial Systems

When two observers moving relative to each other view the same motion, they ascribe to it different velocities and paths. These two different descriptions may, however, be brought into agreement by applying a *transformation* to one observer's equations. Such a transformation takes into account the relative motion of the observers. The problem of transforming a motion from one insertial system to another was first solved by Galileo in his work with projectile problems. Consequently, the equations of this transformation are called *Galilean transformations*, to distinguish them from the *relativistic transformations* established by the Einstein theory. Galileo (and Newtonian dynamics) assumed that distance and time as measured by two observers were identical and independent of their relative motion. Thus a meter rod in each observer's system is the same and clock hands on a moving train rotate at the same rate as those on the earth; that is, measurements of distance and time performed in one system on objects moving with the other system agree with the usual standards. These ideas are easily expressed mathematically by considering two systems of coordinates S and S^*, with S^* moving along the $+x$ direction with a velocity V. Let the origins of the two systems coincide at the instant $t = 0$. Then at some later time point P which has a coordinate x in system S has a coordinate x^* in system S^* where (see Fig. 20.1)

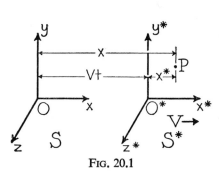

FIG. 20.1

$$x^* = x - Vt \qquad\qquad [\,20.1\,]$$

The other coordinates obey the equations

$$y^* = y \qquad\qquad [20.2]$$
$$z^* = z \qquad\qquad [20.3]$$

We see that Eqs. 20.1, 20.2, 20.3 assume that lengths measured in the two systems are the same. The equivalence of time in the two systems is expressed by the equation

$$t^* = t \qquad\qquad [20.4]$$

Equations 20.1, 20.2, 20.3, 20.4 are the Galilean transformations for the situation in Fig. 20.1.

The Galilean transformation of velocities from one inertial system to another proceeds in a similar fashion. Suppose point P to be moving with a velocity v^* along the $+x^*$ direction as measured by an observer in S^*. By this we mean that it moves from x_1^* to x_2^* in the time interval $(t_2^* - t_1^*)$ where

$$v^* = \frac{x_2^* - x_1^*}{t_2^* - t_1^*} \qquad\qquad [20.5]$$

The velocity measured in S is

$$v = \frac{x_2 - x_1}{t_2 - t_1} \qquad\qquad [20.6]$$

where

$$x_2^* = x_2 - Vt_2$$
$$x_1^* = x_1 - Vt_1$$
$$t_2^* = t_2$$
$$t_1^* = t_1$$

from Eqs. 20.1 and 20.4. Substituting these relations into Eq. 20.6,

$$v = \frac{x_2^* + Vt_2 - x_1^* - Vt_1}{t_2 - t_1}$$

$$= \frac{x_2^* - x_1^*}{t_2 - t_1} + \frac{V(t_2 - t_1)}{t_2 - t_1}$$

$$= v^* + V \qquad\qquad [20.7]$$

We see that according to the Galilean transformations, velocities are transformed by simply adding (or subtracting) the relative velocity of the two systems.

The results of this analysis are "self-evident" to almost everyone without the detailed calculations which we have performed. Their only purpose was to show that the "self-evident" results are based on the assumption that distances and times are not affected by the motion of the observer. It is these "self-evident" assumptions which underlie all pre-relativity physics. They are born of ordinary experience, and previous to the theory of relativity they were never questioned.

20.3   Relativistic Transformations

In considering the conflict between Newtonian dynamics and the constancy of the velocity of light, Einstein accepted the Michelson-Morley experiment, not as an example of the perversity of light propagation and moving bodies, but as a proof that there is *no preferred inertial system for light waves*. The theory of special relativity proposes two postulates on the basis of this assumption.

I The laws of physical phenomena are the same for all inertial systems.
II The velocity of light in any given inertial system is independent of the velocity of that system.

The second postulate represents an experimentally verified fact. The first postulate constitutes a generalization that is on the same level as the law of the conservation of energy; it is not self-evident, but like all assumptions made in physical theories, it forms a hypothesis to be confirmed or denied by subjecting its deductions to experimental evidence. The two postulates combine to establish the *relativistic transformations* between two inertial systems.

The new transformations can be shown by considering the propagation of a light wave in two inertial systems, imposing the condition that the measured light velocity is the same in the two systems. Consider the same set of coordinate systems as in Fig. 20.1; S^* moves along the $+x$ direction with velocity V relative to S, and let the origins O and O^* of the two systems coincide at time $t = 0$. At this instant let the crest of a light wave be emitted from O along the $+x$ direction. Its position in system S is given by

$$x = ct \qquad\qquad\qquad [\,20.8\,]$$

and if the light velocity is also c in system S^*, its position in that system is

$$x^* = ct^* \qquad\qquad\qquad [\,20.9\,]$$

where t^* is the time interval measured in system S^* and is not necessarily equal to t. According to the Galilean transformations, Eqs. 20.1 and 20.4, $x^* = x - Vt$, and $t = t^*$; but we see, as expected, that these transformations are not compatible with Eqs. 20.8 and 20.9 since they demand different light velocities in S and S^*. Consider instead, the transformations

$$x^* = \frac{x - Vt}{\sqrt{1 - V^2/c^2}} \qquad\qquad [\,20.10\,]$$

$$y^* = y \qquad\qquad [\,20.11\,]$$
$$z^* = z \qquad\qquad [\,20.12\,]$$

$$t^* = \frac{t - Vx/c^2}{\sqrt{1 - V^2/c^2}} \qquad\qquad [\,20.13\,]$$

Substituting Eqs. 20.10 and 20.13 into Eq. 20.9, we get

$$\frac{x - Vt}{\sqrt{1 - V^2/c^2}} = c\frac{t - Vx/c^2}{\sqrt{1 - V^2/c^2}}$$
$$x(1 + V/c) = ct\,(1 + V/c)$$
$$x = ct$$

which is just Eq. 20.8. Hence we conclude that Eqs. 20.10 and 20.13 are suitable transformations for preserving the equivalence of the velocity of light in all inertial systems.* A similar proof shows that Eqs. 20.11 and 20.12 also satisfy the principle of the equivalence of the velocity of light in the two systems. Equations 20.10 to 20.13 are the cornerstones of the theory of relativity and constitute the relativistic transformations.

It is clear that the assumption that light propagates with the same velocity in all inertial systems is compatible with the negative result of the Michelson-Morley experiment—there is no interference shift, since there is no difference in the light velocity along the two paths in the apparatus, or indeed along any other paths. However, Eqs. 20.10 to 20.13 demand some rather astounding interpretations of space and time.

1. Consider a rigid measuring rod placed parallel to the x^* axis and fixed in system S^*. (So $v^* = 0$ and $V = v$, the velocity of the rod as measured by the observer.) Its length is l^*, where

$$l^* = x_2^* - x_1^*$$

and x_2^* and x_1^* are the coordinates of its two ends. Now suppose the rod's length to be measured by an observer in system S, say by comparing the two ends at the same instant t_0 with a rod in his system (Fig. 20.2). The measured length is

$$l = x_2 - x_1$$

where, by Eq. 20.10 (making $v = V$)

---

* A more general mathematical proof shows that these are the only possible transformations consistent with Eqs. 20.8 and 20.9, which also satisfy the equivalence of the relative velocities of the systems.

$$x_2^* = \frac{x_2 - vt_0}{\sqrt{1 - v^2/c^2}}$$

$$x_1^* = \frac{x_1 - vt_0}{\sqrt{1 - v^2/c^2}}$$

so that

$$l = x_2^*\sqrt{1 - v^2/c^2} + vt_0 - x_1^*\sqrt{1 - v^2/c^2} - vt_0$$
$$= l^*\sqrt{1 - v^2/c^2}$$ [20.14]

Since l is less than l^* Eq. 20.14 states that the length of the rod measured by an observer in motion with respect to the rod is shorter than the length meas-

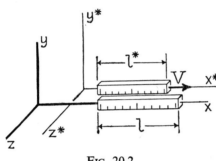

FIG. 20.2

ured by an observer at rest with respect to the rod. Equations 20.11 and 20.12 state that the rod's dimensions perpendicular to its direction of motion, i.e., its motion relative to the observer, are unaffected by the motion. So in general, *all bodies are contracted in their direction of motion by a factor* $\sqrt{1 - v^2/c^2}$, *where v is the velocity of the body.*

2. Consider next a certain clock kept fixed at a point x_0 in system S, whose ticks are spaced $(t_2 - t_1)$ seconds apart as observed in system S. In system S^* the ticks are spaced by $(t_2^* - t_1^*)$ seconds where by Eq. 20.13 (making $V = v$):

$$t_2^* - t_1^* = \frac{t_2 - vx_0/c^2 - t_1 + vx_0/c^2}{\sqrt{1 - v^2/c^2}} = \frac{t_2 - t_1}{\sqrt{1 - v^2/c^2}}$$ [20.15]

$(t_2^* - t_1^*)$ is thus greater than $(t_2 - t_1)$; Eq. 20.15 states that the time between ticks is longer for an observer moving with respect to the clock than for an observer fixed with respect to the clock. *Or in general all moving clocks are slowed down by a factor* $\sqrt{1 - v^2/c^2}$, *where v is the velocity of the clock.*

It is of interest to note that the italicized statements refer only to the relative motion of the measuring rod or clock and the observer. They could equally well be proved by considering the rod to be at rest in system S and the clock at rest in system S^*.

20.4   Relativistic Addition of Parallel Velocities

The contraction of moving measuring rods and the slowing down of moving clocks make certain changes in the Galilean addition of velocities.

Suppose, for example, that a particle is moving along the $+ x^*$ direction with a velocity v^* as measured in system S^* of Fig. 20.1. By this we mean that it travels from x_1^* to x_2^* in the time interval t_1^* to t_2^*. The velocity measured by an observer in system S is, by definition, the distance $(x_2 - x_1)$ divided by $(t_2 - t_1)$ where the x's and t's are the transformed values of the observations in system S^*. Now, by the usual ideas of space and time as expressed in the Galilean transformation, Eq. 20.7, the velocity in system S is simply $v = v^* + V$. However, this formula does not hold in the relativity theory. By Eqs. 20.10 and 20.13,

$$v^* = \frac{(x_2 - x_1) - V(t_2 - t_1)}{(t_2 - t_1) - (V/c^2)(x_2 - x_1)}$$

Dividing numerator and denominator by $(t_2 - t_1)$ and putting $v = (x_2 - x_1)/(t_2 - t_1)$

gives
$$v^* = \frac{v - V}{1 - Vv/c^2}$$
[20.16]

or solving Eq. 20.16 for v we have

$$v = \frac{v^* + V}{1 + Vv^*/c^2}$$
[20.17]

Equations 20.16 and 20.17 are the relativistic velocity transformations. They have several interesting interpretations.

1. We see that v is less than $v^* + V$. This must be the case, for if v^* is the velocity of a light wave in system S^*, i.e., $v^* = c$, then the wave must also have a velocity c in the system S. Putting $v^* = c$ in Eq. 20.17 we have

$$v = \frac{c + V}{1 + Vc/c^2} = \frac{c(1 + V/c)}{1 + V/c} = c$$

which confirms this statement.

2. Also, we see from Eq. 20.17 that if a particle velocity measured in one system is less than c, then in any other system its velocity is also less than c. For suppose $v^* = 0.99c$ and $V = 0.99c$, then

$$v = \frac{0.99c + 0.99c}{1 + (0.99)^2c^2/c^2} = \frac{1.9800}{1.9801}c = 0.99995c$$

20.5   Relativistic Mass

Newton's second law of motion, which is included either explicitly or tacitly in virtually every aspect of classical physics, now appears to be incorrect when applied to a system moving with a velocity near that of light. According to the second law a steady force must produce a constant acceleration, and as long as the force is applied the velocity of the body must increase without limit. Hence the velocity of the body could exceed the velocity of light; a direct conflict with the theory of relativity. We see, therefore, that it must be increasingly difficult to accelerate a mass as its velocity approaches the velocity of light. The property of all matter which opposes change in motion is its inertia (mass). The relativistic velocity transformation suggests that the mass of a body must increase as its velocity is increased.

Relativity theory subjects the above argument to quantitative analysis and shows that the mass of a body moving with a velocity v is

$$m = \frac{m_0}{\sqrt{1 - v^2/c^2}} \qquad\qquad [\,20.18\,]$$

where m_0 is its mass at zero velocity, that is, its *rest mass*. Evidently, if $v = c$ then $m = \infty$; only an infinite force can cause a body to move with the velocity of light, for then the mass of the body is infinitely large. This prediction of relativity has been amply confirmed in measurements of e/m of high-speed electrons; m is observed to vary with electron velocity as Eq. 20.18 demands. The mass of a moving particle is called its *relativistic mass*. The difficulty of forming a picture of the increased mass due to motion arises directly from our limitations of defining any mass. In classical dynamics we have accepted as a

Table 20.1
Relativistic mass increase of high-speed electrons

ELECTRON VELOCITY	% OF VELOCITY OF LIGHT	% INCREASE IN MASS	KINETIC ENERGY IN ELECTRON VOLTS
3.0×10^8 cm/sec	1	0.005	25.0
3.0×10^9	10	0.50	2.57×10^3
9.0×10^9	30	5.0	2.47×10^4
1.5×10^{10}	50	15.	7.90×10^4
2.1×10^{10}	70	40.	2.04×10^5
2.7×10^{10}	90	129.	6.61×10^5
2.97×10^{10}	99	609.	3.12×10^6

working description of mass the concept of opposition to change of motion, that is, inertial mass. Relativity declares that this opposition increases with velocity. If we call up that vague and circular description of mass which served the eighteenth century physicist, namely, "quantity of matter," we gain nothing. Does a high-speed electron have more "matter" than a slow electron? The question is without meaning because we are unable to define matter. Relativity theory says simply that it will require a greater force to accelerate a fast electron by a given amount than will be needed for a slow electron.

Example. Consider an electron moving with a velocity of 1.50×10^{10} cm sec. Then $v/c = \frac{1}{2}$ and

$$m = \frac{m_0}{\sqrt{1 - \frac{1}{4}}} = \frac{m_0}{\sqrt{\frac{3}{4}}} = 1.15\, m_0$$

so that its mass is increased by 15% over the rest mass. This factor, of course, increases as v approaches c. Table 20.1 collects the results of this and similar calculations together with the electron energies.

20.6 The Conservation of Momentum and Energy in Relativity Theory

In dynamics considerable emphasis was placed on the validity and utility of the laws of the conservation of momentum and dynamical energy. Relativity theory acknowledges the great body of experimental evidence that confirms these laws, but shows that the method of calculating momentum and dynamical energy must be altered somewhat to preserve their validity. In order to preserve the conservation of momentum it is necessary to define relativistic momentum as the product of relativistic mass and velocity. As in Newtonian dynamics, relativistic momentum is a vector. It is given by

$$\mu = m\mathbf{v} = \frac{m_0}{\sqrt{1 - v^2/c^2}}\mathbf{v} \qquad [20.19]$$

where $\mathbf{v}$ is the vector velocity of the particle. With this definition of momentum the conservation of momentum applies to all inertial systems regardless of their relative motions—as the first postulate of special relativity demands.

Einstein likewise accepted the conservation of energy; his first postulate requires that if an observer in one system finds that a certain group of particles has a constant dynamical energy, the observers in all other inertial systems must find the same constancy. (The principle can be generalized to include all forms of energy.) The transformations needed to conserve energy have been derived in relativity theory; for our purposes, the most significant result lies in the new formula for calculating dynamical energy; namely, the relativistic dynamical energy is the product of the relativistic mass of the particle and the square of the velocity of light:

$$W = mc^2 = \frac{m_0 c^2}{\sqrt{1 - v^2/c^2}} \qquad [20.20]$$

For most bodies the velocity v is small compared with the velocity of light, hence v^2/c^2 will be small compared with unity. The binomial theorem* in mathematics allows us to make the following approximation for small v.

---

* The binomial theorem: $(1 + x)^n = 1 + nx + \dfrac{n(n-1)}{2}x^2 + \cdots$.

$$\frac{1}{\sqrt{1 - v^2/c^2}} = 1 + \tfrac{1}{2}\frac{v^2}{c^2} + \text{negligible terms}$$

Therefore,

$$W = m_0c^2/\sqrt{1 - v^2/c^2} = m_0c^2 \left(1 + \tfrac{1}{2}\frac{v^2}{c^2} + \cdots\right)$$

$$W = m_0c^2 + \tfrac{1}{2} m_0v^2 \qquad\qquad\qquad [\,20.21\,]$$

The second term is just the classical kinetic energy of the particle. However, the relativistic formula for energy states that even if the kinetic energy (classical) is zero, the particle has a residual energy of m_0c^2. This is called the rest energy or *mass energy* of the particle. The expression

$$\text{Mass-energy} = m_0c^2 \qquad\qquad\qquad [\,20.22\,]$$

is possibly one of the most significant conclusions to be drawn from special relativity theory. We devote the next section to its interpretation.

Example. Consider an electron accelerated to a high velocity by means of an electric field between two plates. Suppose the potential difference between the plates to be 2.04×10^5 volts, i.e., a 0.204-Mev electron. The work done on the electron is still eV in relativity theory, so that its kinetic energy is

$$eV = \frac{(4.80 \times 10^{-10})(2.04 \times 10^5)}{300} = 3.26 \times 10^{-7} \text{ ergs}$$

and its total relativistic energy is

$$\begin{aligned} W &= eV + m_0c^2 \\ &= (3.26 \times 10^{-7}) + (9.11 \times 10^{-28})(9.00 \times 10^{20}) \\ &= 11.5 \times 10^{-7} \text{ ergs} \end{aligned}$$

Its relativistic mass is

$$\begin{aligned} m &= \frac{W}{c^2} \\ &= \frac{11.5 \times 10^{-7}}{9.00 \times 10^{20}} = 12.8 \times 10^{-28} \text{ gm,} \end{aligned}$$

so that

$$\frac{m}{m_0} = \frac{12.8 \times 10^{-28}}{9.11 \times 10^{-28}} = 1.40,$$

or a 40% increase in mass over the rest value (see Table 20.1). Its velocity is obtained from

$$W = 11.5 \times 10^{-7} = \frac{m_0c^2}{\sqrt{1 - v^2/c^2}}$$

Thus

$$1 - \frac{v^2}{c^2} = \left(\frac{8.20 \times 10^{-7}}{11.5 \times 10^{-7}}\right)^2 = (0.713)^2 = 0.51$$

$$v = c\sqrt{0.49} = 2.1 \times 10^{10} \text{ cm/sec}$$

20.7   The Mass-Energy Equivalence

As we know from *classical* dynamics, the total dynamical energy of a particle is the sum of two terms: kinetic energy and potential energy. When work is done on a free particle, as, for example, by accelerating it along a horizontal frictionless plane, only the kinetic energy is changed, whereas in other situations the work may change only the potential energy. In any case it is only *changes* of energy which are measurable, so that we can always assign a fixed amount of some hypothetical form of energy in addition to its energy of position and motion since the hypothetical energy will cancel out in measured energy changes. This is a useless procedure, however, unless this new form of energy is observed to change into dynamical energy on occasion. Thus we say that a falling stone has heat energy in addition to its dynamical energies, since this heat energy can be increased at the expense of the kinetic energy when the stone hits the earth.

In the theory of relativity it appears that we should assign energy to the *rest mass* of a particle; and this is not an empty procedure since in certain processes changes in *rest mass* are found and are accompanied by compensating changes in the kinetic energy. (Even if v is too large to allow the binomial expansion, the interpretation remains unaltered.) The same proposal could have been followed in pre-relativity physics, although it is true that no similar clue existed for evaluating the amount of the rest energy. The important point is that changes in energy which are directly assignable to changes in rest energy are indeed observed and agree in amount with the relativistic formula. This agreement is a direct consequence of the relativistic transformations and the relativistic dynamics to which they lead.

In mathematical terms, the total relativistic energy of a particle is

$$W = \text{K.E.} + m_0 c^2$$

If in some process energy is conserved, but kinetic energy is converted into mass energy, then (bars denote quantities measured after the process)

$$\overline{W} = W = \overline{\text{K.E.}} + \overline{m}_0 c^2 = \text{K.E.} + m_0 c^2$$

and so

$$\text{K.E.} - \overline{\text{K.E.}} = (\overline{m}_0 - m_0)c^2$$

Decrease in kinetic energy of a particle = (increase in rest mass) $\times c^2$

or

$$\Delta W = (\Delta m)c^2 \qquad\qquad [\,20.23\,]$$

(where Δ before a quantity means "change of" that quantity). Thus we see the significance of assigning rest energy $m_0 c^2$ to every particle.

In ordinary large-scale dynamics these changes in rest mass are extremely small since the kinetic energy of a particle at ordinary speeds is very much smaller than its rest energy, and any changes in mass are too small to be measurable.

Example 1. A bullet of mass 100 gm has a velocity of 4×10^4 cm/sec (about 900 mi/hr). If its kinetic energy were completely converted to mass energy what would be the mass increase?

$$\text{K.E.} = \tfrac{1}{2}mv^2 = \tfrac{1}{2} \times 100 \times (4 \times 10^4)^2 = 8 \times 10^{10} \text{ ergs}$$

$$\text{Mass increase} = \frac{\Delta W}{c^2} = \frac{8 \times 10^{10}}{9 \times 10^{20}} = 8.9 \times 10^{-11} \text{ gm}$$

Clearly, this is an entirely unmeasurable mass increase, simply because the bullet has a K.E. of 8×10^{10} ergs whereas its rest energy is

$$m_0 c^2 = 100 \times 9 \times 10^{20} = 9 \times 10^{22} \text{ ergs}$$

In contrast with large-scale dynamics, atomic and nuclear particles often have kinetic energies as large or greater than their rest energies and frequently the interactions of such particles dissipate an appreciable part of their kinetic energies so that the rest mass may change by a measurable fraction.

Example 2. A 0.204-Mev electron (see Table 20.1) has a kinetic energy of 3.26×10^{-7} ergs and a rest energy of 8.20×10^{-7} ergs. If its kinetic energy were converted to mass energy the mass increase would be

$$\Delta m = \frac{\Delta W}{c^2} = \frac{3.26 \times 10^{-7}}{9.00 \times 10^{20}} = 3.62 \times 10^{-28} \text{ grams}$$

or a percentage mass increase of

$$\frac{3.26 \times 10^{-28}}{9.11 \times 10^{-28}} \times 100 = 40\%$$

Of even greater significance than increases in rest mass brought about by kinetic energy dissipating processes are the reverse processes in which energy is released by *decreases* in the rest mass of a group of particles. Here the large factor c^2 multiplies the mass changes so that the energy changes are very large by ordinary standards. For example, a decrease in rest mass by 1 gm releases an energy of 9×10^{20} ergs $= 9 \times 10^{13}$ joules $= 25$ million kw-hr. A large hydroelectric generator would convert this amount of water power into electrical energy in about 500 hr. It is enough energy to fly a four-motored airliner for about 4000 hr.

Finally, it must be realized that the relativity theory does not tell *how* to make this mass energy available in some other form. However, it does make such processes seem natural and reasonable, it supplies the conversion factor, c^2, between mass and energy, and it shows the conditions under which such conversions are large enough to be measurable.

20.8   The Theory of General Relativity

The foregoing material describes in a qualitative manner part of the theory of special relativity announced by Einstein in 1905 (at the age of 26!). It is termed "special" because it applies only to systems moving with constant velocity, that is, inertial systems. In the following eleven years he succeeded in extending the theory to accelerated systems, culminating in the theory of general relativity. The mathematical complexities of this theory are great, for the transformations of the four-dimensional space describing motion—three space coordinates plus a time coordinate—require a special mathematical technique known as tensor analysis. The results of the theory have been applied mainly to astronomical phenomena, and observations have confirmed its predictions in several cases. The most interesting outgrowth of general relativity is the new light in which gravitational forces are viewed.

It is common experience that the occupants of an upward accelerating elevator car have a feeling of increased weight; an airplane pilot pulling out of a dive will push against the seat with several times his normal weight. These are instances where an acceleration apparently increases weight. Suppose an observer were so unfortunate as to be enclosed in a rapidly whirling room that is isolated in empty space; to him "gravity" would not be acting "up" or "down," but radially away from the axis of rotation. If he should drop a book, it would move radially out from the axis of rotation. Such an observer could establish a law of "gravity" that would have complete validity for his system. In view of such considerations Einstein came to the conclusion that in the neighborhood of any given system there could be no measurable distinction between gravitational forces and "apparent" forces due to the acceleration of the system. This postulate—that no experiment can distinguish between gravitational forces and forces due to acceleration of the reference system—is called the principle of equivalence. It is the fundamental postulate of the general theory of relativity. As a corollary it states that it is not possible to determine whether a system of reference is an inertial system, and hence that the laws of physics should be formulated without regard to inertial systems. This conclusion undermines the philosophy of Newtonian dynamics, just as the special theory demolished the absolute space of Maxwell's electrodynamics.

A final word of caution may be needed. Though Newtonian dynamics and relativistic dynamics are conceived on diametrically opposite premises, the former on the existence of absolute space and time, the latter emphasizing the completely relative nature of these concepts, it would be a mistake to think of the work of Newton and his successors as a collection of fortunate errors. The predictions of the theory of relativity rely on the effect of the term $1 - v^2/c^2$ or its square root; only in the case of the extremes, astrophysics and atomic physics, does this term become observable. Newtonian dynamics serves well and faithfully in the realm of macrophysical phenomena; relativity theory has shown it to be an approximation, but the failures of classical theory require the most ingenious of experiments for their detection. It is a remarkable fact that the physics of the extremely large—astrophysics—and the physics of the extremely small—atomic physics—join to establish a new understanding of the workings of the physical world.

PROBLEMS

1. An airplane moving with a velocity of 200 meters/sec (about 500 mi/hr) fires a bullet straight ahead. If the muzzle velocity of the bullet is 500 meters/sec, find its velocity relative to an observer on the ground. Repeat the calculation for the bullet fired directly backwards.   *Ans.* 700 m/sec; 300 m/sec.

2. An atom is accelerated to a velocity of 10^9 cm/sec, at which instant it ejects an electron directly ahead with a velocity of 2×10^{10} cm/sec relative to the atom. Find the electron's velocity as measured by an observer in the laboratory, using (a) Galilean transformation, (b) relativistic transformation.
Ans. 2.10×10^{10} cm/sec; 2.055×10^{10} cm/sec.

3. Two electrons, each moving with a velocity of 2.5×10^{10} cm/sec, approach one another. Find the velocity of one relative to the other, using (a) Newtonian dynamics and (b) relativistic dynamics.   *Ans.* 5×10^{10} cm/sec; 2.95×10^{10} cm/sec.

4. Find the relativistic mass of an electron moving with a velocity of 2.7×10^{10} cm/sec.   *Ans.* See Table 20.1.

5. An electron has an energy of 1 Mev. Find its relativistic mass; find its velocity. (*Hint:* Example of §20.6.)
Ans. 2.95 times rest mass; 2.83×10^{10} cm/sec.

6. It requires a time of 2 microsec for a certain event to occur within an atom. If the atom is moving with a velocity of 10^{10} cm/sec, what time for this event will be measured by an observer in the laboratory?   *Ans.* 1.89 microsec.

7. How much energy is available when one electron (at rest) is annihilated? Express the answer in Mev.   *Ans.* 0.51 Mev.

8. The heat released by combustion of anthracite coal is about 30,000 joules/gm. How many times as effective is mass annihilation compared to combustion?
Ans. Three billion times.

Suggested Reading

BARNETT, L., "The Universe and Dr. Einstein," New York, Wm. Sloane Associates, 1948.
    Superb presentation of the simpler aspects of relativity for the non-scientist.

BERGMANN, P. G., "Introduction to the Theory of Relativity," New York, Prentice-Hall, Inc., 1942.

    Chapter III of this advanced and mathematical treatise is a good elementary account of the bases of relativity theory in optical phenomena. Chapter IV treats the relativistic transformation equations.

DAMPIER, SIR WILLIAM, "A History of Science," New York, The Macmillan Co., 1946.

    Pages 416–28, historical account of the birth of the theory of relativity.

EDDINGTON, SIR ARTHUR, "The Nature of the Physical World," New York, The Macmillan Co., 1929.

    Chapters I–III, bases and nature of the theory of relativity by one of its ablest popular interpreters. Chapter VI and VII discuss the problem of gravity in relativity.

EINSTEIN, A., "Relativity," London, Methuen & Co., 1920.

    Popular lectures, non-mathematical. Good and certainly authoritative.

EINSTEIN, A., and INFELD, L., "The Evolution of Physics," New York, Simon & Schuster, 1938.

    Thorough and thoughtful treatment of our physical concepts. Slow but rewarding reading.

GAMOW, G., "Mr. Tompkins in Wonderland," New York, The Macmillan Co., 1940.

    An amusing description of a man caught in a world in which relativistic effects are everyday experiences.

JEANS, SIR JAMES, "The Mysterious Universe," New York, The Macmillan Co., 1937.

    Chapter IV, good discussion on the problem of the ether. Written for the layman.

The Birth and Growth of the Quantum Theory

21.1 Hot-Solid Radiation

We have mentioned that the problem of the radiation of light led to the birth of the quantum theory. Specifically it was in connection with the light emitted by hot solids.

The two most conspicuous features of the radiation from a heated solid are best indicated by the graphs in Fig. 21.1, namely, the continuous spectrum

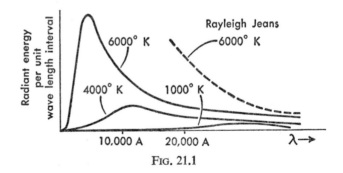

FIG. 21.1

produced and the shift of its maximum energy to shorter wave lengths with increase in temperature. At 1000° K the maximum energy is at 29,000 Å (the far infrared), and there is only a very slight amount of visible energy. The solid would appear a dull red color. At 4000° K the maximum is at 8000 Å, but a much larger amount of energy is in the visible range than before; we would describe the body as "white hot," i.e., radiates all the visible wave lengths. At 6000° K which is the sun's surface temperature the maximum has moved into the visible at 5000 Å, and the solid becomes a very brilliant source of white light. Measurements of these energy maxima revealed that the wave length at maximum energy was inversely proportional to the absolute temperature of the emitter, a relation first noted by Wien in 1893.

An empirical relation such as Wien's is always a stimulating thing in physics, as is the graphical relation—the shape of the curves in Fig. 21.1. What mechanism can we assign to a hot solid that permits it to radiate energy that is distributed in the manner the curves indicate? Is there any way of theoretically predicting these curves?

Such theoretical attempts were made at the end of the nineteenth century, using a model in which the atoms and molecules in the solid vibrated at all frequencies and sent out electromagnetic waves at these frequencies. The intensity of radiation for the various frequencies was supposed to depend on the number of vibrations at that frequency and the energy of each vibration. The former is proportional to ν^2 and the latter proportional to the absolute temperature. While we shall not present the details of this calculation, it will not account for the curves of Fig. 21.1. It does, however, agree with these curves at low frequencies; the dotted curve labeled Rayleigh-Jeans (6000° K) is plotted from the formula of this theory. The principal points to note are: The Rayleigh-Jeans theory departs greatly from the measured distribution of hot-solid radiation at short wave lengths; the curve has no maximum; and worst of all it approaches infinity at very high frequencies. This latter result implies an infinite total energy of radiation, which is utterly unreasonable. The resolution of the difficulties in the theory of hot-solid radiation resulted in a concept which is now of primary importance in all atomic physics—the *quantum of energy*.

21.2 Planck's Quantum Hypothesis

The early theories of hot-solid radiation were based on the assumption that the atoms and molecules in the solid were vibrating with a continuous range of frequencies, emitting waves of light much as a huge number of vibrating strings of various pitch might emit sound waves. In 1900 Max Planck, working with this model, tried to employ a well-known mathematical device that is fundamental to the mathematics of calculus. The trick was this: One first assumed that atoms (or molecules) did not radiate continuously but rather in discontinuous or discrete amounts; then one could mathematically allow the size of these discontinuous amounts to get smaller and smaller until they blended into the continuous flow of energy the model demanded. This is like assuming that water flowing from an open tap is coming out in bursts, but if we imagine the bursts to get smaller and closer together we will arrive at the continuous flow of water actually observed.

The result of this mathematical procedure was startling. If the calculations were carried through to completion the result was no more satisfactory than previous ones. But Planck found that if he retained his discontinuous "chunks" of radiation, not allowing them to get smaller, but instead assigning to each one a definite amount of energy which was proportional to the frequency of the radiation, he arrived at a correct and complete agreement with the entire experimental curve. This would seem to demand that an atom or molecule does not radiate continuously, but only in bursts or chunks, these chunks having a definite amount of energy. Planck called such a discontinuous amount of energy a *quantum* (the plural is *quanta*), a term meaning a definite amount of anything, usually an irreducible amount. (Thus a human being represents a quantum of population—there are no fractions of human beings; similarly the electron charge represents the quantum of electricity.) The theory demanded that the amount of energy (W) possessed by a quantum must be proportional to its frequency (ν). Thus, a quantum of radiation is not only a definite amount of energy, it is also of a single definite frequency. The constant of proportionality is represented by h and is known as *Planck's constant.* Hence, the quantum of radiant energy of frequency ν is

$$W = h\nu \qquad\qquad [21.1]$$

Though the mathematical results of Planck's work are too involved to be presented here, the effectiveness of the quantum in explaining the radiation curves can be shown very qualitatively. An atom or molecule radiates a chunk of energy $W = h\nu$; so that the shorter the wave length, i.e., the greater the frequency, the more energy the atom must have in order to radiate that wave length. Hence, only a relatively small number of atoms ever succeed in radiating very short wave lengths, accounting for the decreased energy shown by the curve on the short wave-length side of the peak. On the other hand, many atoms may acquire enough energy to radiate a long wave-length quantum, but such a quantum does not have much energy. Intuitively it seems reasonable that for a given temperature there will be a point of compromise between the energy-rich but rare quanta and the moderately energetic but more frequent ones, and this compromise forms the maximum energy peak observed. Increasing the temperature favors the formation of more energetic quanta as the curves demand.

21.3 Implications of the Quantum Hypothesis

Planck's idea of quanta of energy was accepted, reasonably enough, with caution and restraint, for its implications were revolutionary. Since it requires light to be radiated in discrete amounts, it therefore presumably follows that light must travel out into space as discrete quanta. Hence, according to the quantum hypothesis light is *not* a continuous flow of energy, but has a granular structure. We are attributing a type of particle nature to light, though, true, these are particles apparently without mass. We seem to be placing electromagnetic waves in a separate category, for there is no evidence that the usual types of waves, such as sound and water waves, possess this property of discreteness. A piano string emits waves continuously as long as it is vibrating at all, and these waves form a continuous train in traveling through the air. But a light quantum consists of a limited train of oscillations. Indeed we could justifiably ask what is meant by a light "wave" if it is composed of such a discontinuous set of waves (with gaps between).

Another aspect of Planck's assumption which is no less drastic is the restrictions placed on the *source* of the quantum. The theory stipulates that an atom cannot radiate just any energy it receives, but must wait for just so much ($h\nu$) and then radiate that and no more. For if an atom could radiate any amount of energy it is hard to conceive how a large quantum of energy (high frequency) could ever be formed. The quantum hypothesis seems to impose rules of conduct on the atom. If this is true, we may have gained important insight into its interior mechanism. Discovering to what "laws" the components of the atom submit will lead us far in constructing a reasonable picture of them. Planck's hypothesis would suggest that the atomic components are restricted in their motions by rules of *quantization* since only discrete, discontinuous energy changes are allowed.

The scrutiny we have given to Planck's quantum hypothesis would not be merited if the concept were inapplicable to problems other than the radiation of a hot solid. The cautious but concerned attention with which it was received by other physicists turned to widespread acceptance in the years that followed. There are three milestones that were largely responsible for this success: Einstein's application of the quantum hypothesis to the theory of the photoelectric effect (1905); Bohr's quantized atom model (1913); and Compton's success in accounting for quantum-electron collisions (1923). Since these bear directly on our effort to construct a picture of the atom, we shall consider them in some detail in this and succeeding chapters.

21.4 The Photoelectric Effect

The phenomenon of photoelectricity was discovered by Hertz in 1887, when he observed that a spark between two metal electrodes occurs at lower than normal voltages if ultraviolet light is shining on the electrodes. Eleven years later J. J. Thomson, and independently P. Lenard, succeeded in demonstrating that a metal surface on which ultraviolet light fell emitted negative charges. Figure 21.2 shows a simple way of confirming this. A negatively charged electroscope connected to a piece of zinc metal slowly loses its charge

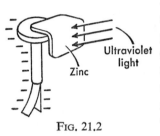

as light continues to fall upon the zinc plate. If the experiment is repeated with the electroscope positively charged the leaves do not fall. We conclude that under the action of the light negative charges leave the zinc plate (and hence the electroscope connected to it) if the zinc plate is negative so as to release them; a positive plate would retain any negative charges attempting to leave.

Fig. 21.2

The emission of negative charge by the action of light on a surface is called the *photoelectric effect*, and the emitted charges are called *photoelectrons*. It was soon determined that photoelectrons are no different from all other electrons; the name is used simply to indicate the manner in which they are set free.

21.5 Characteristics of the Photoelectric Effect

A systematic survey of photoelectricity disclosed several facts that are worthy of attention.

1. For any given material there is a minimum light frequency (maximum wave length) below which electrons will not be emitted. Suppose the light from a carbon arc (a hot solid) were dispersed into its continuous spectrum by a diffraction grating (Fig. 21.3), and a screen with a slit allowed only a small band of wave lengths to fall on a zinc surface. As the slit is moved from the red end of the spectrum toward the ultraviolet there is no effect on the electroscope leaves until the slit reaches 3500 A; for this and all shorter wave lengths photoelectrons are emitted. This maximum wave length is called the *photoelectric threshold*. All elements exhibit the photoelectric effect, but each element has its own characteristic photoelectric threshold. The elements in the first and second columns in the periodic table (the chemist refers to them as the "alkali metals" and "alkaline earths" respectively) have the longest threshold wave lengths, i.e., will emit electrons with the reddest light. For some of these the wave lengths in visible light are sufficiently short.

2. For a given surface the *number* of photoelectrons emitted per second, in other words, the photoelectric current, is directly proportional to the intensity of the light. Though this characteristic is scarcely surprising, the appa-

ratus used in its verification is worth examination. Figure 21.4 shows a block of sodium mounted with a collecting chamber in a vacuum (to allow unimpeded collection of the electrons). With a fixed collecting voltage the current varies directly with intensity of the light source.

3. *For a given surface, the kinetic energy of the emitted photoelectrons depends only on the light frequency and is independent of light intensity.* To de-

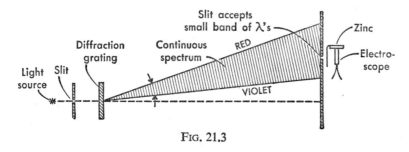

Fig. 21.3

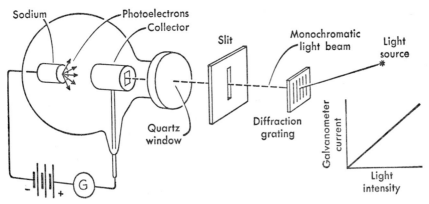

Fig. 21.4

termine this, the apparatus in Fig. 21.4 is used in the following manner. The incident monochromatic light is chosen with a wave length considerably shorter than the threshold value. It is found that even if the potential difference between the sodium surface and the collecting cup is made zero there is still a photoelectric current, indicating that the electrons were emitted with some kinetic energy. To find how much this kinetic energy amounted to, a "retarding" potential is applied, that is, the sodium is made slightly *positive* relative to the collecting chamber (rather than negative as in Fig. 21.4). As this positive potential is increased a point is reached when no current flows; if it requires 5 volts of potential difference to hold the electrons back then they must have had 5 ev of energy. By this method the amount of energy given to an electron by the incident light can be measured as both the intensity and frequency of the light are varied. Figure 21.5 indicates the results. *The electron energy was found to be independent of light intensity.*

The above result is italicized because the wave theory of light is completely unable to account for it. If light is depicted as a form of wave motion, increasing the intensity of the light must increase the amplitude of the wave and hence its energy. For instance, the sound waves from a siren sounding a single frequency set the eardrum in motion; the energy received by the eardrum depends on the amplitude of the sound wave; the louder the siren the greater is the amplitude of vibration of the eardrum, and, in fact, a sufficiently intense sound can rupture the ear. Yet increasing light intensity fails to give the photoelectrons more kinetic energy; it only causes the ejection of more electrons. Higher photoelectron energies can be produced only by increasing the light frequency.

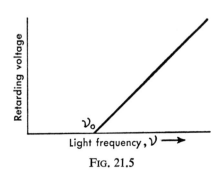

Light frequency, $\nu \longrightarrow$

FIG. 21.5

21.6 Einstein's Photoelectric Equation

Contrary to popular supposition Einstein was awarded the Nobel Prize (in 1921) for his photoelectric theory (1905), not his work in relativity. Few men have had the genius to make basic contributions in relatively unrelated problems, yet on several counts Einstein's researches have merited the Nobel Prize.

His explanation of the photoelectric effect is simply presented. Light is not a continuous wave but consists of quanta of energy, the same quanta proposed by Planck. When a quantum ($h\nu$) of light hits a surface it may give up its energy to an electron which then spends it in two ways: (1) A certain amount is needed in getting away from the atoms it is leaving behind and away from the surface; this energy we can call the "photoelectric work," W_p; it is the same work that we encountered in thermionic emission (§16.1); that is, for metals $W_p = W_t$. (2) The remaining energy received from the quantum appears as kinetic energy of the electron, $\frac{1}{2}mv^2$. Therefore, in symbols, we can write

$$h\nu = W_p + \tfrac{1}{2}mv^2 \qquad\qquad [\,21.2\,]$$

or in words:

Energy received from the quantum = energy to escape + kinetic energy.

This is Einstein's now famous photoelectric equation. At once it succeeds in explaining all the observed phenomena listed in §21.5. Let us see how.

1. Minimum frequency. If the frequency is reduced, the energy of the quantum is less ($W = h\nu$), and hence the kinetic energy of the electron is less. At the point where $\frac{1}{2}mv^2 = 0$ the quantum energy is entirely exhausted in getting the electron out of the metal; the light frequency corresponding to this minimum energy is the photoelectric threshold already mentioned and is designated ν_0. Hence $W_p = h\nu_0$. Quanta of any frequency less than this will not liberate photoelectrons.

2. Number of electrons emitted depends on the intensity of light. The *intensity* of the light depends on the *number* of quanta (*not* their energy, as in the case of waves). Thus if more quanta fall upon a surface then more electrons are emitted, the light intensity and number of electrons being proportional.

3. Energy of individual electrons depends on the frequency of the light, not its intensity. This major stumbling block is now removed by the photoelectric equation. The greater the frequency ν the greater the kinetic energy $\frac{1}{2}mv^2$. Increasing light intensity does not change ν or $\frac{1}{2}mv^2$. (It should be noted that we must assume that the electron absorbs the energy of one quantum only.)

Einstein's photoelectric equation served to elevate Planck's quantum theory to the rank of a basic principle of atomic physics. In addition it pointed out to Millikan a means of measuring Planck's constant h, a constant which, like the velocity of light, seems to permeate all atomic theory.

21.7   Millikan's Determination of h

Using an apparatus similar to that of Fig. 21.4, Millikan was able to measure all the quantities in the photoelectric equation except h, and thus to evaluate Planck's constant. Rewriting Einstein's Eq. 21.2,

$$h\nu = W_p + \tfrac{1}{2}mv^2 = h\nu_0 + \tfrac{1}{2}mv^2$$

or

$$h(\nu - \nu_0) = \tfrac{1}{2}mv^2 \qquad\qquad [\,21.3\,]$$

The incident frequency ν is known from the constants of the spectrometer (see §10.9). By observing the retarding potential which just prevents collection of electrons their kinetic energy is obtained. Finally, changing the frequency of light by moving the slit locates the minimum frequency for which no electrons are emitted. With these data h can then be calculated. (The experiment is far more difficult than this description would imply. The major trouble comes in observing when zero current occurs; also, great care must be taken to have extremely clean surfaces, for otherwise there will be a mixture of W_p's.) The result of Millikan's work (in 1912), together with other methods developed later, gives for the accepted value of Planck's constant:

$$h = 6.624 \times 10^{-27} \text{ erg-sec}$$

21.8   The Photocell

A modified form of the apparatus of Fig. 21.4 has become a widely used engineering and industrial device, called a *photocell*. A half-cylinder is coated with one of the alkali metals and approximately at its center is a collecting electrode (Fig. 21.6). Connecting wires are brought out through the base of the glass envelope, and the cell is highly evacuated. (There are gas-filled photocells in which a small amount of a gas is introduced; in such a cell the current is increased by the ionization of the gas.) The photosensitive surface is made negative relative to the collecting electrode and will thus cause a current to flow in the circuit when light falls on the cell. Such a "light switch" has found wide application in talking motion pictures, television, burglar alarms, package counting, and other processes too numerous to mention.

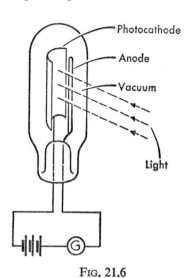

Fig. 21.6

PROBLEMS

1. How much energy is a quantum of green light ($\lambda = 5000\text{Å}$)?

    Ans. 3.96×10^{-12} ergs.

2. What is the energy of the quantum of Problem 1 expressed in electron volts?

    Ans.   2.48 ev.

3. Under ideal conditions the maximum sensitivity of the ear is about 10^{-17} watts/cm² of sound while that of the eye is about 5 quanta/sec/cm² of yellow light ($\lambda = 6000$ Å). Which is more sensitive, the ear or the eye?

    Ans.   The eye, but only by a factor of about 6.

4. The photoelectric threshold of a certain solid is 4.25 ev. What is the longest wave length of light which will produce a photoelectron?   *Ans.*   2900 Å.

5. It was found that to just stop photoelectrons of a certain photocell required a retarding potential of 3 volts. Find the energy of the electrons in ev and ergs.

Ans. 3 ev, 4.8 × 10⁻¹² ergs.

6. The photoelectric threshold for a certain material occurs for light of wave length 5000 Å. How much kinetic energy (in electron volts) have the photoelectrons produced by light of wave length 3000 Å?   *Ans.* 1.65 ev.

Suggested Reading

Darrow, K. K., "Introduction to Contemporary Physics," New York, D. Van Nostrand Co., 1926.
   Review of the status of quantum theory in 1926. Well written.

Eddington, Sir Arthur, "The Nature of the Physical World," New York, The Macmillan Co., 1933.
   Chapter IX discusses the growth of quantum theory. Well presented.

Hoffmann, B., "The Strange Story of the Quantum," New York, Harper & Brothers, 1947.
   Written for the layman. The unusual aspects of the quantum are pointed up. Good reading.

Jordan, P., "Physics of the 20th Century," New York, Philosophical Library, 1944.
   Chapter IV, critical account of the nature of the quantum theory in nontechnical language by one of the founders of quantum mechanics.

Millikan, R. A., "Electrons (+ and −)," Chicago, University of Chicago Press, 1947.
   Chapter X, Einstein's photoelectric theory and its test by the author. Very readable.

CHAPTER 22

X Rays

22.1 Discovery of X Rays—Roentgen

The gas-discharge tube which, in the hands of J. J. Thomson, led to the discovery of the electron was also instrumental in the discovery of x rays. This discovery is often described as one of the fortuitous "accidents" of experimental research, by which it is meant that the work was not the result of a controlled experiment, guided by definite hypotheses and designed to confirm these hypotheses. Roentgen, the discoverer, was working in his laboratory in Germany, investigating the properties of the cathode rays generated in a gas discharge. A photographic plate, completely wrapped in black paper and lying near the discharge tube, was found to be fogged upon development. Several other experimenters had observed that a plate shielded from light became fogged in this manner, but it remained for Roentgen in 1895 to investigate this "accident" in a truly careful and controlled way.

22.2 The X-Ray Tube

Roentgen found that cathode rays were essential for the production of these rays which penetrated opaque paper. Furthermore, the source of the radiation was the anode of the discharge tube. If the cathode rays were interrupted in their progress to the anode by interposing a piece of metal between anode and cathode, the metal became the source of the unknown rays. Hence he concluded that *x rays are generated when high-speed electrons (cathode rays) hit a solid target.* The modern x-ray tube employs a filament source of electrons backed by a concave reflector for focusing the cathode rays and a heavy anode target inclined at an angle to the incident electrons (Fig. 22.1). The very large amount of kinetic energy given up by the electrons upon hitting the target generates intense heat; hence the target is usually of material such as molybdenum or tungsten which does not melt readily. Other targets must be water-cooled; this is accomplished by making the anode hollow and circulating water through it.

22.3   Characteristics of X Rays

The property of x rays which led to their discovery was the fogging of a photographic plate. This and the other methods of x-ray detection result from the *ionizing* ability of the rays. In their passage through matter electrons are liberated from the atoms in the material, producing a path of ionization along the beam. As we shall see, x rays are simply high-energy quanta (electromagnetic waves), and the ionization may be likened to the photoelectric effect on an atomic scale. On the other hand, the great energies of the x-ray quanta reduce the chance of photoelectric and other

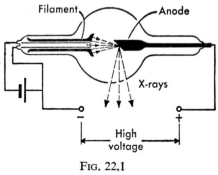

FIG. 22.1

ionization processes and give the rays a great penetrating power. Various specific methods of x-ray detection and the processes upon which they are based are listed below.

Photographic.   The fundamental process of photography is the ionization of a silver halide grain. Subsequent processing (developing, fixing, etc.) of the plate or film is based on chemical reactions which affect these ionized grains differently from the others. In ordinary photography the ionization event is a direct photoelectric process. In x-ray photography the ionization can result directly from the quantum or from secondary events. Evidently, any ionizing radiation will (and does) produce a photographic image.

The penetrating power of x rays, together with their photographic effect suggested their usefulness in studying the bone structures of the human body. Since x rays penetrate flesh more readily than the denser bones they produce a shadowgraph of the bones. The widespread use of x rays for this purpose needs no further mention.

Gas ionization.   When x-ray ionization is produced in solid materials the ions cannot, of course, be collected directly since they cannot move in an applied electric field. However, in a gas, both the + ions and the electrons can be collected, producing an "ionization current" proportional to the x-ray intensity. A simple demonstration of this is furnished by a charged electroscope (see §11.8) whose leaves drop when exposed to an x-ray beam. The ion currents to the electroscope case neutralize the charged leaves. Simple, portable electroscopes are carried by workers who are exposed to radiation. The electroscopes are charged at the beginning of the day, and the remaining charge is measured later to determine the total amount of radiation which has passed through the instrument (and the worker).

Fluorescence. When a gas-discharge tube is operated at high voltages a greenish glow is seen around the anode. This *fluorescence* is, in part, due to the action of the x rays on glass. The effect is greatly enhanced by using zinc sulfide powder or other metallic oxides and sulfides instead of glass. The details of the process are complex, but in general we may say that they result from the light-emitting ability of electrons as they return to their stable positions after being set free (ionized) by the x rays. The process is similar in the case where cathode rays impinge directly on the fluorescent material, as in the television picture tube. In x-ray technology such screens are used in the common fluoroscope.

22.4 Penetrating Power of X Rays

As we have stated, x rays in their passage through matter become weaker in proportion to the ionization which they have produced. In terms of the quantum theory we say that a beam of x rays is a collection of quanta. Each time a quantum produces an ionizing event it *disappears* and so is lost from the beam. In addition, some of the quanta are scattered from the beam either elastically (without loss in energy) or inelastically (see §24.2). Both of these processes contribute to the *absorption* of the beam in its passage through matter. Both processes are dictated by a certain chance or probability of their happening in a given path length in the material.

If all the quanta are of the same frequency, it is clear that these processes are repeated with only a change of numbers of quanta in each succeeding layer of material. There is, for example, a certain thickness for which the number of quanta is reduced by half. In double this thickness the number will be reduced to $\frac{1}{2} \times \frac{1}{2} = \frac{1}{4}$ of the original, etc. Since the beam intensity is proportional to the number of quanta, the beam intensity decays by this rule as it passes through matter (see Fig. 22.2). Note clearly that no thickness, however great, is sufficient to reduce the intensity entirely to zero.

22.5 The Wave Nature of X Rays

We have observed several characteristics of x rays, but we have not yet shown how they were established to be quanta. It is immediately demonstrated that they carry no charge, for their motion is unaffected by either

electric or magnetic fields (thus ruling out the idea that x rays might be reflected cathode rays). Their high penetrating power suggests the possibility of
a wave similar to but more energetic than a light wave. The critical test for a
wave is its ability to exhibit constructive and destructive *interference* (Chapter

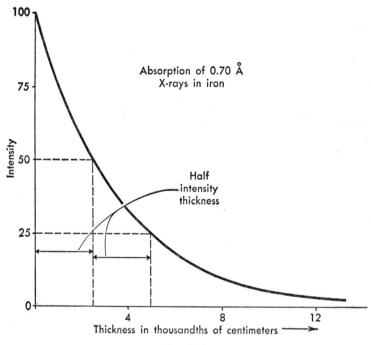

FIG. 22.2

10). However, neither the usual double-slit experiment (Young's experiment)
nor the diffraction grating yielded the expected diffraction patterns. The
difficulty was resolved in 1912 by von Laue. He reasoned that if x rays are
truly waves the failure to obtain an interference pattern with a diffraction
grating must be attributed to the small diffraction in the pattern, that is, the
diffraction angle was too small to separate the pattern from the non-diffracted
image. The diffraction grating equation (Eq. 10.2) is

$$n\lambda = d\frac{x}{L}$$

The spread of the diffraction pattern is determined by x, the distance of the
diffracted image from the zero image; since d, the grating spacing, and n, the
order of the diffraction image, are both constant for a given grating, then a

small x must be due to a small wave length, λ. To obtain an observable spread of diffraction images the small wave length must be compensated for by using a grating of smaller spacing, d. It therefore occurred to von Laue that a crystal would serve as a suitable grating; the atoms in a crystal are uniformly spaced with quite small values for d. There was some evidence at that time

FIG. 22.3

that for most crystals the value of d was the order of 10^{-8} cm; the most finely ruled man-made diffraction gratings have rulings no closer than 10^{-4} cm. However, since the crystal possesses points (atoms) instead of lines (rulings), we would expect a diffraction pattern of points rather than of lines. If the crystal is perfect, that is, if the spacing is uniform throughout the entire crystal, the pattern is a series of points that are the interference images of a point source (Fig. 22.3). Such patterns are called Laue patterns. Their interpretation is often complicated, especially if the crystal is not a perfect one. However, from the measured diffraction angles it is demonstrated that the usual x rays are waves of length in the range of 1 Å (10^{-8} cm). (The wave length of visible light is of the order of 5000 Å.) Subsequent experiments showed conclusively that x rays exhibit the properties of visible light (interference, polarization, etc.); they differ from light quanta only in wave length. Incidentally, the success of the von Laue experiment confirmed the idea that a crystal is a regular, fixed array of atoms, which even in a large crystal may be reasonably well maintained.

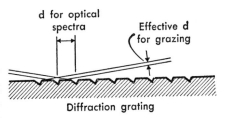

Diffraction grating

FIG. 22.4

Once it had been clearly demonstrated that x rays were waves having a very short wave length it was possible for A. H. Compton to show that the ordinary optical diffraction grating could produce a detectable x-ray diffraction pattern if the x rays were directed at grazing incidence. Along a line of sight almost parallel to the grating surface the effective line spacing is very much smaller than when viewed perpendicularly to the surface (Fig. 22.4). Hence by allowing the x-ray beam to just graze the grating, a pattern could be observed which resembled the ordinary optical line spectrum.

22.6 X-Ray Spectra

If the x-ray beam from a tube such as that of Fig. 22.1 is analyzed into its component wave lengths a pattern such as that of Fig. 22.5 is obtained. It consists of two components, a *continuous* radiation having a high-frequency cutoff and a superposed *line* spectrum. It is found that the line spectra are characteristic of the x-ray producing material, i.e., the anode, while the form and position of the continuous spectrum depends only on the energy of the electrons striking the anode.

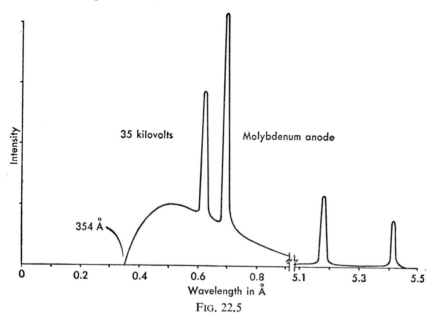

FIG. 22.5

In view of the quantum theory it is clear that the high-frequency cutoff corresponds to those quanta which have received the *entire* electron energy and that no higher frequency quanta are possible. This means that

$$W = Ve = h\nu \qquad\qquad [\,22.1\,]$$

where V is the difference in potential across the tube and e the electronic charge.

Example. What is the high frequency cutoff for $V = 35{,}000$ volts (see Fig. 22.5)?

$$\nu_{max} = \frac{Ve}{h}$$

$$= \frac{35000}{300} \times \frac{4.80 \times 10^{-10}}{6.62 \times 10^{-27}} = 8.46 \times 10^{18} \text{ per sec}$$

so that the cutoff wave length is

$$\lambda_{min} = \frac{c}{\nu_{max}}$$
$$= \frac{3.00 \times 10^{10}}{8.46 \times 10^{18}} = 0.354 \text{ Å}$$

Since both λ_{min} and V can be measured accurately such experiments furnish a precise determination of the ratio h/e.

The details of the shape of the continuous spectrum will not occupy us here. Except at the cutoff the quanta receive less than the energy Ve because of energy loss of the electrons as they penetrate the anode.

The line spectra have received a great deal of attention, particularly since the development of the quantum theory. We shall see that they arise in much the same manner as do optical spectra, and correspond to changes in internal energy in atoms (see §23.9).

PROBLEMS

1. What fraction of x rays will penetrate 10 cm of an absorber if their intensity is reduced by one-half in going through 2 cm of the same absorber? *Ans.* 3.1%.

2. What is the frequency of a 5-Å x ray? *Ans.* 6×10^{17} vibrations/sec.

3. What is the energy of a 5-Å x ray in ergs and electron volts?
Ans. 3.97×10^{-9} ergs; 2480 ev.

4. A certain x-ray tube uses a potential difference of 100,000 volts. What is the wave length of the shortest x ray generated? *Ans.* 0.124 Å.

5. The betatron (§28.6) can produce electrons of 100 Mev. What is the shortest x ray that these can generate? What is its frequency?
Ans. 0.00012 Å; 2.5×10^{22} vibrations/sec.

Suggested Reading

JAUNCEY, G. E. M., "The Birth and Early Infancy of X-rays," *American Journal of Physics*, Vol. 13, pp. 362–79, 1945.
    The intriguing story of the popular reception of Roentgen's discovery.

MOULTON, F. R., and SCHIFFERES, J. J., "The Autobiography of Science," New York, Doubleday Doran & Co., 1945.
    Pages 484–90, Roentgen's account of his discovery of x rays.

Bohr's Quantum Theory of the Atom

23.1 Atomic Models and Atomic Mechanics

The development of the atomistic concept of matter in the nineteenth century kept in step with the observations of chemical processes and the thermal behavior of matter, particularly gases. The atom arose as an entity in bulk matter and remained in that role until the present century. Atoms were endowed with motion (the kinetic theory), with mass (atomic masses), with size, with chemical affinities (valency), but not until 1911 were they given a structure and an internal mechanics. Before this they were conceived of as the primary constituents of matter, as the possessors of many properties, but these properties were not *explained* in terms of any atomic theory. Atoms acted as they did simply because they were "made" that way by man in his search to correlate natural phenomena in terms of a model. The gropings of speculation and theory had not yet passed the stage of atomic form and substance to the sharper picture of the atomic interior.

Shortly after the turn of the century this sharper picture began to take shape as a result of the discoveries of many new atomic processes. The gas-discharge tube showed the electrical nature of the atomic constituents. Thomson's cathode-ray experiments and positive-ray studies demanded that the atom contain electrons. Photoelectricity showed the interaction of the atom with light; x rays were discovered and clearly indicated their atomic origin. Within a few years the weight of new evidence pressed very strongly on the vague atomic models of the time and demanded a much more detailed structure.

Throughout this period there were, of course, many speculative attempts to correlate the atomic processes in terms of an atomic model. Most of these attempts are of only historical interest and need not concern us here. However, in 1911 Ernest Rutherford proposed the *nuclear* atom model, and shortly afterward Niels Bohr used this model in a theory to explain the nature of line spectra. The success of these attempts was immediate and far reaching.

Within a few years the new theory had been applied to explain chemical valency, x-ray spectra, and the general connection of light with atomic processes. The theory was not perfect and had to be amended, particularly by the new quantum theory in 1926, which verified its predictions and corrected its deficiencies. Today, in historical perspective, the progress from Rutherford's atomic model to the completeness of present day atomic theory is an interesting and exciting story.

23.2   The Nuclear Atom Model

By 1911 several kinds of experiments had been performed which could be explained only by detailed atomic models. One of these models was proposed by J. J. Thomson to explain the scattering of x rays by matter. Thomson's atom was a continuous distribution of electrically charged matter of atomic dimensions, a sea of positive electricity with embedded negative electrons. Rutherford's model was quite different; it consisted of a very small positive core (some ten-thousandths of the size of the atom) surrounded by a diffuse cloud of electrons. Rutherford arrived at this model from the consideration of α-particle scattering.

We shall discuss the radioactive process responsible for α-particle emission in Chapter 25. For the present it suffices to state that certain elements spontaneously emit positively charged (charge of $+2e$) particles of 4 atomic mass units with energies of several million electron volts. These are called α (alpha) particles. Beams of these high-speed projectiles were found to be dispersed or scattered by passage through thin metallic foils. It was clear that such energetic particles must penetrate into the atoms in the foil and that the scattering resulted from the electrical forces between the α particles and the atoms' constituents. Most important it was necessary to explain the infrequent but measurable number of large angle scattering events.

On Thomson's atom model the α particle would not be turned aside by the diffuse cloud of electrical matter in the atom but would penetrate through the structure and suffer a number of small pushes from the positive and negative matter. These impacts would disperse the α-particle beam but practically never cause any changes of direction of more than a few degrees. Rutherford recognized that this was not in agreement with experiment and proposed a nuclear atom model which could produce large angle scattering by virtue of the highly charged and massive nuclear core. Further, his 1911 calculations agreed quantitatively with the observed scattering at all angles and showed convincingly that the nuclear atom was a fruitful concept.

With a few modern interpolations Rutherford's nuclear atom model proposed that:

1. Practically all the mass of the atom is concentrated in a particle of some 10^{-12} cm diameter—the central core or *nucleus*.

2. This nucleus is positively charged. The number of units of charge (each numerically equal to the electron charge) on the nucleus is equal to the *atomic number* of the atom. (This was in the nature of a good guess, since scattering experiments at that time indicated the charge of the nuclear scatterer only roughly. Later scattering experiments with foils of various metals sustained this conjecture.) In view of the fact that the atom is electrically neutral and contains negative electrons as well as a positive nucleus the model proposed that:

3. *Electrons* are diffusely spread through a region of atomic dimensions (10^{-8} cm) around the nucleus. The number of electrons is equal to the atomic number.

A picture of this model has been given in Fig. 11.3.

23.3 The Bohr Atom and Spectroscopy

Rutherford's nuclear atom model was concerned only with the distribution of mass and charge in the atom and did not explain the internal atomic processes. It did not, for example, say why the atom was stable, why it didn't collapse due to the Coulomb attraction between the negative electrons and the positive nucleus. Nor did it in itself predict the various known atomic processes from the mechanics of the structure. The first internal process explained by an atomic theory was the emission and absorption of line spectra by atoms with one electron (hydrogen, helium ionized once, lithium ionized twice, etc.). This connection between atomic theory and spectroscopy began with Bohr and has been a most fruitful alliance ever since.

Bohr was not working in a completely uncharted field when he proposed his theory of spectra. A great deal of observational data and empirical correlation in spectroscopy had been collected, beginning in the middle of the nineteenth century with the development of the modern spectroscope. The wave lengths of spectral lines from known sources were tabulated, various classes of spectra had been recognized, and empirical rules were known which correlated the positions of the lines in some of the simpler spectra. Still, however, previous to Bohr's work in 1913 there was no *theory* of spectra but only a collection of spectroscopic data and rules for its classification.

In essence, Bohr faced the problem of explaining the known stability of atoms by a model which included the possibility of internal processes to accord with the emission and absorption of light by atoms. We have already seen that electrodynamics fails to explain these facts; indeed it predicts instability for a structure composed of charged particles. Bohr avoided this instability by simply denying that classical electrodynamics applies in detail in the atom and proposed a new set of dynamical assumptions for the atom. The calculations which he then carried out agreed excellently with the spectroscopic facts and provided a theory on which future spectroscopic measurements could be interpreted.

As we now know, the successes of the Bohr theory are sharply limited. However, although the details of the theory and its model are no longer accepted, Bohr introduced certain general concepts into the laws of atomic behavior which have survived and become basic to all theories of the atom. In addition, the Bohr theory gave us a "picture" of the atom (and its processes) which has not been improved upon, and probably will not be, for the theory which corrected, extended, and supplanted the Bohr theory tells us that atomic pictures are no longer possible at all. Instead it substitutes for them a set of abstract concepts which have no parallel in the macroscopic world, and so is beyond picturing. The new theory is called *quantum mechanics*. Yet man's mind seems so constructed that is is impossible to think continually in terms of complete abstractions; consciously or not we are prone to call up an image, and the Bohr model supplies this image.

23.4   The Postulates and Results of the Bohr Theory

The Bohr theory of the atom rests on the model that had been proposed by Rutherford. With the aid of three fundamental postulates or assumptions Bohr attempted to establish the laws of the internal operation of the atom.

Bohr assumed the nucleus to be a heavy central core with a number of positive charges equal to the atomic number Z of the atom. Each charge making up the total was the same size as the charge of the electron (4.8×10^{-10} esu); hence there must be Z electrons surrounding the nucleus. To prevent these electrons from collapsing into the positive nucleus he assumed that they rotated in circular orbits with the nucleus at the center. Bohr first developed his theory for the simplest of all the atoms, the *hydrogen atom*, which is also the first in the periodic table ($Z = 1$). Calling the mass of the electron m, its orbital radius r, and its charge e (Fig. 23.1), Bohr made three basic postulates about the behavior of the electron.

First postulate: The centripetal acceleration of the electron is due to electrostatic attraction by the nucleus. Putting this in the form of an equation,

$$F = ma = \frac{mv^2}{r}$$

$$\text{Coulomb force} = \frac{ee}{r^2}$$

Therefore,

$$\frac{mv^2}{r} = \frac{e^2}{r^2} \quad \text{(first postulate)} \qquad\qquad \text{[23.1]}$$

The second and third postulates were more radical; in them Bohr introduced into the atom the idea of *quantization* proposed by Planck and so suc-

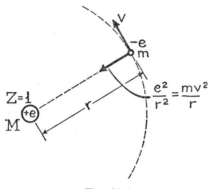

$$\frac{e^2}{r^2} = \frac{mv^2}{r}$$

FIG. 23.1

cessfully used by Einstein in the photoelectric theory. They had required that energy must be quantized; Bohr went a step further—not only the energy but the *orbit* of the electron about the nucleus can have only certain values, that is, is quantized. How does one express the quantization of such a quantity? In the case of energy Planck wrote $W = h\nu$, or W can only be ν times a fixed constant h, Planck's constant. To quantize the electron orbit requires a consideration of the radius of the orbit (r) and the momentum (mv) of the electron moving in this orbit; the product, mvr, is called the *angular momentum* of the electron, and it was this product that Bohr quantized. In actuality it was 2π times the angular momentum, that is, $2\pi mvr$ which is quantized to be equal to certain multiples of Planck's constant h; the use of 2π allows these multiples to be integers. These integers we will represent by the symbol n, meaning that n may have any integral value, 1, 2, 3, 4, $\cdots$, etc. This apparently devious manipulation is necessary to satisfy the demands of quantization, namely, that only certain multiples of h are possible; the introduction of 2π allowed these multiples to be integers. Summing up:

Second postulate: 2π times the angular momentum of the electron must be a whole number times h. In equation form:

$$\text{Angular momentum} = \text{Linear momentum} \times \text{Radius}$$
$$= mvr$$

so
$$2\pi mvr = nh \quad \text{(second postulate)} \qquad [23.2]$$

where
$$n = 1, 2, 3, \cdots, \text{etc.}$$

Though this postulate is arbitrary, it at once leads us to a calculation of the possible orbits of the electron, and to the size of the hydrogen atom. To see this, eliminate v from Eqs. 23.1 and 23.2. Squaring Eq. 23.2,

$$4\pi^2 m^2 v^2 r^2 = n^2 h^2$$

Solving Eq. 23.1 for v^2,

$$v^2 = \frac{e^2}{mr}$$

and substituting

$$4\pi^2 m^2 \frac{e^2}{mr} r^2 = n^2 h^2$$

or

$$4\pi^2 m e^2 r = n^2 h^2$$

finally

$$r = n^2 \frac{h^2}{4\pi^2 m e^2} \qquad [23.3]$$

Now n is any integer, and all the other quantities are constants:

$$h = 6.62 \times 10^{-27} \text{ erg-sec}$$
$$m = 9.11 \times 10^{-28} \text{ gm}$$
$$e = 4.80 \times 10^{-10} \text{ esu}$$

(e must be in cgs units, not coulombs, to give the cgs unit for r.) So

$$r = n^2 \frac{(6.62 \times 10^{-27})^2}{4\pi^2 \times 9.11 \times 10^{-28} \times (4.80 \times 10^{-10})^2}$$
$$= n^2 \times 0.529 \times 10^{-8} \text{ cm}$$

Thus the *allowed* orbits have radii that are 1, 4, 9, 16, 25, etc. times 0.529×10^{-8} cm. When the electron is in its smallest orbit the diameter of the hydrogen atom is 1.06×10^{-8} cm, certainly the order of magnitude already known for atomic diameters (see §9.8). Yet Bohr got this quantity using such apparently unrelated constants as Planck's constant and the mass and charge of the electron.

Equation 23.3 demonstrates, as the second postulate required, that the electron can travel only in certain orbits—those whose radii are

$$r_1 = 1 \times 0.529 \times 10^{-8}\text{ cm}$$
$$r_2 = 2^2 \times 0.529 \times 10^{-8}\text{ cm}$$
$$r_3 = 3^2 \times 0.529 \times 10^{-8}\text{ cm}$$

Thus $r_2 = 4r_1$, $r_3 = 9r_1$, $r_5 = 25r_1$, etc. (Fig. 23.2).

It is utterly impossible for an orbit of $1.5 \times n_1$ or $7.3 \times n_1$ or any other non-integral multiple of n_1 to exist. What keeps the electron out of such orbits? The answer is the law of quanti-zation—this is accepted by the theory and leads to agreement with experiment; questioning its valid-ity is thus questioning a necessary part of a successful theory and is unprofitable unless something better or more palatable is ad-vanced.

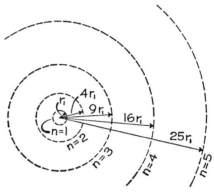

FIG. 23.2

The integers represented by n, each one of which identifies a par-ticular orbit, are known as *quan-tum numbers*. Thus the quantum number of the smallest orbit is $n = 1$, of the fifth orbit $n = 5$, etc.

With the third postulate Bohr answered the question of what happens when an electron is displaced from one orbit into another. To see this it is now necessary to find how much *energy* the electron has in any given orbit. The electron has kinetic energy ($\frac{1}{2}mv^2$) due to its circular motion, and also has potential energy $(-ee/r)$* due to the electric field of the nucleus. Hence, the total energy of the electron in its orbit r is

$$\text{Energy} = W = \tfrac{1}{2}mv^2 - \frac{e^2}{r}$$

But from Eq. 23.1

$$mv^2 = \frac{e^2}{r}$$

so

$$W = \tfrac{1}{2}\frac{e^2}{r} - \frac{e^2}{r} = -\frac{e^2}{2r} \qquad\qquad [\,23.4\,]$$

---

* Potential energy is the work which must be done on the electron to move it from its position r cm from the nucleus to infinity. The force being overcome is the Coulomb attraction of the electron by the nucleus. However, the force (ee/r^2) is not constant and there is no elementary way of calculating this work. Consequently, one must resort to calculus to obtain the correct result. This problem was also encountered in deriving Eq. 12.3.

(The negative sign means that work must be done *on* the electron to move it away from the nucleus—its ability to do work in the direction of increasing r is negative, at infinity its P.E. is zero.) Equation 23.4 can be put in terms of fundamental constants by substituting the expression for r, Eq. 23.3.

Then
$$W = -\tfrac{1}{2}e^2\frac{4\pi^2me^2}{n^2h^2} = -\frac{2\pi^2me^4}{n^2h^2}$$
[23.5]

We see that the larger the orbit (represented by n) the less work we would have to do to remove the electron from the atom—as we expected from simple reasoning. The electron has more energy the farther out from the nucleus it gets (it has less negative energy, we have to do less work on it) rising to the surface of zero energy, as it were. For it to move from an inner orbit to an outer one this additional energy must be supplied externally; conversely, if the electron returns from an outer to an inner orbit, it must give up the energy difference between the two orbits. How does an electron "give up" energy in moving to an inner orbit?

Third postulate: When an electron makes a transition from an outer orbit of energy W_o to an inner orbit W_i a quantum of electromagnetic radiation is emitted, of energy $h\nu = W_o - W_i$. This postulate is bold, for in one step it denies Maxwell's theory of the radiation of an accelerated electron. Bohr has postulated that the only way the electron can radiate is to change orbits; in any given orbit, even though it is accelerating (centripetal acceleration) the electron is *not* radiating. Hence, the orbit of lowest energy ($n = 1$) is a *stable* orbit in which the electron can move indefinitely without loss of energy. We have avoided the suicide of the accelerated electron which Maxwell's electromagnetic theory predicted by the arbitary device of denying that a quantized electron radiates so long as it remains in its quantized orbit. Yet at the risk of confusion, let us hasten to get on record that we have not completely discarded Maxwell's ideas. A *free* electron *does* radiate when accelerated, but it *does not* when it is a part of the structure of the atom. We are discovering, as we shall continue to re-discover, that classical (pre-Planck) laws of particles often must suffer change and revision when applied to atomic structure.

To return to the third postulate, let us put it in mathematical form. Calling n_o the quantum number of an *outer* orbit, n_i of an *inner* orbit, we can write Eq. 23.5

$$\text{Energy in outer orbit} = W_o = -\left(\frac{2\pi^2me^4}{h^2}\right)\frac{1}{n_o^2}$$

$$\text{Energy in inner orbit} = W_i = -\left(\frac{2\pi^2me^4}{h^2}\right)\frac{1}{n_i^2}$$

Then
$$hv = W_0 - W_1$$

$$hv = \frac{2\pi^2 me^4}{h^2}\left(\frac{1}{n_i^2} - \frac{1}{n_0^2}\right) \quad \text{(third postulate)} \qquad [23.6]$$

Since spectrometers are usually calibrated for wave length, rather than frequency, we write

$$v = \frac{c}{\lambda}$$

and
$$\frac{hc}{\lambda} = \frac{2\pi^2 me^4}{h^2}\left(\frac{1}{n_i^2} - \frac{1}{n_0^2}\right)$$

or
$$\frac{1}{\lambda} = \frac{2\pi^2 me^4}{ch^3}\left(\frac{1}{n_i^2} - \frac{1}{n_0^2}\right) \qquad [23.7]$$

Equation 23.7 agreed exactly with the known empirical formula for the wave lengths of the hydrogen spectral lines. In addition it predicted a spectrum

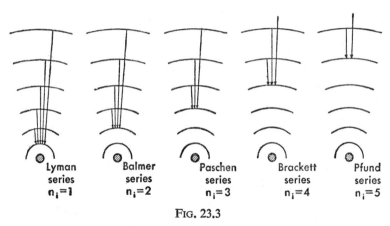

Lyman series $n_i=1$ Balmer series $n_i=2$ Paschen series $n_i=3$ Brackett series $n_i=4$ Pfund series $n_i=5$

Fig. 23.3

(for $n_i = 1$) which was not discovered until the following year; and most remarkable it predicted the wave lengths of the light radiated by the hydrogen atom from a collection of known constants and some assumed quantum numbers. Whenever the electron moves inward from some orbit n_0 to some inner orbit n_i a certain wave length of light must be radiated.

The dominant term in Eq. 23.7 is $1/n_i^2$, since for a given value of n_i the general spectral region for the various transitions $n_0 \rightarrow n_i$ is the same, while for different values of n_i the whole set of lines lies in a different spectral region. This was the fortunate circumstance which allowed the lines to be empirically arranged in series, each series corresponding to a given inner orbit or final energy state of the atom. The several series are shown in Fig. 23.3 together with the names of their discoverers.

We can calculate the constant coefficient of Eq. 23.7:

$$\frac{2\pi^2 me^4}{ch^3} = \frac{2\pi^2 \times 9.11 \times 10^{-28} \times (4.80 \times 10^{-10})^4}{3.00 \times 10^{10} \times (6.62 \times 10^{-27})^3} = 1.10 \times 10^5 \text{ per cm}$$

By letting $n_i = 1$ and $n_0 = 2, 3, 4, 5, 6$, etc., we calculate the wave lengths of the *Lyman series*, which lies in the far ultraviolet. For $n_i = 2$ and $n_0 = 3, 4, 5, 6$, etc., we get the *Balmer series*, the first three members of which are in the visible spectrum and easily measured (Fig. 23.4). *The measurements confirm*

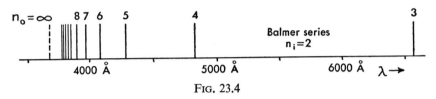

FIG. 23.4

Eq. 23.7 to within the accuracy of the constant coefficient! In fact, all the hydrogen lines predicted by Bohr theory have been found and measured; prediction in every case has been experimentally confirmed. Both the Lyman and Pfund series were discovered after Bohr's predictions.

23.5   Considerations of the Bohr Model

It might be profitable at this point to summarize the Bohr model of the hydrogen atom. It has one electron (1/1837 the total mass) rotating about a positively charged nucleus, with the centripetal force supplied by the electrostatic attraction (first postulate). The electron's angular momentum is quantized, which thus allows only certain specified orbits to exist (second postulate); these orbits are specified by integers, quantum numbers. The atom radiates energy only when the electron moves from an outer to an inner orbit, this energy being just one quantum, $h\nu$ (third postulate). The model answers no questions about why this happens, or about how the electron gets from one orbit to another. Furthermore, it gives no explanation of how the quantum radiated could have the properties of a wave, but it is startlingly successful in explaining the hydrogen atomic spectrum, and predicts a reasonable size for the hydrogen atom—all done using apparently unrelated constants.

It gave satisfaction on another point. The absorption spectrum (§19.7) of an element proved that an atom will absorb the same frequencies it radiates. On the Bohr model the absorption of energy is accomplished when the electron is displaced from an inner to an outer orbit; it may then return by radiating this energy. If the conservation of energy still holds in the atom (and that is one of the macrophysical laws that has required no modification) then the energy radiated must be just the energy absorbed, as is experimentally observed. The absorption in the original beam results since on re-emission light waves go in all directions and the re-emitted light in the original beam is small. This was further checked by a different kind of experiment. The hydrogen electron is normally in its smallest orbit ($n = 1$), for there it has the least energy. The state of least energy of an atom is called its *ground state* (it has hit bottom and has no further energy to radiate). If the electron is displaced to an outer orbit the atom is said to be in an *excited state* (it has been endowed with energy, as it were). The Bohr model demands that the excitation energy be quantized—to displace an electron to a given orbit requires a definite, fixed amount of energy. Suppose this energy of excitation be supplied by collisions with a stream of electrons moving through the hydrogen. In order for hydrogen to radiate the first line (1215 Å) of the Lyman series ($n_o = 2$, $n_i = 1$) these electrons require an energy which we can readily calculate from quantum theory:

$$\lambda = 1215 \times 10^{-8} \text{ cm}$$
$$W = h\nu$$
$$= \frac{hc}{\lambda}$$
$$= 6.62 \times 10^{-27} \times \frac{3.00 \times 10^{10}}{1215 \times 10^{-8}}$$
$$= 1.63 \times 10^{-11} \text{ ergs}$$

1 electron volt $= 16 \times 10^{-13}$ ergs so

$$W = \frac{1.63 \times 10^{-11}}{16 \times 10^{-13}} = 10.2 \text{ ev}$$

The energy of the bombarding electrons is accurately controlled by the difference of potential through which they are accelerated. It was found that the 1215-Å line did not appear in the hydrogen spectrum until the bombarding electrons had 10.2 ev; increasing their energy brought in the higher members of the series in succession, clear evidence of the quantized nature of the atom.

Still another demand we can put on the Bohr atom is to explain the existence of continuous spectra, for even hydrogen has continuous spectra. Suppose a collision, either by a bombarding electron or by another atom (gas discharge) forces the electron *completely out of the atom*. In other words, suppose the atom is ionized. Being positive, the ion is prepared to capture a passing "free" electron; when it does so the captured electron will sink to the ground state orbit either in one jump or in several. In so doing, the amount of energy it will radiate as a quantum will be the difference in energies of the outermost orbit ($n = \infty$) and that orbit in which it rests *plus* any kinetic energy it had when it was captured. The kinetic energy of a free electron is not quantized; it can have any value (remember the continuous distribution of thermal velocities revealed in kinetic theory).

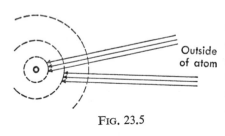

Outside of atom

FIG. 23.5

Hence, though a single captured electron will have a unique kinetic energy, another electron will have a slightly higher or lower kinetic energy. The result of millions of such captures by millions of positive ions will be the radiation of a continuous spectrum of quanta of all energies rather than a series of lines. It is evident that for hydrogen there should be several regions of continuous spectra, each one corresponding to the capture of a free electron into a particular orbit (Fig. 23.5); each will lie on the high-frequency side of a particular series, since the continuum of kinetic energies represents greater energy than the outermost orbit. All these continuous spectra are observed exactly as predicted.

23.6 Nuclear Mass Effect and Isotopic Spectra

In Bohr's first postulate, as we have presented it, the electron is supposed to move around the nucleus as a fixed center. In fact, this is not exactly true, both electron and nucleus rotate dumbbell fashion about a point somewhere between them (Fig. 23.6). If the electron and nucleus were of the same mass, it is clear from the symmetry that this point would be halfway between the two. However, as the nucleus is the more massive, the

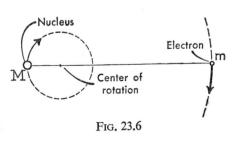

FIG. 23.6

center of rotation is quite near to the nucleus, and the electron's orbit and energy are only slightly altered from the values of Eq. 23.3 and Eq. 23.5.

The easiest way to correct for this effect is to replace the true electron mass m by a fictitious mass slightly less than m by an amount depending on the nuclear mass. Thus the constant term in Eq. 23.7 depends on the nuclear mass as well as electron mass, being smaller for light nuclei. This was first observed by comparing the Balmer series of hydrogen with the spectrum of ionized helium (helium atom minus one electron), which also can be treated by the Bohr theory. In 1932 the nuclear mass effect led to the discovery of *heavy hydrogen* (mass number 2). The effect appears in many other spectra where more than one isotopic species is present, and several new isotopes have been discovered in this manner. By careful measurement of these isotope shifts the masses of the isotopes can be determined.

23.7 The Electron Spin

Long before the advent of the Bohr theory it was known that many spectral lines consisted of two very close lying components. For example the first Balmer line at 6563 Å appears as two lines separated by 0.14 Å. In other

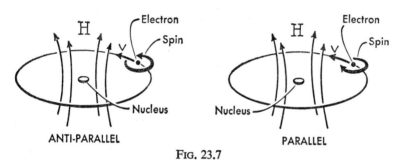

ANTI-PARALLEL   PARALLEL

FIG. 23.7

atoms the separation is larger and easily seen with simple spectrographs. For example, the yellow sodium line consists of two components separated by 6 Å. In 1925 this doubling was explained in terms of a new property of the electron, its *spin*.

Consider the electron spinning around a central axis. As such it constitutes an electric current of small dimensions and generates a magnetic field (see §14.5) as if it were a small magnet lined up with the axis of spin. Now when a classical magnet is placed in a magnetic field it tends to line up with the field. The spinning electron, by reason of quantum properties, has two stable positions in a magnetic field, either parallel or anti-parallel. In the atom such a magnetic field is produced by the *orbital* motion of the electron, similar to a current loop (Fig. 23.7). Thus the spinning electron in this field has two stable positions, and each energy state is doubled by the electron spin. The spectral lines arising from transitions between such states are double.

23.8 Electron Shells and Valency

The Bohr model's successes were not limited to the prediction and correlation of spectra but were of much wider scope. Bohr proposed, on the basis of quantum properties, that the electrons in atoms heavier than hydrogen are arranged in orbits or *shells*. This scheme satisfied the needs of both spectroscopy and of chemistry, as indeed any successful atomic theory must, and predicted the electron arrangements responsible for chemical valency.*

Bohr's shell model was based on a rule deduced from the study of spectra and provides that: (1) possible electron shells are numbered by a quantum number n where $n = 1, 2, 3 \cdots$; (2) no shell may contain more than $2n^2$ electrons; (3) the shells are generally filled in sequence since this procedure results in the lowest energy for a given atom, i.e., if filled otherwise the atom would radiate and transfer to the lowest energy state; (4) a filled shell is chemically inert.

Starting with hydrogen, the ground state shell is $(n = 1)$ and contains but one electron. Helium has two electrons in the $(n = 1)$ shell and fills it $(2 \times 1^2 = 2)$. Helium is, of course, chemically inert. Lithium has two electrons in the $(n = 1)$ shell and one in the $(n = 2)$ shell, and has a valence of 1 as a result of its outer $(n = 2)$ electron. Beryllium has two $(n = 1)$ electrons and two $(n = 2)$ electrons and a valence of 2. The $(n = 2)$ shell is filled with $(2 \times 2^2 = 8)$ electrons which occurs for neon which has 8 $(n = 2)$ electrons, 2 $(n = 1)$ electrons, and is chemically inert. Addition of one more electron results in sodium (atomic number 11), a single electron in the $n = 3$ shell, and sodium's well-known valence of 1.†

This correlation with chemical valency continues throughout the periodic table (see Table E). Thus the first column contains all the atoms with one electron in an unfilled shell, the second column has those with two such electrons. The seventh column has those with one electron less than is necessary to fill a shell, e.g., fluorine has $2(n = 1)$ electrons and $7(n = 2)$ electrons. The eighth column contains the chemically inert noble gases with their filled shells.

The formation of salts such as NaCl is the lending of an electron by sodium to chlorine resulting in "filled" shells for both atoms. This is spoken of as

---

* The chemical valence of an atom is the number of electrons in the outer shell (+ valence) or the number required to fill the outer shell (− valence.) In some cases fewer electrons than the valence number are involved in chemical combinations.

† It might be asked why argon with 2 $(n = 1)$ electrons, 8 $(n = 2)$ electrons and only 8 $(n = 3)$ electrons (rather than 18) is also a noble gas. We have oversimplified the existence of the particularly stable *subshells*, which are responsible for this fact.

ionic binding—Na$^+$ to Cl$^-$. The model also predicts other chemical facts whose discussion would be out of place here.

23.9 X-Ray Line Spectra

The Bohr theory is successful in predicting the main features of x-ray line spectra (§22.5). X rays occur, of course, only when the target is composed of heavy atoms. The frequency of the x-ray lines increases with increasing atomic number. These facts are made clear if we assume that x-ray line spectra result from electron transitions to the *inner* orbits of heavy atoms (Fig. 23.8).

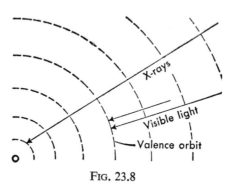

FIG. 23.8

In an x-ray tube the bombarding electrons may knock out an electron from an inner shell, e.g., the ($n = 1$) shell, leaving a sort of internally ionized atom. Immediately this inner gap is filled by an electron from an outer shell, emitting an x-ray quantum in the process. Several alternative inner and outer shells are possible for the transition giving rise to several different x-ray lines.

To gain some idea of the frequencies emitted in such processes consider a heavy atom of atomic number Z. Disregarding the effects of the other electrons, Bohr's first postulate would read $Ze^2/r^2 = mv^2/r$. Indeed, each e referring to the hydrogen nucleus is replaced by Ze so that the energy of the electron state is (by Eq. 23.5)

$$W = - \frac{2\pi^2 me^4}{n^2 h^2} Z^2 = - 13.6 \, Z^2 \text{ electron volts}$$

To remove an electron from the ($n = 1$) shell of copper ($Z = 29$) thus requires $13.5 \times (29)^2 = 11,400$ ev (as compared with 13.5 ev for hydrogen) on this model, and the bombarding electron must have at least this amount of energy to accomplish the process. Transitions between inner shells of moderately heavy atoms will be in the range of several tens of thousands of electron volts. Since 10^4 ev $= 16 \times 10^{-9}$ ergs, a transition giving up 10^4 ev produces a quantum ($W = h\nu$) of wave length

$$\lambda = \frac{c}{\nu} = \frac{hc}{W} = \frac{6.6 \times 10^{-27} \times 3.0 \times 10^{10}}{16 \times 10^{-9}} = 1.2 \text{ Å}$$

The highest frequency x-ray lines result from transitions to the inner ($n = 1$) shell when an electron has been removed from that shell. This is called the "K series" and is somewhat analogous to the hydrogen Lyman series. It is clear that the frequencies of the K lines will increase as Z^2, which is in accord with experiment.

It should be apparent that there is no fundamental distinction between x rays and visible light except for their wave length. Each is born when an electron undergoes a transition between orbits; if the final orbit is a valence orbit the quantum is visible (or near the visible region), if an inner orbit an x-ray quantum is produced. Indeed the hydrogen Lyman series is the x-ray spectrum of hydrogen.

23.10 Failures of the Bohr Theory

The Bohr theory quantitatively explained the spectra of hydrogen and the other one electron atoms (ions) He$^+$, Li^{++}, etc. However, neutral helium has two electrons, and the question now arises: which electron undergoes transition or is it both? This question becomes even more acute for an atom such as fluorine which has *seven* valence electrons. Do six of them remain quiet and leave the seventh to radiate quanta, or do they interact in some manner? For these questions the Bohr theory, even with modification, had few unambiguous answers. It was still quite useful for the "hydrogen like" elements, i.e., the alkali metals (column I of the periodic table, Table E) which had only one valence electron; even here, however, a problem of the interpenetration of orbits arose.

Consequently, ten years after the announcement of the Bohr theory the verdict on its progress was roughly this: It works well with the hydrogen and ionized helium spectra, fairly well with the other monovalent atoms, but not at all well with the atoms of higher valency. Also, a certain uneasiness existed about the arbitrariness of the Bohr postulates; they were not to be condemned on that basis, but they were an object of questioning. That they transgressed Maxwell's electromagnetic theory ("an accelerated electron must radiate") was no crime, for this theory gave incorrect answers in atomic problems. Yet it was disturbing that a *free* electron does radiate when accelerated, but one bound into an atom does not.

Most of the answers to these inadequacies have been supplied by the newer theory of quantum mechanics which, as mentioned earlier in the chapter, offers no atomic model, but does supply a method of calculation. In the next chapter we shall see the basic starting point for quantum mechanics.

PROBLEMS

1. Assuming the diameter of an atom is of the order of 1 Å, the diameter of the nucleus 10^{-12} cm, and that each is spherical, find the ratio of the volume of the atom to that of the nucleus.   *Ans.* 10^{12}.

2. The nucleus of the hydrogen atom is thought to have a radius of 1.5×10^{-13} cm. If it were magnified to 0.1 mm (a grain of dust) how far away would the ground state electron be?   *Ans.* 3.5 m.

3. On the Bohr theory what is the orbital velocity of the ground state ($n = 1$) electron of the hydrogen atom?   *Ans.* 2.2×10^8 cm/sec.

4. Calculate the wave lengths of the first three lines of the Balmer series.
                                  Ans. 6563 Å, 4861 Å, 4340 Å.

5. Compute the ionization potential (energy in ev required to ionize an atom in its ground state) of the hydrogen atom. (The coefficient term in Eq. 23.6 is 2.17×10^{-11} ergs.)   *Ans.* 13.6 ev.

6. Upon losing one electron by ionization helium becomes a one-electron atom and obeys the Bohr theory. Compute the radius of the innermost He+ orbit. (Hint: Rewrite Eq. 23.1 for a nucleus with charge ($+ 2e$), and combine with Eq. 23.2.)
                                  Ans. 0.265×10^{-8} cm.

7. List the electron populations in the shells of the inert gas atoms: Helium, neon, argon, and krypton.

Suggested Reading

BORN, MAX, "The Restless Universe," London, Blackie & Son, 1935.
    Chapter IV on the Bohr atom. Clear, simple.

"Foundations of Nuclear Physics," New York, Dover Publications, 1949.
    Page 111, facsimile of Rutherford's paper proposing the nuclear atom. Parts can be read easily.

GERLACH, W., "Matter, Electricity, Energy," New York, D. Van Nostrand Co., 1928.
    Chapter XVI sums up very well the nature of energy transitions in the Bohr atom.

The Duality of Waves and Particles

24.1 The Birth of Light "Particles" and Particle "Waves"

At the present juncture it is well to review and consolidate our picture of the quantum of radiation, since we shall see shortly that this picture has been greatly expanded. From its invention by Planck in the theory of hot-solid radiation (1900) to Bohr's theory of line spectra (1913) the quantum of radiation appeared only in connection with the *emission* and *absorption* of radiation by matter. New quantum processes were discovered in this period, but the quanta themselves gained no new properties of importance. Thus in the emission of a hydrogen spectrum line the electron in the atom gives up energy which is radiated as a light quantum of a particular frequency, $\nu = (W_0 - W_i)/h$, but except for its frequency nothing about the quantum is specified. In photoelectric emission a quantum disappears when its energy transfers to an electron in the photocathode; the quantum enters the theory only by virtue of its energy $h\nu$. We were led by all this to think of a light wave as a stream of quanta—a spectral line is not a continuous wave but a collection of limited waves, each of the same frequency, each from a single radiating atom, and each associated with one quantum. But this picture is not demanded by the theories mentioned, for they are concerned only with the birth and death of quanta, and we may entertain various ideas of their existence in-between.

Until 1923 no evidence existed which bore directly on the properties of "free" quanta, or *photons* as they are called to distinguish the quantum of radiation, $h\nu$, from other quantized quantities, e.g., Bohr's quantized angular momentum and energy in atoms, the electronic quantum of charge e, and others. However, in that year A. H. Compton found that photons could undergo a *change of frequency* upon being scattered and that this could be explained by assigning mechanical properties (limited extension and momentum) to the photons. This revolutionary discovery answered many of the questions about individual quanta in their free state.

The photon's mechanical properties are on an entirely different level from its role as an electromagnetic wave. Interference, for example, is by virtue of these waves, as is the ordinary scattering of light and x rays by particles (ordinary in the sense that frequencies are unchanged). Even the association of momentum with a wave is not a quantum effect, for light pressure is observed and is explained on Maxwell's theory as the momentum change caused by the reflection of the waves. But in all wave theory there is no possi-

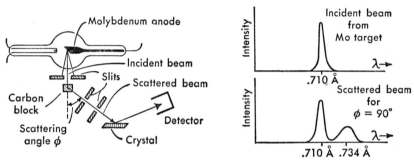

FIG. 24.1

bility of a wave changing its frequency in the manner of the Compton effect. This must be viewed as resulting from the particle nature of the photons.

Shortly following this revolution in the theory of light, Louis de Broglie proposed in 1924 that *particles* would have a "wave length" and might exhibit interference effects. In 1926, Schroedinger extended these ideas to the electrons in atoms, and in representing them as waves he found that quantization of the atom's energy was a natural result of the necessity of standing wave patterns in the electron's stable "orbits." In 1927, Davisson and Germer first detected the wave properties of free particles when they observed the interference pattern produced by a beam of electrons diffracted by a crystal, verifying both the existence of particle waves and de Broglie's formula for their wave length. Thus the pattern of the wave-particle duality was complete; light waves had particle properties, and atomic particles had wave properties.

24.2   The Momentum of Photons—Compton Effect

Compton was studying the scattering of x rays when he discovered that their frequency could be changed in the scattering process. His experiments were generally like those of previous workers which were designed to incorporate x-ray scattering into the scheme of electromagnetic theory, but unlike previous workers, he employed an x-ray spectrometer to measure accurately the wave lengths in the scattered beam. In addition to the wave length of the incident radiation he found that part of the scattered beam had a longer, but definite, wave length. His experimental arrangement is shown in Fig. 24.1. The anode of the x-ray tube was molybdenum, and one of the K lines (0.710 Å) of molybdenum was used as the incident beam. The long wave length satellite in the scattered beam was detected for various scattering angles, and its wave length was found to depend on the scattering angle, al-

FIG. 24.2

though *not* on the incident wave length or the scattering material. He proposed that this long wave-length line was due to photon collisions with the electrons in the scattering material. The electrons were treated as being at rest before the collisions and free, i.e., unbound to the carbon or other atoms in the scatterer, and the photons were given energy $h\nu$ and momentum $h\nu/c$ in the theory.* Collisions were supposed to be elastic, the photon and electron comprising a two-particle system obeying the conservation of energy and of momentum.

The details of the calculation of the long wave-length shift are most simply carried out for a scattering angle of 90°. Consider this case as shown in Fig. 24.2. We proceed by writing the formulas for energy and momentum conservation. It is clear that the x-component momentum obeys the equation

$$\frac{h\nu}{c} = mv_x$$

and for the y-component momentum

$$\frac{h\nu'}{c} = mv$$

---

* A relativistic particle moving with approximately the velocity of light has a total energy mc^2 and a momentum mc; thus in this case, momentum = energy/c. Consequently one is led to assign a momentum $h\nu/c$ to the photon. One might even assign a mass = momentum/velocity = $h\nu/c^2$ to the photon. However, the photon has *no rest mass*, and such a procedure is somewhat artificial.

where ν' is the frequency of the scattered quantum. Energy conservation is given by the formula (neglecting relativistic effects)

$$h\nu = h\nu' + \tfrac{1}{2}mv^2$$

Since $v^2 = v_x^2 + v_y^2$ we have from the momentum formulas that

$$v^2 = \left(\frac{h}{mc}\right)^2 (\nu^2 + \nu'^2)$$

Substituting this into the energy formula,

$$h\nu = h\nu' + \tfrac{1}{2}\frac{h^2}{mc^2}(\nu^2 + \nu'^2)$$

$$\nu - \nu' = \frac{h}{2mc^2}(\nu^2 + \nu'^2)$$

and putting the result in terms of the x-ray wave lengths $\lambda = c/\nu$ and $\lambda' = c/\nu'$

$$\frac{1}{\lambda} - \frac{1}{\lambda'} = \frac{h}{2mc}\left(\frac{1}{\lambda^2} + \frac{1}{\lambda'^2}\right)$$

$$\lambda' - \lambda = \frac{h}{2mc}\frac{\lambda'^2 + \lambda^2}{\lambda\lambda'}$$

Since the shift in wave length $(\lambda' - \lambda)$ is quite small in comparison with the wave length λ itself, $\lambda'^2 = \lambda^2$ approximately and

$$\lambda' - \lambda = \frac{h}{mc} \quad \text{(approximately)}$$

$$= \frac{6.6 \times 10^{-27}}{9.1 \times 10^{-28} \times 3.0 \times 10^{10}} = 0.024 \text{ Å}$$

This is exactly the wave-length shift as found by experiment for 90° scattering. At smaller scattering angles the shift is less, becoming zero at $\phi = 0°$; at larger scattering angles the shift increases to a maximum at $\phi = 180°$ (back-scattering) where it attains the value $2h/mc$. The quantity h/mc is sometimes called the Compton wave length.

As a result of these experiments and the theory above, it was clear that photons exist as particles—they are localized in space and have momentum. In collisions they behave purely as particles, their wave properties seemingly play no part; and yet they are particles of a unique sort since they have no rest mass. If it is difficult for us to picture a particle without rest mass undergoing a collision, that is simply a weakness we display in wanting a picture from ordinary experience. The photon's *true* nature includes *both* its wave and its particle properties; we simply describe it as a composite of these two entities borrowed from macrophysics.

It might be asked at this point whether all radiation quanta display the properties of x-ray photons. Is there a Compton effect for visible light? We must admit that there is none observed. This is not a deficiency in the photon picture and is readily explained by the theory. It is because there are no electrons free enough for Compton collisions with visible-light photons; the binding of the atomic electrons is not negligible in comparison with the quantum energy as it is for the energetic x-ray photons. This binding reduces the probability of Compton scattering as the wave length increases, until in the region of soft x rays the Compton line is very weak. On further decrease of the quantum frequency it disappears. Meanwhile, as the frequency decreases, the probability of ordinary, i.e., frequency unchanged, scattering increases, so that in the optical region the transition to ordinary scattering is complete.

24.3 The Wave Nature of Particles—de Broglie

As in the case of the birth of the quantum of radiation, the wave nature of particles originated in theory rather than experiment. It was first predicted by Louis de Broglie in 1924. De Broglie was much concerned by the fact that although the quantum theory arose as a description of radiation, Bohr had shown that it must be extended to the motion of atomic particles. Might not the quantum theory which introduced the photon to complement the electromagnetic wave be inverted to endow atomic particles with wave properties? In essence, is there an analogy of the wave-particle dualism of light in the theory of particles?

Such an analogy can be constructed by considering the fundamental relation

$$\text{Momentum} = \frac{\text{Energy}}{\text{Velocity}} = \frac{h\nu}{c} = \frac{h}{\lambda}$$

which relates the wave, i.e., λ, and the particle (momentum) properties of light quanta. In the case of particles de Broglie proposed an analogous relation,

$$\text{Momentum} = mv = \frac{h}{\lambda}$$

or

$$\lambda = \frac{h}{mv}$$

where m is the particle mass, v its velocity, and λ the *de Broglie wave length* of the particle.

It is instructive to calculate from this expression the wave length of a particle. The heavier the particle, or the greater its velocity, the shorter will be its associated wave length. Let us choose an electron having 1000 ev of energy (see §17.10). Its velocity is 1.88×10^9 cm/sec, its mass 9.1×10^{-28} gm, and $h = 6.6 \times 10^{-27}$ erg-sec:

$$\lambda = \frac{6.6 \times 10^{-27}}{9.1 \times 10^{-28} \times 1.88 \times 10^9} = 0.38 \times 10^{-8} \text{ cm} = 0.38 \text{ Å}$$

which is of the order of short x rays. For 100-ev electrons $\lambda = 1.2$ Å. In view of the diffraction of x rays these are reasonable wave lengths to measure, to confirm or deny de Broglie's idea. Its striking confirmation came with the work of Davisson and Germer in the United States, followed by G. P. Thomson in England.

24.4 Davisson-Germer Experiment

To prove experimentally the existence of the matter waves associated with a particle, Davisson and Germer in 1927 employed the same idea that had proved light to be a wave motion, namely, the phenomenon of interference. We have seen (§22.5) that the interference of x rays by a crystal or diffraction grating was the evidence advanced for their wave nature. Since for ordinray energies the de Broglie wave length for an electron is of the order of 1 Å or shorter, a crystal (whose atom spacing is 1 Å or so) should cause interference of electrons.

The experimental procedure is indicated in Fig. 24.3. The regular array of nickel atoms of the crystal serve the same role as the slits in a diffraction grating. The collector consisted of a hollow cylinder which caught the scattered electrons. A galvanometer measured the electron current thus collected. The collector could be swung in an arc from left to right. *A pattern similar to an optical diffraction pattern was obtained.* Knowing the crystal spacing (the *d* of

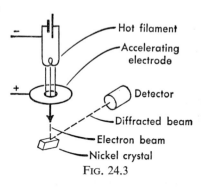

Hot filament

Accelerating electrode

Detector

Diffracted beam

Electron beam

Nickel crystal

FIG. 24.3

the optical grating case) and the angle of diffraction, Davisson and Germer were able to calculate the wave length of the electron wave; the momentum of the electron was determined from the known acceleration voltage and substituted in de Broglie's theoretical expression. The predicted and measured wave lengths agreed! An electron has a readily detectable wave associated with it.

G. P. Thomson used a somewhat different arrangement (Fig. 24.4). A very thin foil of a metal allowed the electrons to penetrate through and onto a photographic plate. Figure 24.4 shows schematically the apparatus and the pattern obtained. Thomson's wave-length measurements likewise confirmed de Broglie's predictions. Particles—electrons—can undergo interference just as light can be made to interfere. There is a symmetry in the duality—both light waves and material particles behave as waves and as particles simultaneously. The following table collects the results of the wave-particle dualism for light waves and atomic particles:

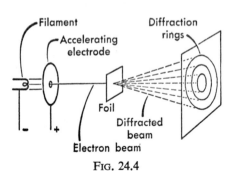

FIG. 24.4

	LIGHT WAVES	PARTICLES
Energy	$h\nu$	$\frac{1}{2}mv^2$
Momentum	$h\nu/c$	mv
Wave length	c/ν	h/mv

24.5   The Interpretation of Particle Waves

De Broglie's formula, $\lambda = h/mv$, contains a mixture of wave properties, λ, and particle properties, mv, and the inevitable quantum label, h. And if v is the particle velocity, as experiment indicates, what then is the wave velocity? We would naturally answer that since the wave is associated with the particle, it must move along with it; and v must be its velocity also. However, ordinary waves do not transport themselves bodily from place to place; they are continuous disturbances which are periodic in space and time. Yet a continuous disturbance filling space is hardly a suitable particle model for it is not localized as a particle must be. How, then, may a wave be localized?

In the theories of light and sound localized wave disturbances such as light flashes and whistle blasts are treated by the principle of wave interference applied to a set of waves of different wave lengths. One assigns to a whistle blast a set of sound waves of various wave lengths ranging around some average value, say λ_0, and constructs the interference pattern of the set in the usual manner of interference phenomena. However, here the pattern is not fixed in space but progresses in the direction of the wave propagation as a pulse or *wave packet* of interference maxima. That is, at each instant the interference maxima are like those of a fixed interference pattern, but the presence of a range of wave lengths causes the maxima to move in the direction of the waves. Such a wave packet is illustrated in Fig. 24.5, moving to the right with velocity v; λ_0 is the average wave length in the packet. Outside the packet there is complete destructive interference to both the right and the left.

With this model in mind let us describe an atomic particle as a wave packet. The particle velocity is the wave packet velocity and the de Broglie wave length is some one of the wave packet wave lengths. Which wave length, we are not yet prepared to say, because of the following complication.

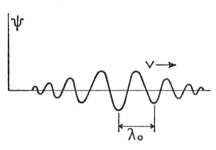

In light propagation in ordinary media, waves of various wave length move with the same velocity. This is

FIG. 24.5

also true for sound waves. Thus the pulse velocity and the ordinary wave velocity are the same. However, in the de Broglie formula λ is strongly dependent on the pulse velocity v, and also on the ordinary wave velocity. There is both a spread in λ and in the ordinary wave velocities in the pulse and no *exact* correlation between a *particular* wave length in the pulse and the pulse velocity. There is an inherent "fuzziness" in the wave packet model; there is no *particular* wave length describing the wave packet but a range of wave lengths, and for a given wave length there is no *particular* particle velocity since this velocity depends on the whole set of wave lengths making up the pulse.

Against the background of classical physics this vagary seems to discredit the wave packet model; but as we shall see it is not the model which is at fault—there is a basic uncertainty in atomic physics of which this is an example.

24.6   The Uncertainty Principle

In 1927 Heisenberg showed that there is a basic uncertainty in atomic physics which is the result of *measurement* itself, a sort of fundamental limit to the precision with which atomic processes can be described. In one form the principle states:

The process of measurement forces an atomic system into a particular state such that the more accurately the velocity is measured the less accurately is the position defined, and the more accurately the position is measured the less accurately is the velocity defined.

The product of these inherent uncertanities is

$$\Delta x \cdot \Delta v \cong \frac{h}{m}$$

where Δx and Δv are the limits of uncertainty of the position and velocity.

This uncertainty is inherent in the wave packet model of a particle. Consider a free electron's wave packet, composed of a set of continuous waves adding to produce a moving interference maximum (the electron) which carries the mass and charge of the electron along in some manner. Suppose we wish to define its position with great precision, i.e., to make the packet shorter. We must add more waves to the packet, and since we recall that each of the component waves must have a different wave length in order to produce a packet, it is clear that there will be a spread of wave lengths in the packet; and this means a spread of velocities, since each wave length has a different velocity according to the de Broglie formula. Furthermore, the more localized the wave packet the greater this spread of velocities, until for complete precision in position the velocities spread over all values. Thus, complete knowledge of the position x destroys all knowledge of the velocity $v;$ $\Delta x = 0$ but $\Delta v = \infty$. Having failed to localize the position except at the expense of uncertainty in the velocity, suppose we try the reverse. We eliminate more and more waves from the packet until the wave velocity is known with high precision. But our packet has spread meanwhile until it fills all space, i.e., if $\Delta v = 0$ then $\Delta x = \infty$. These are the two extreme cases of Heisenberg's uncertainty relation. We shall now see that the general magnitude of h/m in the uncertainty principle is easily derived from the wave packet model. A spread in position of Δx requires a spread in wave lengths, $\Delta \lambda$ of the same magnitude, and from the de Broglie formula this implies a spread in the velocity of the order of $h/m\Delta x$, so that $\Delta v \cong h/m\Delta x$ or

$$\Delta v \cdot \Delta x \cong \frac{h}{m}$$

We see that an observation may force certainty on an observable of an atomic system, but in doing so it produces uncertainty in some other possible observable.

24.7   Heisenberg's Illustration of the Uncertainty Principle

In treating the electron as a wave packet and showing the plausibility of the uncertainty principle it was not entirely clear as to what was meant by localizing the electron's position or velocity; measurements were implied, but their specific nature was not given. This is an important consideration, for the uncertainty principle is the result of the process of measurement itself. Thus a specific example is in order.

We shall imagine a hypothetical experiment. The essence of the experiment is simple. We wish to measure the "state" of an electron, by which we mean its position and its velocity. Since this is a hypothetical experiment we shall employ a hypothetical super-microscope that can magnify the electron to a visible size. However, the light used to illuminate our electron must have a wave length comparable to the dimension of the electron, for a wave length larger than electron would not be reflected appreciably, and hence would fail to betray its presence. Though we are not at all sure of the diameter of the electron (or even if it has a unique diameter) we would guess it to be no greater than that of the atom since it is a component of atomic structure. This means our source of illumination must have the wave length of x rays, if not shorter. Certainly the shorter the illuminating wave length the sharper will be the image in the microscope and the more accurately can we locate the position of the electron. However, the Compton effect has shown that our x-ray photons will give up momentum to the electron which will change its initial motion by an unpredictable amount. Hence our effort to obtain the position of the electron with great accuracy has denied us the possibility of knowing its motion—its velocity—with accuracy. If we reduce the latter uncertainty by using less energetic photons, the diffuse image which results makes the position less certain. That accurate determinations, even in a hypothetical experiment, are doomed to such failures is the content of the Heisenberg uncertainty principle. Of course, the failure arose from the necessity of illuminating the electron; that is, in trying to measure its position and motion we had to disturb it. At best, we have measured the state of an electron interacting with photons. We still have only a limited knowledge of the state of the electron itself.

Example. A translation of the uncertainty principle into the world of ordinary dynamics is in order, for the principle has been loosely interpreted as undermining all physical measurement and experience. A bullet can be considered as a particle of dimensions, say, 1 cm on a side with a mass of 10 gm and a velocity of 1000 ft/sec $= 3 \times 10^4$ cm/sec. Suppose we measure its velocity to within 1 part in 10^4, i.e., $\Delta v = 3$ cm/sec. Its uncertainty in position is

$$\Delta x = \frac{h}{m \Delta v} = \frac{6.6 \times 10^{-27}}{10 \times 3} = 2 \times 10^{-28} \text{ cm}$$

a totally unmeasurable quantity. Clearly, the uncertainty principle plays no practical part in the dynamics of macroscopic bodies, and no generalizations from such dynamics can either affirm or deny its validity.

24.8   Particle Waves and Probability

The localization of a particle within its wave packet is seen to suffer a lack of precision in comparison with classical models. For this reason the concept of *probability* is introduced to describe with all *possible* precision what we can know about such particles. This probability is usually developed for the position of the particle in the following way.

In ordinary wave theory the wave *intensity* is equal to the square of the wave *amplitude*. If intensity is to mean something for particle waves, it must be related to the amplitude in the same manner. If one takes the probability of finding the particle in a certain range of x as equal to the intensity of the particle wave in that range, the analogy is completed. Suppose for example that ψ (psi) is the wave amplitude of free electron (Fig. 24.5). Suppose it to be equal to ψ_0 in the range of positions from x to $x + \Delta x$. Then $\psi_0^2 \Delta x$ is the probability that the electron is in that range, provided that x has been multiplied by a suitable constant so that $\psi^2 \Delta x$ summed over all x values equals 1, i.e., the *total* probability of finding the electron is unity or 100%. In terms of the wave intensity ψ^2 our discussion of the free particle's wave packet says that $\psi^2 \Delta x$ summed over all x equals unity for a short packet (well-defined position), in which case ψ is large only in a small range of x; for a long packet (well-defined velocity) ψ is smaller but extends over a larger range of x.

In terms of the wave intensity ψ^2, the Thomson experiment (Fig. 24.4) shows that the probability of observing the electron at a certain radius oscillates, being large at the rings and small between rings, this behavior being the result of diffraction of the electron waves.

24.9   Electron Waves in Atoms

The association of waves with particles is not confined to the "free" electron and its wave packet but can be extended to electrons moving in electric and magnetic fields. The first application of this kind was by Schroedinger in 1926 in which he invented the wave equation for a single electron moving in the electric field of the nucleus (the hydrogen atom) and solved the equation to find the wave amplitudes and quantum energies of the atom. This work of Schroedinger's was the beginning of the modern theory called *quantum mechanics*. Since that time quantum mechanics has developed rapidly until at present there is no atomic problem which cannot in principle be solved by its methods, and the only limitations are mathematical complexities which force the use of approximate methods for the solutions of the equations.

Although we cannot digress to examine the methods of Schroedinger's quantum mechanics, it is instructive to see what form the electron waves take in the nuclear electric field. If we think of the stationary states of the hydrogen atom as arising from wave interference, there would be an integral number of de Broglie wave lengths in each of the stationary states; the waves are folded around in a circular "orbit" of radius r, where

$$\text{Orbit circumference} = 2\pi r = n\lambda = n \frac{h}{mv}$$

so that

$$2\pi mvr = nh$$

This is Bohr's quantization of angular momentum viewed in the light of wave mechanics. The $n = 1$ orbit contains but one de Broglie wave length; the $n = 2$ orbit contains two wave lengths, etc.

This view of the atom's stationary states shows only a qualitative feature of the Schroedinger theory. One must include the uncertainty principle and other considerations. When this is done, the hydrogen atom's energies are found to agree with the Bohr theory (and experiment). As might be expected from the uncertainty principle, the wave intensity is not confined to a set of orbits. Figure 24.6 shows the calculated wave intensity for the ground ($n = 1$) state of the hydrogen atom. We see that the wave intensity is a maximum (probability of finding electron greatest) for r = 0.53 A, which is just the radius of the first Bohr orbit. However, the probability is not zero outside or inside this orbit—there is an uncertainty in the electron's position. We might say that the Bohr theory gives too precise an answer; the electron does not stay in its Bohr orbit for its wave "leaks out" on both sides of it.

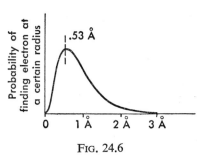

FIG. 24.6

We should not assume from the foregoing discussions that there are no certainties on the atomic scale, for this is far from true. When each physical quantity assignable to an atomic particle or system is examined, it is found that some pairs of quantities can be certain at the same time whereas others (like x and v) cannot. The exact frequencies of spectral lines implies precisely defined energies in the atom (the energy levels). Thus for the radiating atom the energy values are certainties, while the electron's position is uncertain. On the other hand, the energy values are not certain with respect to time; we cannot say precisely *when* the atom radiates.

24.10   Quantum versus Newtonian Mechanics

The material presented in the first two parts of this book—the dynamics of a particle and the electrodynamics of a particle—is part of what is often called "classical" physics; and except for the relativistic modifications it can be described as Newtonian physics, since Newton's laws of motion have been used repeatedly and without exception to describe every type (linear, circular, periodic) of motion encountered. It has been necessary to inquire into the nature of the forces producing these motions, and we have considered linear forces, central forces (such as centripetal force), periodic forces, electrostatic and magnetic forces. We found the influence of some of these forces was often better described in terms of fields, magnetic field, electrostatic field, etc., and the climax of this study of fields was undoubtedly Maxwell's electromagnetic field theory of light. The underlying philosophy of Newtonian physics (§9.10) has been called by the philosophers "mechanistic determinism," that is, the world consists of matter in motion whose behavior is governed rigidly by the "laws" of nature, and the prediction with unlimited accuracy of the characteristics of nature is limited only by man's limited mental processes and measuring techniques. A threatening inroad on this faith of nature's rigid pattern was made by the kinetic theory of gases; for in this theory we can describe the pressure due to a gas only by treating statistically a large number of molecules and can make no statement about an individual molecule. The random nature of collisions between the molecules casts doubt on their determined order of motion—the velocity of a given molecule at a given instant seems more a matter of chance than of plan.

The attack that kinetic theory started has been continued by quantum mechanics with its uncertainty principle. The physical world is not planned to the last infinitesimal detail; it is not possible to predict exactly the position of an electron an instant from now because we don't know its present position or velocity exactly, nor can we ever know this. A school of philosophy has seized on the Heisenberg uncertainty principle as a physical proof of free will, extrapolating it from the limited freedom of action allowed by the uncertainty principle in the world of inanimate particles. Whether this extrapolation from the inanimate to the animate is justified is not for us to decide in this discussion.

What can we say about the onslaught made by quantum mechanics on the laws and theories of Newtonian physics? Mass now exhibits wave properties; energy may have only certain values; light has a granular structure. Is Newtonian mechanics wrong? The answer to this question is made by quantum mechanics itself. Newtonian mechanics is a completely satisfactory approximation in macrophysics; it is only in the finer details of microphysics that its errors are made evident. De Broglie has pointed out that the extent of under-mining of classical physics is all due to the magnitude of Planck's constant h. If h were infinitely small, a quantum of energy would be infinitely small, and we would correctly consider light as a continuous flow. On the other hand, if h had been very large, the quantum nature of light "would leap to the eye of the least attentive physicist" and there would have been no "classical" and "quantum" divisions in physics. Actually, of course, h is very small but not infinitely small. It required the highly ingenious and delicate experiments of the present century to reveal its effects.

PROBLEMS

1. Calculate the momentum of a 5000-Å photon; also of a 0.5-Å photon.
   Ans. 1.32×10^{-22}; 1.32×10^{-18} gm-cm/sec.
2. What is the momentum of a 50,000 ev x-ray photon?
   Ans. 2.67×10^{-18} gm-cm/sec.
3. Write the laws of conservation of momentum and energy for a head-on elastic collision between a photon and an electron at rest.
4. An 0.1-Å x-ray photon undergoes a 90° Compton collision with an electron. What is the wave length of the scattered x ray? *Ans.* 0.124 Å.
5. Show that the de Broglie wave length of a classical particle of mass m and kinetic energy W is given by $\lambda = h/\sqrt{2mW}$.
6. Calculate the de Broglie wave length of an electron which moves with a velocity of 3×10^9 cm/sec (Table 20.1). *Ans.* 0.242 Å.
7. What is the de Broglie wave length of a neutron ($m = 1.67 \times 10^{-24}$ gm) whose energy is 1 ev? *Ans.* 0.286 Å.
8. Show that if the uncertainty in position of a particle is just its de Broglie wave length, then the uncertainty in the particle velocity is equal to the average velocity, in other words, the uncertainty in velocity measurement is 100%.

Suggested Reading

BORN, MAX, "The Restless Universe," London, Blackie & Son, 1935.
   Chapter III. Excellent discussion of quantum theory and the role of prob-ability. Readable.
DE BROGLIE, L., "Matter and Light," New York, W. W. Norton & Co., 1939.
   Popular, non-mathematical book on wave mechanics and its meaning (difficult to assign fragmentary references).

EDDINGTON, SIR ARTHUR, "The Nature of the Physical World," New York, The Macmillan Co., 1933.
  Chapter X contains an illuminating description of the contributions of Schroedinger and Heisenberg.
HEITLER, W., "Elementary Wave Mechanics," Oxford, University Press, 1945.
  Chapters I–II of this delightful book summarize the bases and nature of quantum mechanics. Mathematics may not be understood but physical arguments are very clear.
JORDAN, P., "Physics of the 20th Century," New York, Philosophical Library, 1944.
  Chapter V treats the philosophical content of quantum mechanics.

Natural Radioactivity

25.1 Nuclear Physics

Historically, as well as in the order of this book, the atom has evolved from a kinetic theory projectile to a complex structure of sub-atomic particles, the nucleus and the electrons. The masses and charges of these atomic structures are known; the atomic number Z and atomic mass A describe them completely. The mechanics of the atomic structure, the dynamic stability of the electron waves in the nuclear electric field, the quantization of the electron energies, and the absorption and radiation of quanta as the electron system changes from one quantum state to another are all well established. We have touched only a few of the applications of the new mechanics of the atom—the quantum mechanics of Schroedinger and Heisenberg. It is amazingly successful with its wave functions and energy states, not only in purely internal atomic affairs, but also in all molecular and chemical physics as well. Indeed the whole realm of microphysics in which atoms appear as entities, *atomic physics*, is well understood today, and future progress in this field appears to be largely in the application of quantum mechanics to specific problems.

The atom has acquired a structure and a mechanics. But what of its nucleus, does it also possess a structure? What are the fundamental particles at the present extent of physical knowledge? The electron is one such fundamental particle, according to present day concepts. Are there others, and if so what role do they play in microphysics?

There are, as we recall, 92 naturally occurring chemical elements with atomic numbers (nuclear charges in units of e) ranging from 1 to 92. Their atomic masses are approximately integral numbers if one takes the hydrogen mass as unity (or O^{16} as 16.00) and these masses increase roughly in proportion to the atomic numbers. As we have seen, most elements have several isotopes, differing in mass by one or more mass units from one to the other; and we recall that the atom's mass is largely (about 99.95%) in the nucleus itself. These regularities would seem to suggest that the nucleus itself is a structure of particles of, say, one mass unit each, some of them carrying a unit positive charge as well.

The experimental information and theories which concern the internal structure and internal processes of atomic nuclei comprise *nuclear physics*. The primary components of the nucleus are called *nucleons*. The recent advances into applied nuclear science and technology are sometimes called *nucleonics*.

25.2 The Discovery of Natural Radioactivity

The first evidence of internal processes in nuclei came with the discovery of natural radioactivity by Henri Becquerel in 1896. Its discovery was thus contemporary with the beginnings of atomic physics and the discoveries of x rays and electrons, but its progress has been more complex, its ramifications more numerous. Becquerel was experimenting with phosphorescent compounds (light absorbers which show delayed re-emission); he irradiated them with sunlight and placed them near a photographic plate shielded with black paper to see if they emitted any penetrating radiation. The technique was very similar to Roentgen's in his discovery of x rays in the previous year. One compound tried was a uranium ore; with this Becquerel obtained a fogging of his plate whether the compound had been irradiated with light or not. Without external aid the uranium was emitting rays which could penetrate several layers of paper and affect a photographic plate. We now know, of course, that light-induced phophorescence cannot give the atom enough energy to produce x rays; the connection between Becquerel's discovery and phosphorescence was entirely coincidental. An intensive search in the next few years revealed that the compounds of the elements beyond lead ($Z = 82$) showed similar radiating characteristics. Furthermore, it made no difference in what chemical compound the element occurred, nor could temperature, pressure, or other outside influences discourage the effect; these atoms radiated energy continuously regardless of how they were treated. The phenomenon was called *natural radioactivity*. In the process of investigating the radioactivity of the elements Marie Curie and her husband, Pierre Curie, observed that the ore pitchblende, from which uranium was extracted, showed more activity, that is, would fog a photographic plate faster, than could be explained by its uranium content. In fact, upon chemical separation it become evident that something was being left behind in the pitchblende that was more active than the uranium taken from it. A very careful chemical separation of all the components in pitchblende yielded a new radioactive element, called *polonium* ($Z = 84$) by Madame Curie in honor of her native country, Poland. However, some of the other products of this separation still exhibited strong activity. By a laborious effort the Curies succeeded in isolating a second new element which they named *radium* ($Z = 88$), an element that was exceedingly radioactive.

25.3 Nature of the Nuclear Radiations

The complete understanding of natural radioactivity involved a long and complicated chain of investigations to which many physicists contributed. Beginning with those of Becquerel himself, many experiments with the rays were carried out. By 1900 it was recognized that there were several components, differing with regard to their ability to penetrate solid materials, and also separable by electric and magnetic fields. This work culminated with the experiments of Rutherford in 1903 which clearly showed that there were *three* kinds of rays. In the long list of workers in radioactivity and nuclear physics, Rutherford stands out for his many brilliant experiments extending over a period of more than thirty years.

The essentials of the schemes used by Rutherford and others to separate the three radioactive rays are shown in Fig. 25.1. A small amount of radioactive substance (radium or thorium was most commonly used) was dropped into a hole in a lead block. Above the open channel in the lead was placed either an electric field or a magnetic field. The observations showed that there were

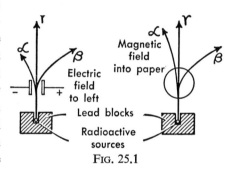

FIG. 25.1

three components, one that was positive which was called alpha (α) particles, one that was negative, called beta (β) particles, and one that carried no charge called gamma (γ) rays. (The early practice of calling all three of these "rays" established a terminology that is still in use despite its misapplication.) The existence of charge strongly suggested that both the α and β components were particles, while γ rays were high-energy photons.

The nature of the β particles was definitely established by measuring their charge-to-mass ratio and by indirect charge measurements. *The β particles were found to be electrons* of high energy, in the range up to say 5 Mev. The γ rays were found to behave like high-energy x rays and subsequent diffraction experiments confirmed their identification *as photons* in the energy range of

0.1 to 3 Mev. The charge-to-mass ratio for the α particles was measured in crossed electric and magnetic fields and found to be that of the *helium nucleus*, i.e., charge of $+2e$, mass of 4 atomic mass units. The charge was measured independently by measuring the current in an α particle beam and counting the number of particles in the beam. Still further measurements showed that α particles when stopped in air collected two electrons and formed helium gas which could be identified by its line spectrum. α particle energies were found to be as high as 10 Mev. All these identifications had been made in the first ten years of the present century.

25.4 Ionizing Power and Range

One of the earliest observations with radioactivity was the ability of the rays to ionize (make conducting) the air around a radioactive source. This ionizing ability differs markedly for the three kinds of rays. Thus it is of great experimental importance in identifying rays of unknown composition. Let us consider this ionizing power and its relation to the absorption of the rays.

It is readily observed that α particles have a short range; only a few centimeters of air or thousandths of inches of aluminum foil are required to block their passage completely, and it seems reasonable to conclude that ionization accounts for the exhaustion of the α-particle energy. As this relatively massive

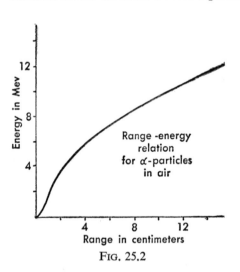

FIG. 25.2

particle, carrying two positive charges, forces its way through matter, it brushes atomic electrons out of its path and produces a large ionization. It has been experimentally determined that on an average each act of ionization costs the α particle about 30 ev of energy. Thus, a 3-Mev α particle will produce 100,000 positive ions before it captures two electrons and settles down to thermal energy as a normal helium atom. Furthermore, since α particle ranges are short, a few centimeters of air, this ionization is very dense, and the trail of an α particle is marked by tens of thousands of ions per centimeter. This ion density varies along the path and is greatest near the end of the range, where the α-particle velocity is least.

It was early observed that the α particles from a particular radioactive substance had a definite range in matter and that the ends of their paths could be rather sharply defined. This fact permits the measurement of α-particle energies in terms of their range in a given substance, say air. The α-particle range-energy curve is shown in Fig. 25.2; the energies for the curve were established by measuring the bending in known magnetic fields.

The ionization of β particles is much less dense than that of α particles for several reasons. The β particle carries only one charge; even at high energies its mass is only about one-thousandth that of the α and grows still smaller as it slows down; and its speed is much greater for a given energy. It has been experimentally determined that per centimeter of path an average β particle

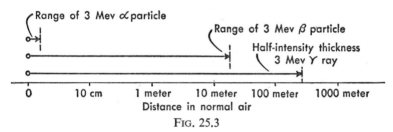

FIG. 25.3

will produce of the order of one-hundredth the number of ions produced by an α particle (Fig. 25.3). Hence a β particle will have roughly one hundred times the range of an α particle of the same energy. However, the range of a β particle is not sharply defined, principally because of the large scattering which it undergoes because of its small mass, and range-energy relations are not very useful for energy determinations.

Gamma rays are less effective ionizers than either α or β particles. Roughly, they are about one-hundredth as effective as the β particle, or 1/10,000 as effective as the α particle. It is not possible to state what thickness of material will *completely* stop γ rays, because, like all photons, they are absorbed "exponentially." This mathematical term simply means that if a certain thickness of material reduces the γ-ray intensity to one-half (the half intensity thickness), then twice that thickness will reduce it to one-fourth, three times to one-eight, etc.; and in theory, no thickness will ever reduce the number of γ rays completely to zero; in practice, however, a few centimeters of lead or a few hundred meters of air effectively eliminate the γ rays. This exponential absorption is a direct result of the nature of γ-ray energy loss. In distinction to α and β particles, γ rays do not lose their energy continuously in small amounts but interact with matter by the photoelectric or Compton effects in which they give all or a principle part of their energy to an electron. Thus the absorption of γ rays is determined by the probability of these processes, which does not change with increased path lengths—one such event effectively eliminates the γ-ray photon. The half-intensity thickness in γ-ray absorption is to be interpreted as that path length for which the probability of γ-ray removal is $\frac{1}{2}$; a further such path length increases the probability to $\frac{1}{2} + (\frac{1}{2} \cdot \frac{1}{2}) = \frac{3}{4}$, etc.

Figure 25.3 shows the relative penetrating powers of 3 Mev α, β, and γ rays in ordinary air.

25.5   Methods of Detection of α, β, γ Rays

All methods of detection of α and β particles and γ rays rely on their ability to *ionize*. There are at least five methods in common use.

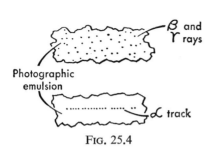

FIG. 25.4

1. The Photographic Plate. The fogging of a photographic emulsion led to the discovery of radioactivity. If this emulsion is viewed under a high-power microscope, it is seen that β and γ rays cause silver bromide grains to develop in a scattered fashion (Fig. 25.4). However, α particles, owing to the dense ionization they produce, leave a definite track of exposed grains in the emulsion (Fig. 25.4). Hence, not only is the α particle detected, but also its range (in emulsion) can be measured. Very recently special photographic emulsions capable of showing β-particle tracks have been developed and extend the usefulness of this popular detector.

2. Scintillations.   The fluorescent screen, e.g., of ZnS, will show the presence of cathode rays and x rays, as we have already seen. Since both β and cathode rays are electrons, and γ and x rays are photons, we should reasonably expect a fluorescent screen to detect both β and γ rays. Unfortunately, the numbers of β particles and γ rays from the ordinary radioactive sample are too small to produce an easily visible effect in a thin fluorescent screen. Recently, however, certain colorless crystals of considerable thickness have been shown to be efficient scintillators for β and γ rays and are being widely used for this purpose. Single

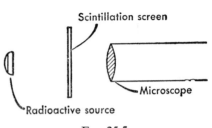

FIG. 25.5

α particles are visually detectable by a ZnS screen; if the screen is viewed with a magnifying eyepiece, localized flashes of light, called *scintillations*, will be observed (Fig. 25.5). The very dense ionization caused by the α particle produces a concentrated effect. By observing scintillations one can not only detect the presence of α particles, but they can also actually be *counted*. The technique is difficult because it requires dark-adapted eyes, and it rapidly tires the observer, but a great deal of early work in radioactivity relied on this visual detection. Recently the scintillation method has been revived, using sensitive photocells to detect the light flashes. Scintillation counters are once more widely used in nuclear laboratories.

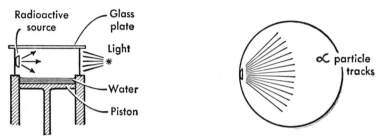

FIG. 25.6

3. Wilson Cloud Chamber. This ingenious device was invented by C. T. R. Wilson in 1912 and still serves as a useful research tool. It depends on the well-known fact that moisture tends to condense around ions (the probable explanation for the formation of clouds in the sky). If an enclosed region of air is saturated with water vapor (this is always the case if water is present), and the air is then suddenly cooled, it becomes supersaturated, that is, contains for the instant more water vapor than it can hold permanently, and a fog of water droplets develops around the ions in the chamber. An α particle, say, traveling through such a supersaturated atmosphere supplies a trail of ions on which water droplets will condense. This trail is thus made visible. An elementary cloud chamber is shown in Fig. 25.6. The cooling to produce supersaturation is accomplished by allowing the gas to expand rapidly. An α particle traversing the chamber just before this expansion leaves a visible track. A collecting electrode with a positive potential relative to the water surface is used to clear out the ions after the expansion, leaving the chamber ready for the next particle. A sketch of α tracks is shown in Fig. 25.6. As described, there is no provision for knowing when a particle enters the chamber, so that the usual technique is to cause an expansion periodically (once or more a minute) and catch what one can. The expansion and photography of the tracks is carried out automatically. In some experiments this is too wasteful of time and film, and the chamber is controlled by a subsidiary detector which trips the expansion in time to catch the ion track. Such controlled chambers are used largely in cosmic ray research where the particles of interest come rather infrequently.

The Wilson cloud chamber can show tracks of both α and β particles. A γ ray, gives rise to a track only by virtue of a secondary (photo or Compton) electron which is produced only infrequently in the vapor. However, if it is first allowed to penetrate a metal foil these electrons are more abundant and hence indicate more readily the presence of the γ rays and allow the secondary-electron energies and those of the γ rays to be determined.

4. Ionization Chamber. This is probably the simplest of all particle-detection devices in principle. It is just a chamber containing two electrodes used to collect the ions produced by the passage of a high-speed charged particle and designed to measure this ion current electrically. Figure 25.7 shows a simple ionization chamber for α-particle detection. The incident particles

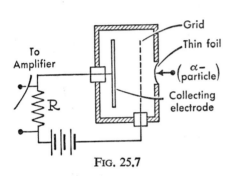

FIG. 25.7

enter through the thin foil (necessary to isolate the gas in the chamber and to complete electrical shielding). The ions left in the particle's wake find themselves in an electric field and move to the electrodes and give up their charge. For an instant there is a small current through the resistance while the battery is neutralizing the collected charges. This momentary current causes a small potential difference across R which is electronically amplified to operate a recording device. Thus each particle entering the ionization chamber produces a voltage pulse or "kick"; the greater the ionization caused by the particle, the larger is the voltage pulse. Like the cloud chamber, the ionization chamber can differentiate between α and β particles. Using secondary electrons, it can also record γ rays, though the pulse produced is very small. Such an ionization chamber *counts* the ionizing particles. In another arrangement (and historically earlier) the ionization chamber measures the total ionization due to a number of particles. The scheme is essentially the same except that R is made larger so that the current pulses decay more slowly and the pulses from successive particles overlap to produce an average current and an average potential difference across R. An electroscope attached to the insulated collecting electrode measures this potential difference and hence the ionization current. Such ionization chambers are frequently used to measure x-ray and γ-ray intensities for health protection.

5. **Geiger Counter.** One of the most widely used of all particle or photon detectors is the Geiger counter, invented in 1908 by Geiger while working in Rutherford's laboratory and improved by many others. It has the merits of high sensitivity, simplicity, flexibility, and ruggedness. In its usual form it consists of an open-ended cylinder along the center of which a wire is stretched (Fig. 25.8). This is enclosed in a glass envelope containing a gas (often a mixture of argon with other gases or vapors) at about 1/5 atmospheric pressure.

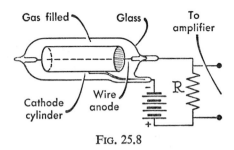

FIG. 25.8

A difference of potential of the order of 1000 volts is applied between the wire and cylinder, with the wire positive relative to the cylinder. The voltage is high enough to be just *under* the breakdown voltage for the gas, that is, a higher voltage would cause conduction (as in a gas-discharge tube). Incident α, β, or γ rays will produce ions in the region between the wire and the cylinder. The electrons (and to a lesser extent the positive ions) set free by this ionization are rapidly accelerated to energies great enough to produce other ions as they move toward the electrodes; the newly released electrons and + ions produce still others, and so on. Hence in a very short time, less than a millionth of a second, there is a veritable avalanche of electrons rushing to the positive wire, and a dense space charge of + ions around the wire. The motion of the electrons and ions to the electrodes causes a large voltage pulse across the high-resistance R due to the induced charges on the cathode and the wire. As soon as the charges are collected by the electrodes and neutralized by the battery the Geiger counter is ready for another entering particle. It is evident, then, that the Geiger counter is a sort of "stepped-up" ionization chamber, employing a greater electric field and cumulative ionization. Indeed, at low voltages it is exactly like an ionization chamber. As the voltage is increased, the ionization (and hence the voltage pulse) also increases until finally further ionization is limited by space charge. In this condition any particle that will produce an original ion gives rise to the same size avalanche, so that the pulse size is the same for α, β, and γ rays. In general each α or β particle entering the counter produces a count; however, the detection of γ rays is less probable. Since the voltage pulse from a Geiger counter is the same for α, β, and γ rays, the counter does not distinguish between them. However, if the glass envelope containing the counter is thick enough, only β and γ rays succeed in getting in. The walls or an end of the counter must be exceedingly thin to permit α particles and slow β particles to enter. Geiger counters and their associated circuits are simple and can, if necessary, be made light and portable.

25.6   Source of Radioactivity

The evidence that the source of α, β, and γ rays is the *nucleus* of the atom is compelling. Consider each type of radiation in turn.

γ **Rays.**   The most energetic *x ray* arises from the transition of an electron to the innermost orbit (the K x ray lines). The higher the atomic number of the atom the more energetic the x-ray quanta. X-ray measurements had shown that even for uranium, which has the largest atomic number of all the elements in nature, this maximum transition involves only 115,000 ev; yet γ rays are found with ten and twenty times this energy. Energy changes in the external structure of the atom are simply not great enough to account for γ rays. It is reasonable to conclude that they must arise in the nucleus.

β **Particles.**   Since these are electrons it might be thought that they are released from the orbits of the atom. However, the most conclusive evidence that β particles have a nuclear, not atomic, origin is in the study of the chemical changes associated with β-ray emission, where it is evident that the atomic number increases by one unit upon ejection of a β ray; hence the nucleus must have *lost* an electronic charge in the process.

α **Particles.**   These are the nuclei of helium atoms. Unless our interpretation of all previous atomic phenomena is wrong, there are only electrons in the external structure of the atom. Furthermore, chemical evidence shows that the α particles must come from the nucleus.

25.7   Spontaneous Nuclear Disintegration

Since the α particle carries two positive charges and four mass units, the nucleus which ejected the α particle must have changed its charge and mass this amount, and also its chemical properties since an element retains its chemical properties only as long as it retains its nuclear charge. *A nucleus emitting an α particle disintegrates to a new element of atomic number reduced by two, atomic mass reduced by four.* This is done *spontaneously* by nature without the help or hindrance of man! Such a conversion of an element to a new element is termed a *transmutation* (the old dream of the alchemists). The elements beyond lead in the periodic table are undergoing spontaneous transmutation.

It has been found that certain species of nuclei emit α particles, other species emit β particles (some few varieties emit either kind; we shall ignore such "isomerism"). A single nucleus never emits both simultaneously.

α **Emitter.** The uranium isotope $_{92}U^{238}$ is an example. When it ejects an α particle its atomic number is then 90, its mass 234. A glance at the periodic table reveals that element 90 is thorium. We may profitably abbreviate the process by writing a reaction in exactly the same manner as chemical reactions are written.

$$_{92}U^{238} \rightarrow {_2}He^4 + {_{90}}Th^{234}$$

There are many other α emitters. For example radium transmutes to radon (a gas) by α emission:

$$_{88}Ra^{226} \rightarrow {_2}He^4 + {_{86}}Rn^{222}$$

β **Emitter.** When an electron is ejected from a nucleus *the nucleus becomes more positive by one unit of charge,* i.e., the atomic number increases by one unit. However, the electron mass is so negligible in comparison with the nuclear mass that there is no change in the atomic mass number. It is observed that the thorium, $_{90}Th^{234}$, that resulted from $_{92}U^{238}$ is a β emitter. The charge on the thorium nucleus increases by one to become 91, the mass is still 234. Element 91 is protoactinium (Pa). The symbol for the electron is $_{-1}e^0$; its mass is negligible, and its atomic number is minus one. Thus,

$$_{90}Th^{234} \rightarrow {_{-1}}e^0 + {_{91}}Pa^{234}$$

Also, $_{91}Pa^{234}$ is found to be a β emitter, transmuting back to another isotope of uranium:

$$_{91}Pa^{234} \rightarrow {_{-1}}e^0 + {_{92}}U^{234}$$

γ **Emitter.** Emission of a γ ray does not alter either the atomic number or the atomic mass, thus does not cause transmutation. It arises from the fact that a nucleus emitting an α or a β particle may be left excited (is left with energy in excess of its normal value). The nucleus gives up this energy by emitting a γ ray. This process is analogous to quantum emission by an atom. A γ ray usually accompanies the emission of a β particle and often accompanies the emission of an α particle.

25.8   Radioactive Disintegration Series

The effect of α-particle emission is to shift the parent nucleus two places to the left in the periodic table; β emission shifts the element one place to the right. It was shown by Rutherford and others that, in the long run, the α emitters win out; there is a seesawing in the transmutation chains that ultimately ends with lead. It was shown further that these complex chains actually form three series, one starting with $_{92}U^{238}$ (called the uranium series), one

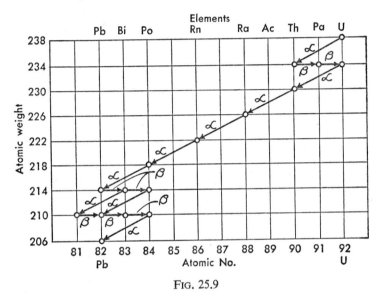

FIG. 25.9

starting with $_{90}Th^{232}$ (called the thorium series), and the third starting with $_{92}U^{235}$ (called the actinium series). The uranium series is diagrammed in Fig. 25.9. All the series end with one isotope or another of lead.

When one realizes that among the three radioactive series there are some 57 transmutations involved, it is with profound awe that one regards the work necessary to unravel them. The problem of isolating each transmutation product was almost prohibitively difficult, and new methods of chemical separation were invented for the purpose.

25.9   Disintegration Half Life

Nothing has been said about the rate at which spontaneous disintegration occurs. Obviously it cannot be fast in every reaction in a chain, or we would have no elements beyond lead left to us today. Disintegration, like the penetration of γ rays, though an entirely different phenomenon, is exponential.

The total *life time* of a radium sample, for instance, is infinite; there will always be a few nuclei disintegrating. Consequently, a more descriptive term is its half life. The *half life* of an element is the time required for one-half of the original number of nuclei to disintegrate. In the case of radium, this time is 1590 years. Thus, in 1590 years a gram of radium has decayed to one-half a gram of radium, the transmutation products accounting for the remaining mass. Uranium 238 has the longest known half life: 4.5 billion years. Some

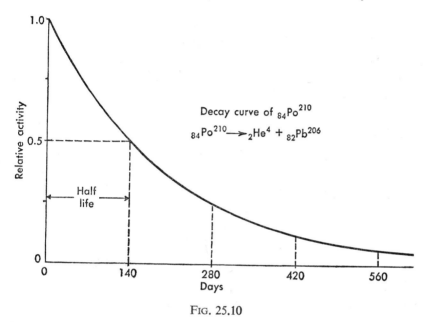

Decay curve of $_{84}Po^{210}$

$$_{84}Po^{210} \longrightarrow {}_2He^4 + {}_{82}Pb^{206}$$

FIG. 25.10

products in the chains leading to lead have very short half lives; thus a sample of polonium 212 (in the thorium series) is half disintegrated in a tenth of a microsecond! The only reason it is observed at all is due to its steady production by its predecessor in the chain, bismuth 212.

It should be emphasized that spontaneous disintegration is random. A given radium nucleus may disintegrate at once or may wait for thousands of years before emitting an α particle; it is completely a matter of chance. All that we can say is that *on the average*, half of all the radium nuclei present will have disintegrated to radon in 1590 years. We know nothing about the "plans" of any particular nucleus. There may always be a few nuclei that will hold out for an infinite time; it is for this reason that the life of a radioactive element is infinite, though its half life is a very measurable quantity. Figure 25.10 indicates a rate of decay curve for one of the radioactive elements.

25.10   Structure of the Nucleus?

Natural radioactivity certainly presents unambiguous evidence that the nucleus possesses a structure of some sort. Our present information would seem to indicate that it must contain α particles and electrons, with γ rays resulting from their internal displacements. It would be precipitous, however, to attempt to build a model on these facts (though, naturally enough, it was attempted at the time) because we now have more information to aid us. We can recognize at once the danger of assuming that all nuclei are built of α particles, for there are many nuclei whose atomic masses are not divisible by four, which would be required if α particles were the only heavy particles in the nucleus. We shall have to wait for the discussion of the evidence against the electron as a component of the nucleus; our present study would indicate that it is present in the nucleus since electrons are emitted in β decay, and it was so believed until 1932. This view has changed and electrons are no longer accepted as nucleons even though, paradoxically enough, they are ejected by the nucleus as β rays.

PROBLEMS

1. Thorium 232 is the parent element of a radioactive series ending in lead 208. How many α particles and β particles are emitted in the successive decay processes of one parent atom?   *Ans.*   6 α particles, 4 β particles.

2. Between thorium 232 and bismuth 212 the sequence of emitted particles is as follows: α, β, β, α, α, α, α, β. Write this chain of reactions, identifying each member with the aid of Table E.

3. The half life of polonium 218 is 3 min. If it is isolated from its parent substance what fraction will remain after a half hour?   *Ans.*   0.1%.

4. Compute the depreciation of 1 gm of radium held for 1590 years assuming the dollar value of Ra is \$25,000/gm throughout the entire period.
Ans. 1.25×10^4 dollars.

5. A certain α-particle counter records 1200 counts/min from a Po^{210} source. What is the counting rate 420 days later?   *Ans.*   150 counts/min.

6. Compute the wave lengths of an α particle and a γ ray each of 1 Mev energy.
Ans. 1.42×10^{-12} cm for α; 1.23×10^{-10} cm for γ.

Suggested Reading

Curie, Eve, "Madame Curie," New York, Doubleday, 1937.
A biography of the discoverer of polonium and radium written by her daughter.

POLLARD, E., and DAVIDSON, W. L., "Applied Nuclear Physics," New York, John Wiley & Sons, 1942.
Chapter 3 on the detection of nuclear particles and Chapter 6 on radioactive decay are written for the non-scientist.

Induced Transmutation and Other Nuclear Processes

26.1 α Particle Scattering and Nuclear Dimensions

If natural radioactivity presented a complex puzzle, it at the same time gave the physicist an *agent* with which to investigate atomic nuclei. This agent is the α particle. Here is a small bullet of great energy that could be used in a frontal attack on the nucleus. Though there is little control over the aim of the bullet, accuracy can be replaced by the technique of saturation bombardment; for the number of atoms in a gram of a radioactive substance is a gigantic figure, and even if only a very small fraction of these atoms was ejecting α particles in any one second this number is still large. Thus a gram of pure radium contains 2.7×10^{21} atoms (Avogadro's number divided by the atomic mass of radium, 226). In any one second 3.7×10^{10} radium atoms are ejecting α particles! Even a milligram of radium is emitting 37 million α particles per second, and these particles have an energy of 4.8 Mev, a potent bombarding agent. In such a rain of bullets some of them must inevitably hit the nuclei of atoms in their path. This saturation technique is essential to all experiments in nuclear bombardment, since we can neither fix the target nor direct the bullet.

We have already seen that Rutherford made use of the results of α-particle scattering experiments in developing the hypothesis of the nuclear atom (§ 23.2). In these experiments (Fig. 26.1) α particles incident on a thin metallic foil were observed to be deflected through various angles as they emerged from the foil. Rutherford employed the nuclear atom to explain these deflections in terms of the electrical repulsion between the α particles and the positive nuclei. The results were consistent with the assumption that the positive charge and most of the mass of the atom were concentrated in the small

(dimensions of 10^{-12} cm) central nucleus, and that the scattering force on the
α particle was that due to the Coulomb field of the atomic nucleus.

If we reflect on the hypothesis of the nuclear atom we may detect an inadequacy in the early Rutherford
model. Admitting that the scattering
force is a Coulomb force, we may
conceive of the nucleus as a charged
mathematical point or a uniformly
charged sphere; both assumptions
give an electric field

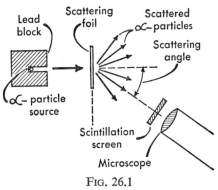

$$E = \frac{q}{r^2}$$

outside of the charged body. For a
point charge everything is, of course,
outside; but for a charged sphere there

FIG. 26.1

is an *inside* region in which the electric
field is not equal to q/r^2. By a macrophysical analogy we would say that the
Coulomb force holds only in the region *outside* of the nucleus and the point at
which it ceases to hold is the *boundary* of the nucleus. Thus a nucleus has a
"size" fixed by the nuclear matter, inside of which the force on a bombarding
particle is not simply the ordinary electric force.

This question of nuclear size is also susceptible to α particle-scattering experiments, for it is clear that the Rutherford scattering formula must be incorrect for those α particles which penetrate the nuclear boundaries. Deviations from the Coulomb law then occur, and the observation of these deviations allows one to estimate the nuclear size.

We may ask how Rutherford's scattering formula can be right and wrong
at the same time. An example may serve to clarify this issue. Consider a 7.7-
Mev α particle bombarding a gold foil. Gold, having an atomic number
$Z = 79$ carries a nuclear charge $+79e$. For a head-on collision the α particle can come to within a distance s of the center of the gold nucleus; at which
point it stops momentarily since its kinetic energy is converted entirely into
potential energy. Thus if $W = \frac{1}{2}mv^2$ is the α-particle energy, then by Eq. 12.3

$$W = \tfrac{1}{2}mv^2 = \frac{(79e)\,(2e)}{s}$$

$$s = \frac{2 \times 79 \times (4.8 \times 10^{-10})^2}{7.7 \times 10^6 \times 16 \times 10^{-13}} \doteq 30 \times 10^{-13} \text{ cm}$$

Therefore 30×10^{-13} cm is the closest distance to which the α particle can approach the gold nucleus.* Since no deviations from the Rutherford scattering formula are observed for 7.7-Mev α particles scattered by gold then the nuclear radius is *less* than 30×10^{-13} cm.

If the scattering nuclei are lighter (and hence of smaller charge) or the α particles more energetic, then s becomes smaller. When s becomes comparable with the nuclear size, deviations from the Rutherford scattering formula should be observed.

In 1919 Rutherford measured the scattering of energetic (7.7 Mev) α particles in hydrogen gas. A head-on collision in the Coulomb field of the hydrogen atom predicts a closest approach distance of 1.9×10^{-13} cm. This distance, it appeared, is less than the nuclear dimensions since large deviations from the scattering formula were observed. It was concluded that the dimensions of the colliding nuclear particles were about 3×10^{-13} cm.

26.2 α-Particle Scattering and Elastic Collisions

The law of force between an α particle and nucleus depends on the closeness of approach. However, the energy imparted to the nucleus by the impact does not depend on the law of force if momentum and kinetic energy are conserved in the collision (see §7.2). It was of utmost importance to find that these conservation laws did indeed apply to the ultimate particles of matter.

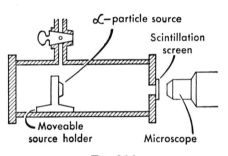

FIG. 26.2

In gases, where the recoiling nucleus can be observed, the laws of α-particle scattering can be studied in detail. Consider, for example, an apparatus like that of Fig. 26.2 with which Marsden and later Rutherford studied the momentum and energy transfers in α-particle-nucleus collisions. For an elastic head-on collision of an α particle of momentum $m_1 v_1$ with a nucleus of mass m_2 at rest, momentum conservation (§7.4) gives

---

* The formula derived assumes the scattering nucleus to remain fixed. Taking its recoil into account the correct formula is

$$s = \frac{ZZ'e^2}{W} \times \frac{m + m'}{m'}$$

where Ze, m, and W are the charge, mass, and kinetic energy of the incident particle and $Z'e$ and m' are the charge and mass of the scatterer.

$$m_1 v_1 = m_1 v_1' + m_2 v_2'$$

and by Eq. 7.7,

$$v_2' = v_1 \frac{2m_1}{m_1 + m_2}$$

where v_1' is the α-particle velocity after collision and v_2' that of the recoiling nucleus. For α-particle-hydrogen collisions $m_1 = 4$ mu and $m_2 = 1$ mu. Thus a hydrogen atom suffering a head-on collision recoils with a velocity of $2 \times 4/(1 + 4) = \frac{8}{5}$ of the incident α-particle velocity. The ratio of the recoil and incident kinetic energies is given by

$$\frac{\frac{1}{2} m_2 v_2'^2}{\frac{1}{2} m_1 v_1^2} = \frac{m_2}{m_1} \times \left(\frac{8}{5}\right)^2 = \frac{1}{4} \times \frac{64}{25} = \frac{16}{25}$$

Thus the recoiling hydrogen nucleus has $\frac{16}{25}$ of the energy of the incident α particle. In this collision the recoiling nucleus moves too rapidly to carry along its electron. Such hydrogen nuclei are called *protons*. Being a lighter particle with but half the charge of the α particle, protons have considerably greater ranges than α particles of comparable energy. Their presence can thus be detected by their great range. In the experiments the incident α particles had energies of 7.7 Mev. Thus the recoil protons had energies up to $\frac{16}{25} \times 7.7 = 4.9$ Mev and ranges of about 130 cm in the hydrogen gas. There will, of course, be other protons of shorter range arising from collisions with α particles which have dissipated part of their energy by ionization. In addition, there will be protons at scattering angles other than 0°. These were likewise found.

26.3 Rutherford's Discovery of Induced Transmutation (1919)

It is clear that the elastic scattering of α particles in gases of heavy atoms will give rise to relatively slow-moving recoil nuclei of very great ionizing power and short range. Yet when Rutherford performed a scattering experiment with nitrogen gas ($_7 N^{14}$) in an apparatus like that of Fig. 26.2, he observed scintillations at ranges much greater than those of the incident α particles and far in excess of those expected for recoiling nitrogen nuclei. To be specific, he was using 7.7-Mev α particles which had a range of about 7 cm in nitrogen at atmospheric pressure. Therefore when the distance between screen and source was made greater than 7 cm, scintillations due to α particles should have disappeared. An elastic head-on collision with a nitrogen nucleus gives it a velocity:

$$v_2' = v_1 \frac{2m_1}{m_1 + m_2}$$

or

$$v_2' = \frac{2 \times 4}{4 + 14} v_1 = \frac{4}{9} v_1$$

Now just how far the nitrogen nucleus could go having four-ninths the velocity of the incident α particle was not well known; however, its large mass and charge should give it a very short range, a centimeter or two at best, and certainly less than the 7-cm range of the α particles. Yet Rutherford observed that if he separated the source and screen by as much as 28 cm he could still get an occasional scintillation! Here is an entirely new kind of collision. It was unthinkable that the heavy nitrogen nucleus could travel such a distance—what would give it the tremendously high energy needed? Possibly the scintillation was due to an α particle which in some manner had been given additional energy by the nitrogen nucleus. But an α particle requires nearly 20 Mev to go 28 cm. On the other hand, from the head-on scattering experiments in hydrogen discussed above, it was known that the *hydrogen nucleus*, because of its small mass and single charge, required only 3.8 Mev to travel 28 cm. in nitrogen gas at atmospheric pressure.

Rutherford proposed a bold and far-seeing answer. In this collision not only was the kinetic energy of the incident particle not conserved, but the identity of the particle itself was not conserved. He proposed that the α particle *entered* the nitrogen nucleus during the collision, and that a hydrogen nucleus (a proton) emerged. If the nucleus $_2\text{He}^4$ was added to the $_7\text{N}^{14}$ at the instant of collision, and $_1\text{H}^1$ was ejected, then the residual nucleus must have gained one positive charge and three mass units in the process. The element of atomic number 8 is oxygen; hence $_7\text{N}^{14}$ was converted into $_8\text{O}^{17}$, and we can write the nuclear equation as

$$_7\text{N}^{14} + {_2\text{He}^4} \rightarrow {_8\text{O}^{17}} + {_1\text{H}^1}$$

When a nucleus is converted into a new nucleus as a result of bombardment, the process is called *induced transmutation*. Since the ejected proton is lighter and has only a single charge, it ionizes less densely than an α particle, and therefore its track in a Wilson cloud chamber would be thinner than an α track. When Rutherford's experiment was repeated in a cloud chamber filled with nitrogen, disintegrations were observed; and the long-range tracks of the emitted protons were clearly evident as well as the short dense tracks of the recoiling $_8\text{O}^{17}$ nuclei.

26.4   Induced Transmutations

In the years since Rutherford's discovery of the transmutation of nitrogen many hundreds of transmutations have been discovered. Until 1932 these were produced only with α particles from naturally radioactive substances, but since the advent of particle accelerators (Chapter 28) other bombarding particles have been successfully used.

The cataloging of the many kinds of transmutations will not be attempted here. They differ not only with regard to the isotope being transmuted and the bombarding particle but also for the several kinds of particles which are emitted. Of the charged particles producing transmutation, alpha particles (symbolized α), deuterons (the nucleus of the isotope of hydrogen of mass 2, symbolized d), and protons (p), are most used. Protons and neutrons (see §26.5) are the most commonly emitted particles. One speaks of (α, p) reactions such as

$$_7N^{14} + {}_2He^4 \rightarrow {}_8O^{17} + {}_1H^1$$

which is written symbolically as

$$_7N^{14}\,(\alpha, p)\,{}_8O^{17}$$

In addition there are (d, p), (d, α), (p, α), and many other varieties of reactions.

Although there is great variety in the transmutation experiments, it is possible to make some generalizations. (1) The atomic numbers, i.e., charges, must balance in the reaction; thus in $_9F^{19}\,(\alpha, p)\,{}_{10}Ne^{22}$ the charges on the left $(9 + 2)$ must equal those on the right $(10 + 1)$. (2) The isotopic masses (expressed as whole numbers) must balance; thus in $_5B^{10}\,(\alpha, p)_6C^{13}$ the mass numbers $(10 + 4)$ and $(13 + 1)$ must be equal. (3) Except for the case of very energetic bombardment only one particle is usually emitted. Even at low energies a few reactions violate this "one particle in and one particle out" rule. At very high energies nuclei often eject several particles. (4) Particle reactions are usually accompanied by γ rays which result from the final nucleus being left in an excited state. These γ rays are of sharply defined energies, characteristic of each nucleus, and prove that the nucleus, like the atom is quantized. (5) Transmutations are effectively instantaneous. Theoretical estimates give about 10^{-15} sec for the duration of the reactions.

26.5   Chadwick's Discovery of the Neutron

A striking parallel exists between Rutherford's discovery of induced transmutation of the nucleus and the discovery in 1932 of the neutron by Chadwick (a former student of Rutherford working in his laboratory in

England). The experiments were superficially similar, the results equally puzzling and the proper explanations were the product of ingenious induction.

Early in 1930 two German physicists, Bothe and Becker, had bombarded beryllium with α particles and found that a very penetrating radiation was given off. It was their guess that the α particle was captured in the beryllium nucleus and a γ ray of very great energy ejected. However, Frederick Joliot and Irène Curie-Joliot (daughter of the discoverers of polonium and radium) tried absorbing these supposed γ rays in various materials, paraffin among them. They found, surprisingly, that protons were ejected from the paraffin (Fig. 26.3), and they assumed that these resulted from a sort of Compton effect for protons. Chadwick was disturbed by this explanation. He very

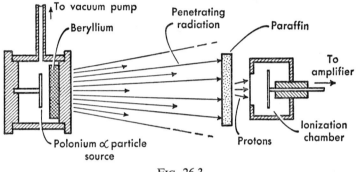

Fig. 26.3

carefully measured the range of the protons ejected from the paraffin (which consists of molecules containing hydrogen and carbon) and found the proton energy to be 8.3 Mev. Now if the proton had been set in motion by an elastic collision with a γ-ray photon, the photon would have had to have 55 Mev of energy (this result comes directly from a simple momentum calculation). Quite possibly it did have and if so, then it should be able to give a nucleus as heavy as nitrogen, say, 0.35 Mev of energy. Substituting nitrogen for the paraffin and measuring the range* of the knocked on-nitrogen nuclei, Chadwick found the energy given the nitrogen nucleus by the alleged γ-ray photon was only about one-half that predicted. On the other hand, if he assumed that the unknown particle was not a photon, but a particle of the same mass as the proton and having just the 8.3 Mev energy of the knocked-on proton, then the predicted energy for the nitrogen was exactly correct. However, the unknown particle could not actually be a proton because it had

---

* By 1932 the range-energy relation for nitrogen ions was reasonably well known.

far too great a penetrating power (low ionization) for a proton of 8.3 Mev. From these arguments Chadwick made the logical but brilliant deduction: The unknown particle must have about the mass of a proton but not the charge of a proton, in fact, no charge at all. He called the particle a *neutron*. *The neutron has approximately the mass of a proton but carries no charge.* The much greater penetrating power of the neutron is due to its lack of charge—it loses energy in traveling through matter only if it collides with a nucleus.

Chadwick was now able to write correctly the beryllium reaction. Using the symbol $_0n^1$ for the neutron we have:

$$_4Be^9 + _2He^4 \rightarrow _6C^{12} + _0n^1 \quad \text{or} \quad _4Be^9 (\alpha, n) _6C^{12}$$

A new particle has come from the nucleus.

26.6 Properties of the Neutron

When a *charged* particle nears an atom its electric field interacts strongly with the electrons and the nucleus of the atom. It is this interaction which produces ionization. A neutron, being uncharged, ignores all electric fields and is slowed down only by direct collisions with nuclei. Since the neutron has effectively the same mass as the proton a single head-on collision with a proton will stop the neutron completely. It was this type of collision that produced the protons Chadwick observed from paraffin. On the other hand, in collisions with a heavy nucleus the neutron simply bounces off in some new direction with only slightly diminished energy. For example, a collision between a neutron and a lead 208 nucleus gives the latter only $\frac{2}{209}$ of the neutron velocity. Hence, lead or any heavy element is a poor neutron shield. The light elements are better and hydrogen is the best. A neutron of a few Mev energy can penetrate many feet of lead but only a few inches of water or paraffin or similar hydrogenous substances.

The *mass* of the neutron cannot be determined by the usual mass spectrographic methods for it has no charge and is not bent in E and H fields. It is, instead, determined by calculations from the masses and energies involved in nuclear reactions. In particular, the disintegration of the deuteron (§27.5) by γ rays yields an accurate neutron mass value. The result is

$$\text{Mass of neutron} = 1.00894 \text{ mu}$$

which is slightly greater than the proton mass of 1.00813 mu.

The only *source* of neutrons is the nucleus. The original beryllium reaction of Chadwick's is still one of the most prolific sources of neutrons. However, many particle reactions are now known in which neutrons are emitted. Once a neutron has been liberated from the nucleus it retains its identity only long enough either to re-enter another nucleus or eventually to disintegrate by a radioactive process. This latter accounts for the disappearance of almost all neutrons. No one has ever had a block of pure neutrons in his laboratory, and even if the neutron did exist as a free entity for long periods of time, it could have no chemical properties, no interatomic forces. The average life of a neutron depends on what it encounters, but is of the order of several minutes.

26.7   The Components of the Nucleus

In the early nineteenth century Prout suggested that all atoms were composed of one or more hydrogen atoms. This, of course, is not true, but Prout's idea that the whole number mass values of atoms argue for common nuclear building blocks has survived to this day. The identity of these common components has changed from time to time. Today the answer seems clear—the primary components (the *nucleons*) of all nuclei are *protons* and *neutrons*. What is the evidence for this view?

If the nucleus has component parts they can be identified only in their detached state, just as the atomic electrons were identified by ionizing the atom. It does not follow, however, that anything detached from a nucleus is a primary nuclear particle. Alpha particles are ejected from the natural radioactive elements, but the α particle cannot be a nucleon since then all atomic masses would be even numbers and atomic numbers exactly one-half of the masses; nor could there be atoms lighter than helium. Electrons (β rays) come from the nucleus, but as we shall see (§26.9) they are not ordinarily found there but are formed just prior to their emission. Gamma rays have no rest mass or charge and may be dismissed as nuclear components. This leaves us with protons and neutrons as components which have been observed to come from the nucleus. A nuclear model of protons and neutrons will explain the known facts:

1. Nuclear Charge. The positive nuclear charge is carried by the protons each of charge $+e$. The atomic number thus equals the number of protons in the nucleus.

2. Nuclear Mass. The number of neutrons + protons equals the atomic mass number, thus explaining its integral value.

3. Nuclear Spin. Nuclei, like electrons, have angular momenta of spin. Both the neutron and proton have spins which are numerically equal to that of the electron, a sort of unit spin* for all fundamental particles. In the nucleus the proton and neutron spins line up either parallel or anti-parallel in pairs. Thus the deuteron (parallel p and n spins) has a spin of two fundamental units. All nuclei with even atomic mass numbers are observed to have spins

---

* The unit spin in quantum theory is $\frac{1}{2}(h/2\pi)$.

of zero or of an even number of fundamental units as predicted by the parallel-anti-parallel rule.

26.8   Induced Radioactivity

Induced transmutations frequently lead to product nuclei which are not found among the natural isotopes. Such nuclei are unstable somewhat in the manner of naturally radioactive elements. This phenomenon is called artificial or *induced radioactivity*.

There are significant distinctions between artificial and natural radioactive disintegrations. Naturally radioactive nuclei emit electrons or α particles, whereas artificially produced radioactive nuclei emit either electrons or a new particle, the positive electron or *positron*. The positron carries a charge of $+e$ and has the same mass as the electron. Positrons, created by another phenomenon, pair production (§27.7), were discovered in 1932.

The first induced radioactivity was reported by Curie and Joliot in 1934. In bombarding aluminum with α particles the following reaction was produced

$$_{13}Al^{27} + {}_2He^4 \rightarrow {}_{15}P^{30} + {}_0n^1$$

They detected the presence of the neutrons just as Chadwick had done in the discovery of the neutron. They found, in addition, that the aluminum target was radioactive and emitted rays which could be detected by a Geiger counter. They concluded that the radioactivity was due to the small amount of phosphorus $_{15}P^{30}$ that had been produced in the nuclear reaction. The measured half life of the phosphorus was found to be 2.6 minutes. By interposing absorbing material and by bending in a magnetic field it was shown that the radiation consisted of positrons.

Table D of the Appendix lists the known stable isotopes of the light elements, as determined by mass spectrograph observations. We observe that only one isotope of phosphorus, $_{15}P^{31}$, is found in nature, and we presume that if any other isotopic form of phosphorus is produced it must be unstable. Such an isotope will achieve stability by transforming to some other element which is stable. The elements beyond lead are undergoing the same process, but with two differences: (1) they are derived from parents with long half lives and are thus still found in nature, and (2) they can decay to stability by two means, electron emission and α-particle emission. The *induced* radioactive elements below lead decay with *only electron or positron emission*, though this may be accompanied by γ rays. In most cases, in contrast to natural radioactive decay, a single radioactive emission leads directly to a stable nucleus.

This rule usually excludes either the electron or the positron process, which-ever fails to lead to a stable nucleus. (There are a few cases in which either electron or positron emission can lead to stability; for these the process is indeterminate, some nuclei of the species following one type of emission, others following the other type.)

To apply this rule let us consider the two possibilities open for the decay of $_{15}P^{30}$:

1. If it emits an electron, then: $_{15}P^{30} \rightarrow _{-1}e^0 + _{16}S^{30}$
2. If it emits a positron, then: $_{15}P^{30} \rightarrow _{+1}e^0 + _{14}Si^{30}$

Consulting the table of isotopes we find no stable sulfur 30, but we do find a stable isotope $_{14}Si^{30}$. Hence, the phosphorus emits a positron. The usual test of deflecting the emitted particle in electric and magnetic fields confirms this.

We can now write the complete reaction observed by the Curie-Joliots:

$$_{13}Al^{27} + _2He^4 \rightarrow _{15}P^{30} + _0n^1$$

$$\xrightarrow[2.6 \text{ min}]{} {}_{14}Si^{30} + {}_{+1}e^0$$

An induced radioactive element is often called a *radio element*. Thus we speak of P^{30} as radiophosphorus. Virtually every element in the periodic table has been made radioactive, and the half life of each one is a unique quantity.

26.9 The Origin of β Rays

We have stated that although nuclei emit electrons (and positrons) they are not stable components of nuclear structure. There are several argu-ments for this view.

Before the discovery of the neutron in 1932 it was thought that the nucleus had enough protons to equal the atomic mass and enough electrons to cancel the charge of those protons in excess of the atomic number. Thus, $_8O^{16}$ was thought to have 16 protons to account for the mass (the electron mass makes only a negligible contribution) and 8 electrons to bring the net charge down from 16 to 8, the atomic number. But in 1932 Chadwick presented the physical world with neutrons from the nucleus. Of course, we could say that $_8O^{16}$ has 15 protons, 7 electrons, and one neutron, or $14p$, $6e$, $2n$, etc. But this is getting arbitrary in our attempt to crowd some neutrons into the nucleus—it looks more like numerology than physics.

One deciding argument came from the attempts to account for the spin properties of the nucleus. The theoretical physicist had long pointed out that 21 particles ($14p + 7e$) assumed in the nitrogen nucleus would not account for its spin which was equal to an even not an odd number of fundamental spin units. But if we assume $7p + 7n$ and no electrons we have the correct number to fit the spin data. Since we must have some neutrons, the data demand that we expel all electrons from our nuclear model.

Another argument against the nuclear electron is its "size" as given by its de Broglie wave length. According to quantum mechanics the electron wave length, $\lambda = h/mv$, must not exceed the size of the nucleus or it could not be contained therein. The energies (hence the momenta) of the nuclear particles are known, and for such energies the electron wave length is much too large to be contained in the nucleus, whereas the neutron wave length is comparable with nuclear dimensions.

In 1934 Fermi proposed a theory of β-ray emission which assumed that the *neutron* can be converted into a *proton* inside the nucleus and give birth to an *electron* in the process. In equation form:

$$_0n^1 \rightarrow _{-1}e^0 + _1H^1$$

Charge and mass are conserved in the process, and we see that the atomic number of the nucleus increases by one unit when the electron is ejected as a β particle. In a similar manner a *proton* changes to a *neutron* and a *positron*

$$_1H^1 \rightarrow _{+1}e^0 + _0n^1$$

giving rise to the positrons emitted by artificially radioactive elements.

Actually the situation is not as simple as we have indicated. There is a third particle, the *neutrino*, involved in the proton-neutron conversions. Of all the nuclear particles, the neutrino is the most elusive. Its presence is invoked to conserve energy and spin in β-ray emission. However, the neutrino does not participate in any observable processes other than β emission and its exact nature is not well understood. It has a very small mass (perhaps zero), no charge, a spin of one unit, does not ionize, and apparently moves through space with almost complete freedom.

For a rather long time it has been known that β rays are emitted with a continuous spectrum of energies, whereas the nucleus is quantized and gives up a definite amount of energy in a β-particle emission. The difference between the quantized energy and the β-particle energy is carried away by the neutrino. Likewise, the neutrino carries away a spin (one fundamental unit) in the reaction so that the observed spins of the initial and final nuclei may be explained.

The spin argument is seen by considering the artificial radioactivity of hydrogen 3:

$$_1H^3 \rightarrow _2He^3 + _{-1}e^0$$

where both $_1H^3$ and $_2He^3$ have observed spins of one fundamental, i.e., electron, unit. Only by adding a third particle (the neutrino) having one spin unit can this be explained, for otherwise $_2He^3$ would necessarily have zero or two spin units if spin were to be conserved.

In conclusion it should be mentioned that the neutron is not conceived of as an electron + proton + neutrino. The electron is emitted in the transformation of a neutron into a proton, just as a quantum of light is emitted when an atomic electron transforms from one atomic energy level to another. One does not say that an atomic electron in an excited state is an electron + quantum; the quantum is emitted at the instant of transformation.

The presence of neutrinos in β emission is fairly definitely established by experiments in which the momenta of the β particle and recoiling nucleus are simultaneously measured. The neutrino momentum is then inferred, using the law of momentum conservation. It is fair to say that the chief role of the neutrino is to preserve the validity of the laws of momentum and energy conservation. Perhaps the existence of the neutrino is at the level of abstraction which produced the ether.

PROBLEMS

1.   A proton makes a head-on elastic collision with a helium nucleus. What fraction of the proton energy is received by the helium nucleus?   *Ans.* $\frac{16}{25}$.

2.   When the neutrons of unknown energy bombard helium gas, α particles moving head-on are found to have 3.50 Mev energy. What was the energy of the neutrons?
Ans.   5.47 Mev.

3.   List the numbers of protons and neutrons in the nuclei He^4, C^{13}, O^{17}, Al^{28}, and K^{39}.

4.   Write nuclear equations for the (α, p) reactions whose target (initial) nuclei are P^{31}, Al^{27}, F^{19}.

5.   Complete the following reactions:
    (a) $Li^7 + ? \rightarrow B^{10} + n^1$
    (b) $F^{19} + H^1 \rightarrow O^{16} + ?$
    (c) $C^{12} + H^1 \rightarrow ? + \gamma$
    (d) $? + H^2 \rightarrow Li^7 + He^4$
    (e) $N^{14} + ? \rightarrow N^{15} + H^1$

6.   If the average angle through which neutrons are elastically scattered by hydrogen atoms were 45°, compute the average number of collisions required to reduce the energy of a 1-Mev neutron to less than 1 Kev (see §7.4).   *Ans.*   10.

7.   From Table D find four examples of isobaric nuclei (nuclei having the same mass numbers but different nuclear charges).

Suggested Reading

"Foundations of Nuclear Physics," New York, Dover Publications Inc., 1949.
   Page 131, facsimile of Rutherford's original transmutation paper, non-mathematical. Page 5, facsimile of Chadwick's original paper on the discovery of the neutron, very readable.

POLLARD, E., and DAVIDSON, W. L., "Applied Nuclear Physics," New York, John Wiley & Sons, 1942.
   Chapter 5 treats transmutation experiments in an easily readable fashion.

CHAPTER 27

Nuclear Forces and Nuclear Energy

27.1 Nuclear Forces

Scattering experiments with light nuclei give some idea of the size of nucleus, the boundaries inside of which the Coulomb force is supplemented by specific nuclear forces. Transmutation proves that these boundaries can be penetrated by high-speed charged particles. α- and β-particle emission shows that nuclear processes sometimes lead to instability and the emission of charged particles. Clearly, there are specific nuclear forces responsible for all these facts and we might inquire as to the laws of these forces.

The problem of nuclear forces is not yet solved and is the most pressing question of present day physics. The nature of the problem is, however, clear; some of its features can be indicated here.

We know that there must be strong forces of attraction between nucleons and that these forces are of an entirely new kind. They are not electrical forces, for the deuteron, which consists of a positive proton and an uncharged neutron, is a stable nucleus. Gravitational attraction is much too small to account for nuclear stability, nor is there any other force in atomic or classical physics which can explain nuclear stability.

As an indication of the strength of the nuclear forces, consider the α particle. Its two protons, some 3×10^{-13} cm apart, repel each other with a Coulomb force of about

$$\frac{e^2}{r^2} = \frac{(4.8 \times 10^{-10})^2}{(3 \times 10^{-13})^2} = 2.6 \times 10^6 \text{ dynes}$$

which is the magnitude of the earth's gravitational force on a 2.6-kg mass! If the α particle is to be kept from flying apart there must be a nuclear force of attraction at least as large as this.

We know that the nuclear forces must be of short range; their effect is felt over distances of the order of nuclear dimensions and quickly falls to zero outside of this. If this were not true α-particle scattering experiments would not agree with Rutherford's Coulomb scattering formula for even moderately small distances of approach. The effect of the short range of the nuclear forces is to define sharply the nuclear boundaries. Inside the nucleus there are strong attractive forces. These quickly die out at the nuclear boundaries, and at larger distances the forces are purely electrical.

These ideas have led to a convenient model for representing the force between a charged particle and the nucleus. Consider, for example, an energetic proton interacting with a nucleus of atomic number Z. The proton, having several Mev of kinetic energy, moves toward the nucleus, converting its kinetic energy into potential energy as it approaches. This potential energy is (see §23.4)

$$W = \frac{e(eZ)}{r}$$

when the proton is a distance r from the nuclear center. The proton acts as if it were a gravitational particle climbing a hill, the height of the hill being given by (constant)/r (Fig. 27.1).

However, the hill does not continue to rise indefinitely as r decreases, for at the nuclear boundary the force suddenly changes from repulsion to attraction, and the hill develops a deep hole which represents the specific nuclear forces. Thus the potential energy of the approaching proton is represented by a sort of volcano whose crater is the nucleus. If the level of the surrounding land

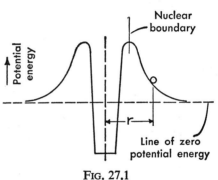

FIG. 27.1

from which the hill rises is taken as the zero of potential energy, the crater falls below this level by an amount depending on the strength of the nuclear forces of attraction. A proton approaching the potential hill rises to a level depending on its kinetic energy and is scattered by the hill's contour if it fails to reach the crater. However, given enough energy (and correct aim) it can reach the crater—this is the threshold energy for a proton-induced transmutation. Of course, the model fails to tell us what happens then. This would be asking a bit too much.

The potential hill model is not so naive as might be supposed. It has been used to explain the observed features of α-particle emission by the naturally radioactive elements. In this theory the hole is supposed to contain an α particle which is represented by its de Broglie wave as a wave interference pattern arising from wave reflections from the sides of the hole. Alpha-particle emission corresponds to the wave "leaking through" the potential barrier and reforming outside as the wave packet of a free α particle. The probability of this leakage is small but finite and can be calculated by quantum mechanics. It is an experimental law that those nuclei having high-energy α particles have short half lives. On the model this is because the potential barrier is narrower near the top and the probability of the leakage is larger for narrow barriers. The theory goes on to show the correct quantitative correspondence of α-particle energy and half life with a potential hole of reasonable width and depth.

The potential hill model also explains the deviations from Rutherford scattering which are observed for light nuclei and high-energy α particles and protons. Here, the inverse of the α-particle emission is invoked, the de Broglie wave of the high-energy projectile leaks into the hole and the scattered wave is modified thereby.

It should not be supposed, however, that this model is completely successful. It is a potential model which describes the interaction of a single particle with a nucleus but does not explain the nature of the nuclear forces.

27.2   Nuclear Binding Energy

The strong forces of attraction in the nucleus give rise to a binding of the nuclear protons and neutrons. This may be described by the *binding energy* of the nucleus, defined as the energy which must be given to the nucleons in order to separate them completely. It is therefore analogous to the binding energy of the hydrogen atom, defined as the work which must be done to remove the electron from its ground state orbit to infinity.

A rough idea of the size of these binding energies can be obtained from the known potential energies of the protons due to their Coulomb repulsion. Fortunately, however, an accurate procedure for determining nuclear binding energies exists that makes use of the Einstein mass-energy equivalence. A nucleus composed of neutrons and protons has a *smaller* mass than the sum of the masses of the separated particles. This *loss* of mass represents the binding energy by Einstein's Eq. 20.23

$$\Delta W = (\Delta m)c^2$$

where Δm is the loss in mass due to binding and ΔW the binding energy. Clearly, this binding energy is negative relative to the zero energy of the unbound particles.

The use of the Einstein mass-energy equivalence is particularly applicable to the measurement of nuclear binding energies because of the large energies and small masses involved. The results are confirmed experimentally with high precision in checks and cross-checks that involve the results of mass spectrograph measurements, the energies of nuclear particle reactions, and several other sources. Some of this evidence we shall discuss in this chapter.

As a beginning, let us consider the mass of the helium atom, measured to be 4.00386 mu (Table D in Appendix) in the mass spectrograph. (Note: In particle reactions it is most convenient to use *atomic* masses rather than nuclear masses; this is permissible because the electron mass balances out in the reaction equation.) Now the helium nucleus is presumed to be composed of 2 neutrons + 2 protons, and the mass of these components would therefore be

$$2 \times \text{(mass of H atom)} + 2 \times \text{(mass of neutron)} = 2 \times 1.00813 +$$
$$2 \times 1.00894 = 4.03414 \text{ mu}$$

This mass is greater than the observed helium mass by the amount, 4.03414 − 4.00386 = 0.03028 mu. This deficiency of mass is taken to be the binding energy of the nucleus. In general, the amount by which the mass of any nucleus is less than the mass of its free nucleons is called the *mass defect*. The mass defect is just the binding energy of the nucleus expressed in mass units.

Let us calculate several mass defects (see Table D of Appendix for atomic masses):

$$
\begin{aligned}
\text{For } {}_1\text{H}^2 \text{ (deuteron): } 1.00813 + 1.00894 \quad &= 2.01707 \text{ mu} \\
\text{Observed mass} &= 2.01472 \\
\text{Mass defect of } {}_1\text{H}^2 &= 0.00235 \\
\text{For } {}_8\text{O}^{16}: 8 \times 1.00813 + 8 \times 1.00894 \quad &= 16.13656 \text{ mu} \\
\text{By definition, mass is} &= 16.00000 \\
\text{Mass defect of } {}_8\text{O}^{16} &= 0.13656 \\
\text{For } {}_{92}\text{U}^{238}: 92 \times 1.00813 + 146 \times 1.00894 \quad &= 240.05 \text{ mu} \\
\text{Observed mass} &= 238.13 \\
\text{Mass defect of } {}_{92}\text{U}^{238} &= 1.92
\end{aligned}
$$

27.3 The Einstein Mass-Energy Equivalence

Although the knowledge of nuclear mass defects is of recent origin, arising with the accurate measurements of atomic masses and the neutron-proton model of the nucleus, the basic reason for their presence was already known in 1905 when Einstein proposed the theory of relativity (Chapter 21). It was evident in this theory that mass changes must be associated with changes in energy, just as heat is produced by mechanical work. Yet the relativistic equivalence of mass and energy is demonstrated most clearly in the nucleus and is quite undetectable in macrophysics and even in atomic physics. Why is this so? A simple calculation of energy per unit mass will be illustrative. The mass defect of $_2$He^4 is 0.03028 mu; by employing the mass energy equivalence this can be put in energy units:

$$W = mc^2$$
$$= 0.03028 \times 1.66 \times 10^{-24} \times (3 \times 10^{10})^2$$
$$= 4.52 \times 10^{-5} \text{ ergs}$$

The energy per particle in the helium nucleus is one-fourth of this or 1.13×10^{-5} ergs, and the energy per unit mass is $(1.13 \times 10^{-5})/(1.66 \times 10^{-24})$ or approximately 7×10^{18} erg/gm. This last figure can be compared to observed macroscopic values. For instance, the gravitational potential energy of a mass is *mgh*, the energy per unit mass is *gh*. For some ordinary value of *h*, say 100 cm, this is $980 \times 10^2 = 10^5$ ergs/gm, or less than the nuclear case by a factor of 10^{14}. Even in a release of chemical energy in an explosion, the energy per mass is only of the order of 10^{12} or 10^{13} ergs/gm. Our detection of mass-energy in nuclear experiments is due to the large amount of energy and the exceedingly small masses of the nucleons. This tremendous energy concentration is a nuclear phenomenon.

Although it is entirely reasonable to expect the mass-energy equivalence to be significant in nuclear phenomena, the relativity theory makes no predictions of how to convert mass energy into some other form of energy. Thus a gram of coal contains about 4×10^{11} ergs in the form of potential heat energy which can be released by oxidation; its mass energy is 9×10^{20} ergs, or about the equivalent of the heat energy of 2500 tons of coal. If we could convert the *mass* of the coal into heat energy, we would get two billion times as much energy! But at the present time physics knows no method for the complete conversion of mass to some other form of energy. The existence of mass defects in all nuclei indicates that a partial conversion must have occurred at the time of the formation of the stable nuclei. Whether this process can be simulated on a laboratory scale is still unknown. In many induced transmutations a small fraction of the total nuclear mass is seen to undergo conversion to kinetic energy (see §27.5). Here, then is an agent for mass conversion.

27.4 Calculation of Binding Energies

Though we are not able to discuss the mechanism in the nucleus by which mass energy can be converted into other forms of energy (observe that it is incorrect to speak of converting mass to energy, for mass *is* one form of energy), we can study the results of this conversion. Since the helium nucleus, for example, weighs less than two free neutrons + two free protons, in an experiment designed to break down a helium nucleus it would be necessary to supply this extra mass before the component particles could be free. Thus, to separate the helium nucleons requires an energy equivalent to its mass defect; and therefore, this must be the energy holding the nucleus together.

To make this quantitative, let us first calculate the relation between energy in mass units and electron volts.

$$W = mc^2$$

if
$$m = 1 \text{ mu} = 1.66 \times 10^{-24} \text{ gm}$$

then
$$W = 1.66 \times 10^{-24} \times (3 \times 10^{10})^2 \text{ ergs}$$
$$= 14.94 \times 10^{-4} \text{ ergs}$$

But we saw (§17.10) that 16×10^{-13} ergs = 1 ev, So

$$\text{Energy of 1 mu} = (14.94 \times 10^{-4})/(16 \times 10^{-13})$$
$$= 931 \times 10^6 \text{ ev}$$

or
$$1 \text{ mu} = 931 \text{ Mev}$$

For helium,

$$\text{Binding energy (= mass defect)} = 0.03028 \text{ mu}$$
$$= 0.03028 \times 931 \text{ Mev}$$
$$= 28.2 \text{ Mev}$$

Though we do not know the form of the forces holding the nucleus together, we have determined the energy of binding and that this energy came at the expense of mass energy. The tremendous binding energies of nuclei can be appreciated by comparing them with the binding energies of molecules. We normally think of water, of sodium chloride, of many of the most common compounds as stable substances which can stand a great deal of mistreatment (in terms of energy) and still retain their structure. Yet molecular binding energies are all of the order of 1 to 10 ev. Compared with these, the nuclear binding energies are many million times greater.

27.5   Energy Balance in a Nuclear Reaction

It is clear that in most nuclear reactions the *conservation of mass is no longer a valid law* since, if a nucleus is transmuted in the reaction, kinetic energy will either be released or absorbed in the mass change in the reaction. Hence the conservation of kinetic energy is likewise not obeyed. However, the total mass plus the mass equivalent of the kinetic energies is conserved in accord with the law of conservation of energy. We shall illustrate this conservation by analyzing several cases. Consider, for example, a particle reaction. If we assume that the target nucleus has negligible kinetic energy (for it is virtually at rest compared to the fast moving bombarding particle) then our energy balance must be the following:

(Kinetic energy of the bombarding particle) + (mass energy of bombarding particle) + (mass energy of target nucleus) = (kinetic energy of emitted particle) + (kinetic energy of residual nucleus) + (mass energy of emitted particle) + (mass energy of residual nucleus)

Quite evidently we can write this equation with all the mass energies and kinetic energies expressed in Mev or expressed completely in mass units. Since masses predominate in the equation, it is usually easier to express K.E. in mass units rather than mass energy in Mev.

Let us apply the conservation of energy to Rutherford's original reaction, $_7N^{14}$ (αp) $_8O^{17}$, noting that the incident α particle in his experiment had 7.7 Mev of kinetic energy. We have on the left-hand side of the equation:

K.E. of α particle	0.0083 mu (= 7.7/931)
Mass of α particle	4.0039
Mass of $_7N^{14}$	14.0075
Total input energy	18.0197 mu

Now on the right-hand side of the equation we do not know the kinetic energy of the proton and the O^{17} nucleus. Let us call their sum K:

Mass of $_8O^{17}$	17.0045 mu
Mass of H^1	1.0081
K.E. of $_1H^1$ and $_8O^{17}$	K
Total energy output	18.0126 + K mu

So 18.0197 = 18.0126 + K, K = 0.0071 mu, K = 0.0071 × 931 = 6.6 Mev. This energy of 6.6 Mev that is released in the reaction is shared by the residual O^{17} nucleus and the emitted proton; because of its much lighter mass the proton gets most of it, roughly 16/17 of it. (The exact manner in which K is shared can be calculated by applying the law of conservation of momentum.) Observe that in this case 7.7 Mev of kinetic energy was put into the reaction and only 6.6 Mev of kinetic energy was released. It is thus an example of the conversion of kinetic energy to mass energy. If the incident α particle had had less than 1.1 Mev (= 7.7 − 6.6) of kinetic energy, the reaction would not have occurred at all. Such a reaction is sometimes called *endothermic* (energy absorbing), a term borrowed from chemistry where it applies to the absorption of heat energy in a chemical reaction.

As a second example of the application of the law of conservation of energy let us calculate the energy balance occurring in Chadwick's experiment. There beryllium was bombarded with 5.3 Mev α particles in the reaction $_4Be^9 (\alpha n) {_6}C^{12}$. The energy balance becomes:

K.E. of α	0.0057 mu ($= 5.3/931$)	Mass of $_6C^{12}$	12.0039
Mass of $_2He^4$	4.0039	Mass of $_0n^1$	1.0089
Mass of $_4Be^9$	9.0150	K.E. of $_0n^1 + {_6}C^{12}$	K
Energy input	13.0246 mu	Energy output	13.0128 $+ K$

So $\qquad K = 13.0246 - 13.0128 = 0.0118$ mu $= 11.0$ Mev

In this case 5.3 Mev of K.E. was spent, 11.0 Mev gained. Mass energy was converted into kinetic energy by the reaction. Such a reaction is often termed *exothermic* (or energy yielding).

As an example of energy conservation in a reaction in which a γ-ray photon rather than a particle is used as the bombarding agent consider the photo-disintegration of the deuteron, a very important reaction which determines the neutron mass. In this reaction

$$h\nu + {_1}H^2 \rightarrow {_1}H^1 + {_0}n^1$$

We assume that the neutron mass is approximately that of the proton, but its accurate value is unknown. The photon simply supplies the deuteron with enough energy to compensate its binding energy and some excess which appears as kinetic energy of the ejected proton and neutron. These two particles being of approximately equal mass carry away about the same kinetic energy upon dissociation. Thus one measures the proton energy, e.g., by its total ionization or its range, and the total K.E. is just twice this. With 2.62-Mev γ rays from naturally radioactive $_{81}Tl^{208}$ (ThC'') the proton kinetic energy is observed to be 0.22 Mev. Writing the conservation law we have

Mass of energy of $h\nu$	0.00282 mu (2.62/931)
Mass of $_1H^2$	2.01472
	2.01754 mu

Mass of $_1H^1$	1.00813 mu
Mass energy of K.E.	0.00047
Mass of $_0n^1$	$_0n^1$
	1.00860 $+{_0}n^1$

so that $_0n^1 = 2.01754 - 1.00860 = 1.00894$ mu is the neutron mass. Thus the binding energy of the deuteron is

$$(1.00894 + 1.00813) - 2.01472 = 0.00236 \text{ mu} = 2.20 \text{ Mev.}$$

Evidently photons of less than 2.20 Mev will not produce dissociation of the deuteron.

27.6   Positron Annihilation

One of the most striking examples of the conversion of mass energy into another energy form is the annihilation of positrons. Positrons, we recall, originate from a proton—neutron conversion in an artificially radioactive nucleus. Yet positrons are not found as free entities in nature and it is pertinent to ask what becomes of them.

Suppose a small amount of radioactive phosphorus is wrapped in a copper foil sufficiently thick to stop the positrons (Fig. 27.2), and a Geiger counter

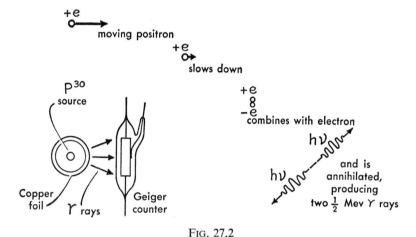

FIG. 27.2

which records gamma rays is placed nearby. Though P³⁰ emits positrons there are no γ rays accompanying them. Yet when copper foil is placed in the path, γ rays are recorded by the Geiger counter. Many experiments had demonstrated that the electrons and positrons are exceedingly ineffective nuclear bombarding agents, and consequently the possibility that these γ rays were induced in the copper nuclei must be ruled out. Instead, we must look to the positron itself as the source of the γ rays. The mechanism is one of conversion of mass energy to electromagnetic energy. A positron is slowed down by collisions in the copper foil; ultimately it encounters an electron (from a copper atom), and the two combine and are annihilated. The mass energy is converted into a pair of photons moving off in opposite directions to conserve momentum (Fig. 27.2). A single positron is unable to undergo self-annihilation because of the law of conservation of electric charge. By applying the conservation of energy to the electron-positron pair we can predict the γ-ray energies (we neglect the small K.E. of the electron and positron):

$$m_{+e}c^2 + m_{-e}c^2 = h\nu + h\nu$$

The mass of the positive electron is identical with that of the negative one, namely 9.1×10^{-28} gm. Hence

$$2mc^2 = 2h\nu$$

and the energy $h\nu$ of each photon is just the mass energy of either electron:

$$W = mc^2 = 9.1 \times 10^{-28} \times (3 \times 10^{10})^2$$
$$= 81.9 \times 10^{-8} \text{ ergs}$$
$$= 0.51 \text{ Mev} = \text{energy of each } \gamma \text{ ray}$$

By placing calibrated lead absorbers in the path of these γ rays their energy can be measured. The result confirms completely the picture we have pre-

Υ ray

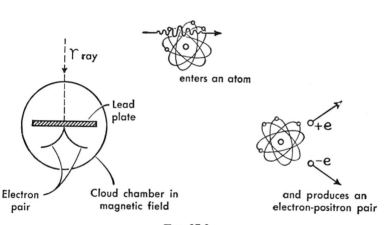

Υ ray

enters an atom

Lead plate

o +e

o -e

Electron pair

Cloud chamber in magnetic field

and produces an electron-positron pair

FIG. 27.3

sented. Thus the life of a positron is brief and ends in a partnership of annihilation to form two γ rays.

27.7   Electron Pair Production

We have often asked the question in physics: Is a given phenomenon reversible? In this case the question takes the form: Can a γ ray create a positive and negative electron? (Conservation of electric charge would demand both.) To create the mass of one electron would require 0.51 Mev; a

γ ray must therefore have at least 1.02 Mev energy to create a pair of electrons. This pair production has been found; the only requirement besides the
energy is the presence of a nucleus (Fig. 27.3). In other words, a γ ray in
empty space will not produce an electron pair regardless of its energy. However, when it penetrates matter and comes close enough to a nucleus it will
produce such a pair of electrons, which in turn move out with equal energies
and in different directions. Not only is this possible, but for γ rays of several
Mev this is the most likely way for them to be absorbed by matter. Of course,
the positron thus created undergoes annihilation promptly. Positrons produced by γ rays were first observed in 1932.

PROBLEMS

(Isotopic masses are to be found in Table D of the Appendix.)

1. Calculate the binding energy of the triton (H^3).   *Ans.* 8.39 Mev.

2. Find the binding energy *per nucleon* in each of the following: He⁴, O¹⁶, A⁴⁰,
Cu⁶³ (62.957), Ag¹⁰⁹ (108.949); Au¹⁹⁷ (197.039), U²³⁸ (238.131). Which nuclei are the
most stable?

3. Compute the energy released in the following reactions:
    (a) C^{12} (d, p) C^{13}, energy of d = 4.50 Mev.
    (b) B^{11} (n, α) L^7, energy of n = 8.26 Mev.

4. α particles are available of 7.7-Mev energy. Is the following reaction energetically possible: C^{12} (α, n) O^{15}?

5. Suggest three possible targets for making radioactive N¹⁶, assuming there are
available with sufficient energy p, n, d, α for bombardment.

6. Compute the maximum energy of β particles emitted when free neutrons disintegrate (neglect the small recoil energy of the residual nucleus). (N.B. The masses
normally quoted, as in Table D, are *atomic* masses.)   *Ans.* 0.75 Mev.

7. Compute the minimum energies required for the photodisintegration of the α
particle into the following products:

   $H^3 + H^1$ *Ans.* 19.8 Mev.
   $H^2 + H^2$ *Ans.* 23.8 Mev.
   $He^3 + n^1$ *Ans.* 20.6 Mev.
   $2H^1 + 2n^1$ *Ans.* 28.2 Mev.

8. Which of the known nuclei of atomic mass number 23 has the greatest binding
energy (Table D)?

Suggested Reading

MILLIKAN, R. A., "Electrons (+ and −)," Chicago, University of Chicago Press, 1947.
   Chapter XIV, lucid account of discovery of the positron and its properties.
POLLARD, E., and DAVIDSON, W. L., "Applied Nuclear Physics," New York, John Wiley & Sons, 1942.
   Chapter 5 discusses the mass-energy balance in nuclear reactions.

Particle Accelerators

28.1 Possible Bombarding Particles

Natural radioactive sources supply high-energy α particles which may be used as bombarding agents in studying nuclear disintegrations. However, there are at least two limitations on such sources: They are weak in yield of particles, and the energy of these particles is determined by the nucleus emitting them and cannot be increased.

Nuclear transmutations are produced by electrons and γ rays only in special cases. One requires heavy particles such as the α particle. However, *protons* ($_1H^1$ nuclei) and *deuterons* ($_1H^2$ nuclei) are even more effective. Their masses are comparable to that of the α particle, but they have only one positive charge to cause repulsion by the nuclei instead of the two carried by the α particle. There are now several devices which artificially produce such high-energy particles in the laboratory. Such devices are called *particle accelerators*. Some of the most common ones will be described.

28.2 Linear Accelerators

The most obvious way to accelerate a charged particle is to allow it to fall through a potential difference in a vacuum. Two electrodes, one at ground potential and one at a high potential (DC), would serve, the ion source being placed near one of the electrodes; as an alternative, several electrodes might be used with a cascading potential difference along them. Such devices in which the accelerated particles move along a straight path through one or more regions of high electric field are called *linear accelerators*.

To produce a 2-Mev proton or deuteron clearly requires a fixed potential difference of two million volts. (This same potential difference would produce a 4-Mev α particle because of its double charge.) Such very large potentials are understandably difficult to produce and maintain in a controlled fashion.

The more obvious methods, such as the use of step-up transformers and rectifiers, have been used for this purpose, but various technical reasons have limited such systems to something less than a million volts.

The most successful of the constant potential linear accelerators is that invented by van de Graaff in 1931. This machine produces its potential difference by the bodily transport of ions or electrons from ground to an insulated conducting electrode, carrying the charges on a moving belt. Since this is essentially an electrostatic process the device is frequently called an electrostatic generator (or accelerator). Figure 28.1 indicates the details of such a generator. The insulating belt (of fabric or rubber) passes a brush-like collector at the bottom of the generator. The brush is maintained positive by batteries or a generator; a gas discharge (the belt is the cathode) is maintained here, and the brush collects electrons from the belt as it passes. When the belt reaches the top of its path it encounters a second collector which is connected directly to the hollow electrode. The deficit of electrons on the belt is partially made up by taking them from the sphere, which thus assumes a positive

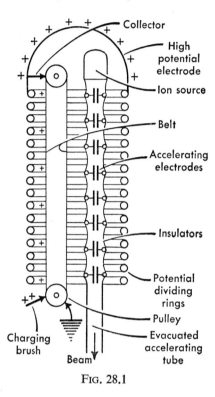

FIG. 28.1

charge. The returning belt is grounded before it starts its cycle over again. The final limit to the charge and potential that the electrode can acquire is set by the leakage into the air and along the supporting insulators. To reduce this the whole unit is often placed in a large pressure tank to gain the increased insulation offered by a gas under high pressure.

A vacuum-tight accelerating tube is mounted inside the supporting column. It is composed of a series of cylindrical conductors (accelerating electrodes) separated by insulating cylinders. The total potential is apportioned evenly along this structure, usually through the agency of a gas discharge between pairs of successive conductors along the outside of the accelerating tube (see Fig. 28.1). Inside the evacuated tube there is a potential difference between successive conductors totaling the potential difference between the upper electrode and ground. These conductors are employed partly to divide the total potential in order to avoid any great potential difference across a single insulator, and partly to focus the beam. Ionized hydrogen, deuterium, or helium enters at the top of the tube, and is then accelerated toward the bottom. A small hole in the bottom electrode allows the *beam* of accelerated particles to impinge on a target. Ionizing the hydrogen, deuterium, or helium initially is a relatively simple process. Across the flow of gas is directed a local beam of accelerated electrons—200 ev is sufficient electron energy—which collide with the molecules of the gas and cause both dissociation of the molecule into its component atoms and ionization of some of these atoms. The gas flow must be kept quite small to maintain a good vacuum in the accelerating tube. This avoids electrical breakdown inside the tube as well as scattering of the beam by gas atoms. The vacuum is maintained by a fast vacuum pump connected to the tube.

The advantages of such an accelerator are many. It supplies an intense beam of protons or deuterons; furthermore, a knowledge of the potential difference between the ends of the tube gives us an exact value of the particle's energy. It is possible to obtain a beam of protons or deuterons amounting to a current of several microamperes; remembering that the charge on the proton or deuteron is 16×10^{-20} coulombs, that one coulomb contains $\frac{1}{16} \times 10^{20}$ of such charges, and that a microampere is 10^{-6} coulombs per sec, we see that a microampere of protons is $\frac{1}{16} \times 10^{14} = 6.7 \times 10^{12}$ protons per second falling on the target. Even if our aim in hitting a nucleus is bad, we still will hit a million or so nuclei every second! To get an equal number of α particles from a radium source would take several grams of radium, or a good fraction of the entire supply of radium on earth. The many practical difficulties in generating and controlling the several million volts and in insulation breakdown or leakage have combined to set an upper limit of about 10 Mev to the energies obtained with the electrostatic type of linear accelerator.

Another type of linear accelerator is being actively developed at the present time, although its basic principles were investigated and tested as early as 1931 by Sloan and Lawrence. In this machine alternating potentials are supplied to a set of electrodes arranged so that the particle is in the accelerating gaps only when the electric fields are in the accelerating direction. (The particles are shielded from the fields during the decelerating half of the cycle, or alternatively, the AC voltages across successive gaps are delayed in time so that each gap picks up the particle in the acceleration part of the cycle.) In the Sloan-Lawrence machine (Fig. 28.2a) the successive electrodes were connected to a transmission line carrying a wave of radio-frequency energy. In one modern variant of this the wave is actually propagated in the same structure (a "wave guide") in which the particle is accelerated (Fig. 28.2b). Another radio-frequency linear accelerator uses a set of "cavities" which act something like transformers in producing very high voltages from the relatively low voltages fed into them from vacuum tube amplifiers (Fig. 28.2c). Some of these machines are being developed for electron acceleration in the billion-electron-volt range of energies.

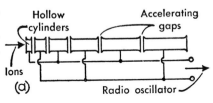

28.3   The Cyclotron

This instrument invented by E. O. Lawrence in 1932 has been one of the most successful of all devices for accelerating protons, deuterons, α particles, or other ions. Its advantage, like that of the radio-frequency linear accelerator, lies in its ability to make a particle fall through a relatively small difference of potential many times, building up an energy equivalent to a large potential difference. To effect this a large magnetic field is used to bend the particles in a circle and bring them back to the region of potential difference for additional acceleration (a circular accelerator).

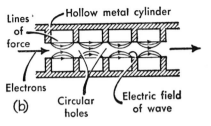

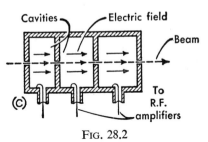

Fig. 28.2

Figure 28.3 shows the essential parts of the cyclotron. An alternating difference of potential is placed between two hollow D-shaped electrodes which lie in a horizontal plane and face each other. A cross beam of electrons at the center of this structure is used to ionize the gas. Suppose that some hydrogen ions are formed between the dees, and consider the instant when the right-hand dee is 50,000 volts negative, relative to the left-hand dee; the proton will move in a horizontal plane across the gap gaining 50,000 ev of energy. It now finds itself moving in the hollow inside of the right dee in a region of no electric field. A strong magnetic field exists in the vertical direction, and the moving charge will undergo a force perpendicular to its motion (see §14.8). If the magnetic field is upward (lower pole N) this will be a clockwise semi-circle as viewed from above. Now if, at the exact moment when the proton is returned to the gap between the dees, the polarity of the dees is reversed, making the left dee negative, the proton will accelerate across a second time, gaining an additional 50,000 ev of energy. It is still being bent by the magnetic field, though because of its increased velocity it will move in a larger circle. Evidently, if we can arrange to alternate the dee polarity at just the right instants, the proton will gain 50,000 ev at each gap crossing, steadily spiraling out toward the edge of the dees. Here a plate, called a "deflector plate," with a high negative potential, is used to pull the particle out from the dee structure, deflecting it into an external chamber where it can bombard a target. As is usual in particle accelera-tion, the region in which the particle moves must be well evacuated.

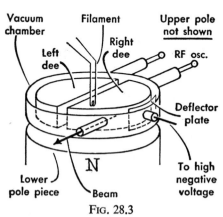

Fig. 28.3

Evidently, this history of events will occur for every hydrogen ion that gets started while the right-hand dee is negative, so we would expect to find protons in all parts of their outward journey, protons crossing the gap at the center, and those which are crossing near the edge and ready to be deflected out. It should be apparent that a large question has been introduced: How is it possible to time the alternation of polarity to be correct for both the particle just getting started and the one already well spiraled out? That this is possible accounts for the success of the cyclotron. Consider the following: The force on a particle of charge e, velocity v in a magnetic field H is $F = evH$. Since the particle is moving in a circle, we know that this must be a centripetal force $F = mv^2/r$. Hence, making this identity we have

$$ evH = \frac{mv^2}{r} \quad \text{or} \quad \frac{r}{v} = \frac{m}{He} \qquad\qquad [\,28.1\,] $$

Now the time for a particle to make a half revolution (from gap back to gap) is just the distance it travels (πr) divided by its velocity (v): $t_{\frac{1}{2}} = \pi r/v$. Sub-stituting the expression above for r/v we get

$$t_1 = \frac{\pi m}{He} \qquad\qquad [28.2]$$

This is just the result we were looking for—the time between gap crossings does not depend on either the radius of the path or the velocity of the proton and will therefore be the same for a beginning particle as for an outer one. (In other words, when the velocity increases, the radius increases by the same factor, that is, their ratio is constant for all particles of the same e/m.)

It is now possible to predict the kinetic energy the particle will have; using Eq. 28.1,

$$\text{K.E.} = \frac{1}{2}mv^2 = \frac{1}{2}m\left(\frac{Her}{m}\right)^2 = \frac{1}{2}\frac{H^2e^2r^2}{m} \qquad [28.3]$$

It is evident that to obtain high-energy particles (having a given e/m) a strong magnetic field (H) covering a dee structure of large radius (r) is desired. This accounts for the large size of the high-energy cyclotron. Existing cyclotrons have diameters varying from 15 to 60 in., requiring magnet structures that vary in weight from 10 to 200 tons.

It is interesting to assume some data and calculate the beam energy attained with a cyclotron. Suppose we have available a magnet that can produce a field of 13,000 oersteds (see §14.7) over a 40 in. diameter circle, and we wish to accelerate deuterons ($_1H^2$). Then

$$\text{K.E.} = \frac{1}{2}\frac{e^2}{m}H^2r^2$$

For the deuteron

$$e = 16 \times 10^{-20} \text{ coulombs} = 4.8 \times 10^{-10} \text{ esu}$$
$$m = 2.01 \times 1.66 \times 10^{-24} \text{ gm} = 3.34 \times 10^{-24} \text{ gm}$$
$$H = 13,000 \text{ oersteds} = \frac{13,000}{3 \times 10^{10}} \text{ esu}$$
$$r = 20 \text{ in.} = 20 \times 2.54 \text{ cm} = 50.8 \text{ cm}$$

Hence

$$\text{K.E.} = \frac{1}{2}\frac{(4.8 \times 10^{-10})^2 \times (13,000)^2 \times (50.8)^2}{3.34 \times 10^{-24} \times (3 \times 10^{10})^2}$$
$$= 1.68 \times 10^{-5} \text{ ergs}$$
$$= \frac{1.68 \times 10^{-5}}{16 \times 10^{-7}} = 10.5 \text{ Mev}$$

An energetic particle! The polarity of the dee must alternate with a frequency which we can obtain from Eq. 28.2. If the time for a half revolution is $t_1 = \pi m/He$, then the time for a full revolution is $2t_1 = 2\pi m/He$. During this time the polarity must have changed sign and returned to its original value. The frequency of this alternation is

$$f = \frac{1}{2t_i} = \frac{He}{2\pi m}$$ [28.4]

Putting in values,

$$f = \frac{13,000 \times 4.8 \times 10^{-10}}{3 \times 10^{10} \times 2\pi \times 3.34 \times 10^{-24}} = 10^7 \text{ cycle/sec}$$

So to keep in step with the circulating deuterons the polarity must change 10 million times a second. In addition, we note that the expression for energy, Eq. 28.3, is independent of the potential difference between the dees; if the potential difference is reduced, the deuteron simply makes more revolutions to attain the same energy. Suppose we are going to put 50,000 volts on the dees. Since the final energy is 10.5 Mev ($= 10.5 \times 10^6$ ev), the deuteron must fall through the gap $10.5 \times 10^6/50,000 = 210$ times; that is, it must make 105 round trips in spiraling outward. While doing this the polarity must therefore have changed 105 times; this requires $105/10^7 = 10.5 \times 10^{-6}$ sec, or about ten millionths of a second for the deuteron's journey. The final velocity of the particle can be calculated at once:

$$\tfrac{1}{2} mv^2 = \text{K.E.} = 1.68 \times 10^{-5} \text{ ergs}$$
$$v^2 = \frac{2 \times 1.68 \times 10^{-5}}{3.34 \times 10^{-24}} = 10.0 \times 10^{18}$$
$$v = 3.16 \times 10^9 \text{ cm/sec}$$

or about one-tenth the velocity of light.

Finally we note from Eq. 28.4 that the oscillator supplying the alternating voltage for the dees must have a frequency that is proportional to e/m for the accelerated particle. This frequency will thus be about the same for deuterons and α particles, since the latter has twice the charge and twice the mass (approximately) of a deuteron. Double this frequency is needed for protons, because their mass is only one-half that of the deuteron. It is not easy to adjust the oscillator frequency over such a range; for this reason cyclotrons are designed either for protons or for deuterons and α particles. If for the latter, the expression for energy shows that the energy of the α particle will be twice that for the deuteron.

28.4 Limitations of the Cyclotron

Consideration of Eq. 28.4 reveals that the frequency of the alternating potential difference on the dees depends on the mass of the accelerating particle. Hence a constant frequency is effective *only* if the particle mass remains essentially constant as it gains speed. For this reason a cyclotron is not used to accelerate electrons to high energies. Even the much heavier proton, deuteron, or α particle begins to suffer appreciable relativistic mass increase when the energy is in the 100-Mev range. This mass increase sets an upper limit to the energy obtainable with a cyclotron, for the particle at the edge will require a different alternation frequency than the one at the center. Existing cyclotrons have successfully obtained beams of protons and deuterons with energies up to 16 Mev and beam currents of as much as a milliampere; α particles of double this energy and about one-tenth the beam current have been produced. For higher energies the cyclotron must be basically modified (§28.5).

28.5 Synchrotron

Since there is no way to prevent the relativistic mass increase, one attempts to compensate for it. Equation 28.4 suggests that if we allowed the magnetic field H to increase at just the same rate as the mass increases, then acceleration would result for a constant frequency. Or as an alternative, we could allow the frequency to decrease proportionately with the mass increase; or we might allow both f and H to vary. Such devices, employing either varying f or H, are called *synchrotrons* (operating conditions are synchronized with the relativistic mass increase).

The F-M cyclotron (or "synchro-cyclotron") first built at the University of California is such a structure. Using a constant magnetic field and a dee voltage of varying frequency (F-M) this machine operates well into the relativistic energy range for deuterons and α particles. The magnet is of the usual cyclotron design; it weighs 4000 tons and has poles 184 in. in diameter. Deuterons of up to 200 Mev and α particles up to 400 Mev have already been produced, and even these figures do not represent the final limitations of the machine. Several new types of nuclear reactions have already been discovered, shedding new light on the nature of nuclear forces.

For still higher heavy-particle energies, magnets of the cyclotron type (with solid cylindrical poles and a surrounding yoke) become much too expensive and bulky. Indeed, the magnet weight increases about as the cube of the pole diameter, or as the 3/2 power of the beam energy. This and other considerations point to the use of a ring-shaped magnet with one or more accelerating sections interposed in the ring; both the magnetic field and the frequency would vary in time. Several such synchrotrons are under construction for the 2- to 10-Bev (billion electron volt) range. A sketch of one is shown in Fig. 28.4.

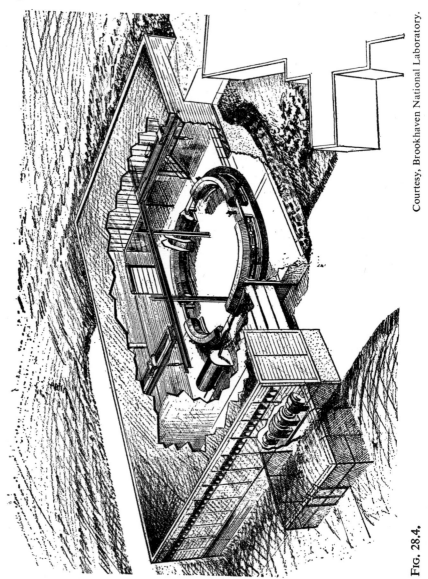

Courtesy, Brookhaven National Laboratory.

FIG. 28.4.

28.6   The Betatron

An ingenious application of the phenomenon of electromagnetic induction was employed by D. W. Kerst in 1940 to obtain high-energy *electrons*.

It is called a betatron, and is illustrated in Fig. 28.5. Between the poles of a large electromagnet is placed an evacuated glass "doughnut" into which electrons are introduced from a filament source. The magnetic field is now varied in an alternating manner. It was emphasized in Chapter 15 that a varying magnetic field produces an electric field, the phenomenon of electromagnetic induction. Suppose we view the situation at the instant that the top magnetic pole is north, the bottom one south, and the field is increasing. As far as the electrons in the vacuum are concerned, this is just the same as if a north magnetic pole were approaching from above. They will move in such a direction that their magnetic field will oppose the apparent approach (Lenz's law). The argument for this direction is identical with that of the coil and approaching bar magnet (Fig. 15.6). Remembering that an electron flow is a current in the opposite direction, we conclude

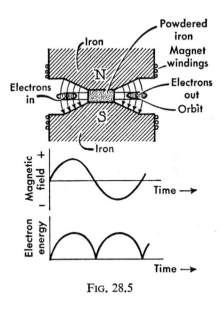

FIG. 28.5

that the electrons will flow clockwise as viewed from the top of the glass chamber. If the magnetic field is large and increasing rapidly, the electrons will make many hundreds of thousands of revolutions in the glass chamber in the short time of increasing field. The conduction is in a vacuum, and hence the electrons steadily gain energy as they circulate. By the time the field stops increasing an electron energy of many million electron volts will be built up. At such energies the electron is traveling with practically the velocity of light, and its mass has become many times its rest mass. As the magnetic field begins to reduce, the induced electric field is reversed, and the electrons are slowed down. However, before this reversal of the induced field the beam is drawn out of the doughnut or caused to impinge on a target by a rapid decrease in the magnetic field brought about by an auxiliary set of magnet coils. Thus the betatron uses only the first quarter of the field cycle in generating a beam of high-energy electrons. At the present time, electrons up to 100 Mev have been produced by the large betatron at the General Electric Research Laboratories. These may be used directly as nuclear bombarding agents, or the very penetrating x rays produced when the electrons hit a target may be used. The full possibilities of such energetic electrons and their accompanying x rays are yet to be exploited.

A result of the betatron operation might be reported that confirms Maxwell's electromagnetic radiation theory. It was pointed out in §19.2 that according to this theory an accelerated electron must be emitting electromagnetic radiation. The Bohr theory denied that this could happen if the electron is associated with an atomic nucleus and substituted the idea of quantized orbits. However, a free electron is presumably subject to no such quantum conditions, and hence, should radiate if accelerated. The electrons in the betatron are free and are being accelerated (centripetal acceleration). And in the high-energy betatron such electrons are observed to radiate electromagnetic waves, some of it being even in the visible region! These accelerated electrons are self-luminous, visibly proving the Maxwell theory. In fact, since this energy radiated out as electromagnetic waves must come at the expense of the kinetic energy of the electrons, a practical upper limit to betatron energies is set by this dissipation of kinetic energy; such a limit is probably well under a billion electron volts. For higher energies electron synchrotrons are indicated. Both the induced emf of the changing magnetic field and electric fields produced by an external oscillator are used to increase the electron energies. At the present time several electron synchrotrons in the hundreds of Mev region are under construction.

28.7   Why More Energy?

This most pertinent question must be answered, at least in part, on somewhat speculative grounds at the present time. The primary problem in most of nuclear physics lies in the nature of nuclear forces and their role in nuclear structure. Past experiments in transmutation have been limited by the available energies to reactions in which only a single particle is ejected. It is reasonable to assume that the introduction of greater energies into the nucleus might cause multiple-particle emission. Evidence for such complex reactions was first obtained in cosmic ray studies. Multiple-particle reactions are now being investigated in detail with the 400 Mev α particles from the California synchro-cyclotron.

Present accelerator design attempts to extend particle energies to the region of those found in cosmic rays. It has been known for many years that our earth is being steadily bombarded by an extremely high-energy radiation coming, presumably, from interstellar space. These *cosmic rays* have been carefully studied with cloud chambers and Geiger counters, ionization chambers and photographic plates placed at many altitudes, and the best evidence indicates that it consists largely, if not solely, of protons with energies of many billions of electron volts. These cosmic particles steadily bombard the atmosphere, and most of the radiation that actually reaches the surface of the earth is the result of atmospheric nuclear reactions from this bombardment. The nature of this secondary cosmic radiation has been thoroughly investigated; it consists of positive and negative electrons, γ rays, protons, neutrons plus a new particle having the charge of an electron but a mass intermediate between the electron and the proton. It has been named a *meson* (meaning intermediate particle). Both positive and negative mesons, with masses ranging from 200 to a 1000 times the rest mass of the electron have been observed (and there is nothing to rule out a neutral meson). The lifetime of the commonest meson (mass about 200) is about two microseconds, after which it converts its excess mass into a pair of neutrinos and a normal positive or negative electron. Now, an impressive feature of the discovery of the meson lies in the fact that in 1935 a Japanese physicist, Yukawa, had *predicted* its existence in order to account for the kind of forces that seem to exist in the nucleus. Like the electron, it was supposed that the meson was not a free particle in the nucleus, but was created by a proton or neutron.

In the cosmic rays it appears that mesons are created in the upper atmosphere by the primary cosmic ray particles (probably protons). Only recently have they been produced in the laboratory. This is because of the large energies involved in meson production. For example, for a meson of mass 200 electron masses the energy required for creation is some $(200/1837) \times 931 = 102$ Mev. Mesons have been produced with the 400-Mev α-particle beam of the California synchro-cyclotron.

A final word that is, at present, just speculation: To create a pair of electrons requires about 1 Mev; to create a pair of mesons requires several hundred Mev (depending on their mass); what is necessary to create a pair of protons? Since the proton is approximately one mass unit, its mass is 931 Mev of energy. Hence a pair would require some two billion electron volts. But the conservation of charge demands that one of them must be negative. The name tentatively given to such a particle is "anti-proton." It has never been observed in secondary cosmic rays, and we have not had sufficient energy in the laboratory to attempt to create it. A proposed 3.5-Bev synchrotron would have enough energy. The anti-proton would be a queer and interesting particle even if it possessed (as it undoubtedly would) a very short life. Might not the anti-proton be an exceedingly effective bombarding agent since it would be attracted, not repeled, by the charges on the target nucleus? How would a nucleus react if such a particle joined its family of nucleons? Such questions may find answers with the development of bigger synchrotrons.

PROBLEMS

1. A certain van de Graaff machine generates a potential difference of 3.5 million volts. It is used to accelerate (a) protons, (b) deuterons, (c) α particles. What energies in Mev will these particles have?

2. Compute the maximum energy of protons obtainable from a cyclotron of 45-in. dee diameter and 12,000 oersted magnetic field.   *Ans.*   22.5 Mev.

3. What frequency of voltage on the dees of the cyclotron of Problem 2 is required?
Ans.   18.4 megacycles/sec.

4. With 60,000 volts between the dees, how many revolutions do the protons of Problem 2 make? What is the total time required?   *Ans.*   187; 10.2 microsec.

5. What is the final velocity of the protons of Problem 2?
Ans. 6.6×10^9 cm/sec or 41,000 mi/sec.

6. Repeat Problems 2, 3, 4, and 5 for deuterons instead of protons.
Ans.   11.2 Mev; 9.2 megacycles/sec; 94; 10.2 microsec; 3.3×10^9 cm/sec.

7. Repeat Problems 2, 3, 4, and 5 for α particles instead of protons.
Ans.   22.5 Mev; 9.2 megacycles/sec; 94; 10.2 microsec; 3.3×10^9 cm/sec.

8. What is the percentage increase in mass of a 200-Mev deuteron as compared with a deuteron at rest?   *Ans.*   10.7%.

9. Calculate the lengths of the first two electrodes of a Sloan-Lawrence accelerator operating with deuterons at 10 megacycles/sec with 50,000 volts across the gaps. (Let the ions start from rest as they enter the gap which precedes the first electrode. Remember that ion velocities inside the hollow cylinders are constant.)
Ans.   22 cm, 31 cm.

Suggested Reading

"Foundations of Nuclear Physics," New York, Dover Publications Inc., 1949.
  Page 23, facsimile of paper by Cockcroft & Walton on the first transmutation induced with accelerated particles. Page 93, facsimile of Lawrence-Livingston paper on the invention of the cyclotron.

KERST, D. W., "Development of the Betatron," January, 1947 issue of *The American Scientist* (Vol. 35, No. 1).
  Page 57, popular account of history of induction acceleration which led to author's development of the betatron.

POLLARD, E., and DAVIDSON, W. L., "Applied Nuclear Physics," New York, John Wiley & Sons, 1942.
  Chapter 4 describes various particle accelerators in simple language.

Nuclear Fission and Nuclear Energy

29.1   Thermal Neutrons

The two conspicuous properties of the neutron are its lack of charge and its mass of (approximately) one mass unit. As was noted in the discussion of the discovery of the neutron, it possesses great penetrating ability. An α particle, a deuteron, or a proton produces dense ionization in traveling through matter; the positive charge on such particles allows them to "pull out" atomic electrons by Coulomb attraction. A high-speed electron likewise interacts with atomic electrons and produces ionization, but to a lesser degree. The photon (γ ray) which has no charge to interact with the electrons in the material loses energy by Compton collisions and the emission of photo-electrons, and if its energy is greater than 1.02 Mev, the photon may completely vanish in the act of pair production.

In contrast to these mechanisms of ionization the neutron, being uncharged, has no electrical interaction with electrons and loses energy only by direct collisions with nuclei. In such collisions the neutron transfers appreciable momentum and energy to the nucleus, since the neutron mass is comparable to nuclear masses. Collisions with hydrogen nuclei led to the discovery of the neutron; if the collision is head-on and elastic, the entire neutron momentum is transferred to the proton. It was pointed out (§7.5) that the most probable angle of elastic collision between particles of the same mass is 45°; at this angle the neutron gives up just one-half of its energy to the proton. In ten such most probable collisions the neutron energy is reduced by the factor $(\frac{1}{2})^{10}$ or 1/1024; or in 20 collisions this factor is roughly one-millionth. Hence a 1-Mev neutron need make only about 20 most probable collisions with hydrogen nuclei to have its energy degraded to 1 ev. (Of course, for practical calculations the average energy loss rather than the most probable energy loss should be used. This is actually somewhat larger than $\frac{1}{2}$.)

It is instructive to calculate how much energy of thermal motion an average neutron would have if it were part of a gas at room temperature (300°K); this is a simple kinetic theory result (see §9.6).

$$\text{Average thermal kinetic energy of an atom} = \frac{3}{2}\frac{R}{N}T$$

where R is the gas constant, 8.3×10^7 ergs/°K, and N is Avogadro's number, 6.02×10^{23}. Then

$$\text{K.E.} = \frac{3}{2} \times \frac{8.3 \times 10^7}{6.02 \times 10^{23}} \times 300 = 6.2 \times 10^{-14} \text{ ergs}$$

$$= \frac{6.2 \times 10^{-14}}{16 \times 10^{-13}} \text{ ev}$$

$$= 0.04 \text{ ev}$$

Hence, if our original 1-Mev neutron suffered about 25 most probable collisions with hydrogen nuclei, its energy would be reduced to thermal energy. Such neutrons are called *thermal neutrons*. For example, neutrons initially having several Mev of energy will be reduced to thermal energies in traversing 10 to 15 cm of paraffin; thereafter they behave much as a gas, though a relatively unstable gas, since the neutron ultimately decays by electron emission to become a proton (the half life for this decay is probably less than 30 min) or disappears in a nuclear reaction with a nucleus. It should be noted that this procedure of degrading the particle energy to thermal values is unique with the neutron. An α particle, a deuteron, or a proton will pick up its required quota of orbital electrons and become neutral atoms at energies very much higher than thermal; likewise an electron will join an atom to become simply an orbital electron. Only the neutron will retain its identity at thermal energies.

29.2   The Neutron as a Bombarding Agent

From this point on in our discussion we shall consider two classes of neutrons: fast neutrons having energies of the order of a million electron volts; slow or thermal neutrons having energies of the order of electron volts or less. Both are used as bombarding agents in inducing nuclear transmutation (though "bombarding" is a somewhat exaggerated term for the randomly moving thermal neutrons). Because the neutron has no charge, the positively charged nucleus presents no repelling barrier to its approach. For this reason the thermal neutron may enter a nucleus to induce a transmutation. Let us consider the two types of reactions.

Fast Neutron Reactions.   The picture we have presented for the slowing down of neutrons relied on elastic collisions between nuclei and neutrons. Such collisions are certainly the most probable kind; however, there exists a small chance that the fast neutron will undergo an inelastic collision, i.e., will actually penetrate into the nucleus to produce an unstable compound nucleus such as we encounter in all induced transmutations. The result is the usual kind of nuclear reaction, in which a proton, an α particle, or even another neutron may be ejected, plus the usual possibility of γ rays. One of the most common methods of obtaining neutrons uses a naturally radioactive source of α particles and relies on the reaction which led to the discovery of the neutron, namely $_4Be^9\,(\alpha,\,n)\,_6C^{12}$. A target bombarded by these ejected neutrons may then be studied. There are also

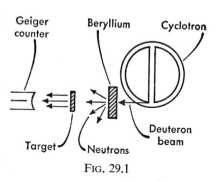

Fig. 29.1

two common methods of obtaining neutrons in conjunction with a cyclotron deuteron beam; these involve the reactions $_4Be^9\,(d,\,n)\,_5B^{10}$ and $_3Li^7\,(d,\,n)\,_4Be^8$; both reactions have a prolific neutron yield. A schematic arrangement is indicated in Fig. 29.1. Except for the technique of obtaining the neutrons in the first place, there is little new to say about fast neutron induced reactions. A few typical ones are listed below:

$$_5B^{10} + _0n^1 \rightarrow _3Li^7 + _2He^4$$
$$_7N^{14} + _0n^1 \rightarrow _6C^{14} + _1H^1$$
$$\longrightarrow _7N^{14} + _{-1}e^0$$
$$_9F^{19} + _0n^1 \rightarrow _7N^{16} + _2He^4$$
$$\longrightarrow _8O^{16} + _{-1}e^0$$
$$_{13}Al^{27} + _0n^1 \rightarrow _{12}Mg^{27} + _1H^1$$
$$\longrightarrow _{13}Al^{27} + _{-1}e^0$$

Thermal Neutron Reactions. As with the fast neutron the most common collisions between slow neutrons and nuclei are elastic. However, a new consideration arises in the case of slow neutrons. Because of their random kinetic motion they are retained in the target material for a relatively long time, and thus the chance of observing a nuclear reaction caused by them is relatively large. As a transmutation agent the slow neutron is very effective, because it collides again and again with the target nuclei, whereas a fast neutron penetrates the target and is gone. Since only a small fraction of the collisions cause transmutation, the increased number of collisions undergone with the slow neutron increases the number of transmutations observed. A second consideration applies uniquely to slow neutrons—contrary to all other types of bombarding particles they bring into the nucleus only a negligible amount of kinetic energy (less than 1 ev). The result of this is usually the capture of the neutron with the newly formed isotope radiating a γ ray (fission is a notable exception, and there are others also). To illustrate, suppose a sodium target is bombarded with thermal neutrons, and we ask what possible reactions could occur. With the aid of a table of isotopic masses (Table D) we can answer as follows:

$$_{11}Na^{23} + {_0}n^1 \text{ (thermal)} \rightarrow ?$$

We have mass energy available of

$$\text{Mass energy} = \text{Mass of } {_{11}}Na^{23} + \text{Mass of } {_0}n^1$$
$$= 22.9964 + 1.0089 = 24.0053 \text{ mu}$$

Suppose we tried the (n,p) reaction:

$$_{11}Na^{23} + {_0}n^1 \xrightarrow{(?)} {_{10}}Ne^{23} + {_1}H^1 = 23.0008 + 1.0081 = 24.0089 \text{ mu}$$

which is energetically impossible. Try the (n, α) reaction:

$$_{11}Na^{23} + {_0}n^1 \xrightarrow{(?)} {_9}F^{20} + {_2}He^4 = 20.0065 + 4.0039 = 24.0104 \text{ mu}$$

which is also impossible. Suppose no particle was ejected, that is, a (n, γ) reaction.

$$_{11}Na^{23} + {_0}n^1 \rightarrow {_{11}}Na^{24} + h\nu = 23.9977 + h\nu$$

Hence

$$h\nu = 24.0053 - 23.9977 = .0076 \text{ mu} = 7.1 \text{ Mev}$$

The sodium 24 will emit a 7.1-Mev γ ray; it is also unstable and decays to $_{12}Mg^{24}$ with the emission of an electron (half life of 14.8 hr). Slow neutron bombardment of sodium is an excellent method of making radiosodium (Na^{24}). It should not be assumed that all thermal neutron reactions are of the (n, γ) type, though this is the most probable one; a simple calculation of the sort just completed will determine those reactions which are energetically possible. The significance of thermal neutrons in nuclear reactions was first pointed out by Enrico Fermi in 1934; he and his co-workers found that for several elements (cadmium, for example) slow neutron capture is a highly probable phenomenon.

29.3   Nuclear Fission—Hahn and Strassmann

After the possibilities of both fast and slow neutron bombardment had been made evident, a new avenue of approach to nuclear reactions was available. One problem in particular seemed amenable, the formation of elements beyond uranium (the transuranic elements). Because of the large Coulomb barrier presented by the 92 positive charges on the uranium nucleus, charged-particle bombardment was not effective at attainable energies. However, a neutron should enter as readily as it enters any other nucleus. Fermi and his collaborators found in 1934 that bombardment of uranium with neutrons produced several new half lives in the target which they attributed to newly formed transuranic elements.

These results aroused considerable interest, and in the next five years a number of workers experimented with slow and fast neutron bombardments of uranium. Many radioactive half lives were found, but attempts at their identification with particular nuclei were subject to great confusion. Finally in 1939 Hahn and Strassmann, working in Germany, showed definitely that one of the supposed transuranic elements was actually an isotope of barium ($Z = 56$), identified by its half life and also chemically. Other isotopes in the middle portion of the periodic table were likewise identified. The interpretation of these anomalous results was suggested by Hahn and Strassmann and promptly extended by Frisch and Meitner (who were former collaborators of Hahn and Strassmann, but were then refugees working in Bohr's laboratory in Copenhagen). A uranium nucleus upon capturing a *slow* neutron *split in two fragments* of which barium must have been one. The phenomenon was termed *nuclear fission*. Workers in many laboratories all over the world continued the investigation of this remarkable new nuclear reaction; within the year some hundred research papers on fission were published.

29.4 Uranium Fission Fragments

The uranium found in nature has three isotopes of the following masses and abundances:

$$_{92}U^{238} (99.28\%); \; _{92}U^{235} (0.71\%); \; _{92}U^{234} (0.005\%)$$

By isolating a few micrograms of uranium 235 with a mass spectrograph, it was determined unambiguously that this was the isotope undergoing slow neutron induced fission. (Uranium 235 will undergo fission with fast neutrons only rarely; such fast neutron fission is negligible compared with that due to slow neutrons.) The U^{236} formed by $U^{235} + {_0}n^1$ is basically unstable, and literally splits apart into two nuclei (Fig. 29.2) of comparable masses.

There are observed two significant features of the fission fragments: (1) On the average one fragment represents about 60% of the original mass the other about 40%; splitting into two particles of equal mass is much less probable. Furthermore, the fragments are highly radioactive, and finally reach stability only after an involved radioactive descent from their original state. (2) In addition to the two nuclear fragments, from two to three fast neutrons on the average are liberated in the fission (Fig. 29.2). To illustrate, let us write down one of the many possible fission reactions:

$$_{92}U^{235} + _0n^1 \text{ (thermal)} \rightarrow _{56}Ba^{144} + _{36}Kr^{90} + 2_0n^1 \text{ (fast)}$$

The barium and krypton nuclei are unstable and can decay to stability in the following chains:

$$_{56}Ba^{144} \xrightarrow{} _{57}La^{144} + _{-1}e^0$$
$$\underset{?}{\uparrow} \qquad \longrightarrow _{58}Ce^{144} + _{-1}e^0$$
$$\underset{?}{\uparrow} \qquad \longrightarrow _{59}Pr^{144} + _{-1}e^0$$
$$\underset{290 \text{ days}}{\uparrow} \qquad \longrightarrow _{60}Nd^{144} \text{ (stable)}$$
$$\underset{17 \text{ min}}{\uparrow}$$

$$\Big\} + \gamma \text{ rays}$$

$$_{36}Kr^{90} \xrightarrow{} _{37}Rb^{90} + _{-1}e^0$$
$$\underset{30 \text{ sec}}{\uparrow} \qquad \longrightarrow _{38}Sr^{90} + _{-1}e^0$$
$$\underset{80 \text{ sec}}{\uparrow} \qquad \longrightarrow _{39}Y^{90} + _{-1}e^0$$
$$\underset{70 \text{ yr}}{\uparrow} \qquad \longrightarrow _{40}Zr^{90} \text{ (stable)}$$
$$\underset{61 \text{ hr}}{\uparrow}$$

$$\Big\} + \gamma \text{ rays}$$

It is evident that unraveling the radioactive chains resulting from fission is a task comparable to the clarification of the natural radioactive series. Though fission occurs almost instantaneously, the subsequent radioactivity of the fragments persists for days or weeks.

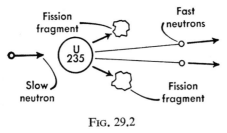

FIG. 29.2

Although the identity of the fission fragments varies from one fission to another, the form of the radioactive chains is generally the same for all. That is, the chains are a succession of β-particle emissions. This is evident from the following consideration. The heaviest elements have more neutrons per nucleon than the stable elements of medium mass numbers. Thus the fission fragments will have an excess of neutrons. Some of these are emitted in the fission process and the remainder are converted to protons with the emission of electrons, forming a chain of three to five members which continues until a stable element is reached.

29.5 Energy Released in Fission

Uranium fission represents a conversion of mass energy on a scale hitherto unheard of. About 0.1% of the mass of the uranium 236 is converted to kinetic energy! This corresponds to a release of about 200 Mev of energy. One method of determining this figure consisted of enclosing the uranium and the slow neutron source in a container that was isolated from external heat sources; by noting the temperature rise of the container and its contents the total energy released can be calculated; a Geiger counter or ionization chamber recorded the number of fission events responsible for this energy release; hence the energy per fission was obtained. A little arithmetic will indicate the magnitudes involved: if every nucleus in a pound of uranium 235 underwent fission the total energy released would be:

$$\text{Energy released per atom} = 200 \text{ Mev}$$
$$= 200 \times 16 \times 10^{-7} \text{ ergs}$$
$$= 3.2 \times 10^{-4} \text{ ergs}$$
$$1 \text{ lb} = 454 \text{ gm} = \frac{454}{235} \text{ moles}$$

in which there are

$$\frac{454}{235} \times 6.02 \times 10^{23} = 1.16 \times 10^{24} \text{ atoms}$$

$$\text{Total energy released} = 1.16 \times 10^{24} \times 3.2 \times 10^{-4}$$
$$= 3.7 \times 10^{20} \text{ ergs}$$

This is the equivalent of the heat from two million pounds of coal.

Rough measurement of the energy of the liberated neutrons and of the γ rays and electrons emitted in the subsequent radioactivity indicates the distribution of the fission energy. About 80% of the 200 Mev goes into kinetic energy of the fragment nuclei. We noted in § 29.1 that thermal energies at room temperature were about 0.04 ev. Hence a fission fragment is given energy corresponding to a few billion degrees Kelvin! We indeed gain respect for the vast amount of kinetic energy locked up in the form of mass, for the above figures result from the conversion of only one-thousandth (0.1%) of the uranium mass. The remaining 20% of the total energy is carried by the neutrons released in the fission and by the fission fragments in the form of radioactive energy.

While one could not have predicted the fission process from the Einstein mass-energy equivalence, it does show the reason for the energy release. If one consults a table of isotopic masses it will be seen that the binding energy per nucleon is larger for nuclei of moderate mass numbers than for the heaviest nuclei. The difference amounts to about 1 Mev per nucleon. Thus if U^{236} splits into two approximately equal fragments there would be a binding energy increase of about 200 Mev (literally 236 Mev by this rough argument). This 200 Mev would then be released as some other form of energy, at least some of which would be kinetic energy of the fission fragments.

29.6   Fission Neutrons

The two to three fast neutrons liberated when uranium 236 undergoes fission open up a new possibility, that of a *chain reaction*. Since a neutron is needed for fission and neutrons are liberated by fission, the process might be made self-sustaining. If this is true then why have we any uranium 235 left, since there are always stray neutrons from cosmic rays that would have touched off the explosion? The answer lies in two facts: (1) The uranium 235 being surrounded by 140 times as much uranium 238 is protected from neutrons. (2) A *slow* neutron is very much more efficient in causing fission than a fast neutron—and the fission-released neutrons are fast. Hence to encourage a chain reaction two problems must be met, enriching the number of uranium 235 atoms, i.e., removing the 238, and slowing down the fission neutrons to increase their effectiveness. In a mass of uranium this slowing-down process must be accomplished by collisions

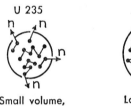

U 235

Small volume, neutrons escape before being slowed down

U 235

Large volume, fewer neutrons escape

FIG. 29.3

with the heavy uranium nuclei, a none too effective means of degrading energy. Thus it is evident that even with a highly enriched sample of uranium 235 we will not have a chain reaction unless that sample has a volume large enough to retain the neutron while it is being slowed down by collisions (Fig. 29.3). Therefore, there must be a *critical* volume, below which too many neutrons escape to sustain the fission reaction. It is for this reason that uranium 235, once it is enriched, can still be handled safely. This suggests a possible mechanism for a nuclear fission bomb: Detonation occurs when two masses, each below critical size, are rapidly hurled together. If the resultant volume were above the critical size a chain reaction would occur with an exceedingly large release of energy. The time for this chain reaction to spread throughout the uranium mass is only a few hundredths of a micro-second!

29.7 Other Fissionable Nuclei

The very difficult process of separating the uranium 235 isotope from 238 (the general problem of isotope separation was taken up in Chapter 18) led to a search for other fissionable nuclei. It had been shown that both thorium ($Z = 90$) and protoactinium ($Z = 91$) exhibit the phenomenon very slightly. However, from theoretical considerations Bohr and Wheeler pre-dicted that the transuranic element of $Z = 94$ should undergo fission with slow neutrons as readily as uranium 235. The transuranic elements are formed by bombarding uranium 238 with *fast* neutrons; the reactions involved are now known to be;

$$_{92}U^{238} + {_0}n^1 \text{ (fast)} \longrightarrow {_{92}}U^{239}$$

$$\longrightarrow {_{93}}Np^{239} + {_{-1}}e^0$$

$$\underset{23 \text{ min}}{\uparrow}$$

$$\longrightarrow {_{94}}Pu^{239} + {_{-1}}e^0$$

$$\underset{2.3 \text{ day}}{\uparrow}$$

Element 93 is neptunium; element 94 is plutonium; it is Pu that undergoes fission easily. Since these elements are not found in nature, it is necessary to manufacture them by transmutation. Though its manufacture from uranium 238 is difficult, plutonium can be separated from its uranium parent chemi-cally, whereas uranium 235 demands much more difficult measures for its separation from uranium 238. To appreciate the difficulties of plutonium manufacture, it should be remembered that any transmutation process is re-latively improbable, since the chance of a neutron entering a nucleus is very small compared to its chance of elastically colliding or missing completely. The maximum amount of any element produced by transmutation in the laboratory had been only a few millionths of a gram. If plutonium is to be used to release nuclear (mass) energy on an engineering scale, it is necessary to have thousands of grams. Thus it is evident that the successful production of plutonium required heroic experimental measures. The solution of the prob-lem was given by Fermi with the invention of the *nuclear reactor* or "pile."

29.8 The Nuclear Reactor—Fermi (1942)

As we have seen, to produce plutonium we must have uranium 238 and fast neutrons; a good source of fast neutrons is the fission of uranium 235;

to keep this source of fast neutrons going we need slow neutrons for fission. The nuclear reactor supplies these requirements.

Consider two small cylinders of ordinary uranium (99.3% of 238, 0.7% of 235) separated by some element that will be effective in slowing down neutrons, but with little tendency to absorb them. Such a substance is called a *moderator*.

We have seen that hydrogen slows neutrons readily, but unfortunately it also absorbs them readily in the nuclear reaction $_1H^1$ (n, γ) $_1H^2$ and hence will not serve as a moderator. The two elements which have been found to be most

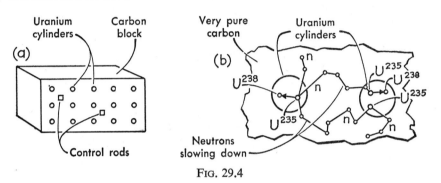

Fig. 29.4

suitable are deuterium $(_1H^2)$ and carbon. The latter is more commonly used. It must, however, be extremely pure to prevent neutron absorption by the impurities.

The course of events in a reactor might be as follows: A neutron introduced in the carbon (from outside, say) is slowed down and finally enters a uranium cylinder; there it collides frequently with uranium nuclei until it finally enters a 235 nucleus and produces fission of the U^{236} nucleus; let us assume that three fast fission neutrons are produced and that one is absorbed by a 238 nucleus, eventually decaying to plutonium; the other two escape out into the carbon and are eventually slowed down by many collisions with carbon nuclei; they now wander into a new cylinder of uranium (or maybe back to the one they come from); if they ultimately hit a 235 nucleus the process can repeat itself (Fig. 29.4). Thus the success of the reactor for manufacturing plutonium lies in using some of the fast fission neutrons to bombard uranium 238, the rest being slowed down to cause fission in 235 to generate more neutrons. For large-scale production of plutonium this system must be multiplied many-fold. Its control is relatively simple. If fission is occurring too frequently a few cylinders of a slow neutron absorber (such as cadmium) may be inserted in the moderator; these will reduce the number of neutrons in the moderator by absorbing them. Removal of the cadmium cylinders speeds up the reaction.

29.9 The Nuclear Reactor as a Source of Heat

Fission of the uranium 235 nucleus releases about 200 Mev largely in the form of kinetic energy. Hence the cylinders of uranium would be heated above their melting points very quickly if they were not cooled. In the manufacture of plutonium this heat energy is dissipated by a tremendous flow of cooling water. (The U. S. Atomic Energy Commission installations use part of the Columbia River.) However, this heat could be put to useful purpose, and the reactor would thus serve as a nuclear energy furnace. This aspect of the use of nuclear energy is being investigated at the present time. The principal problem is the development of high-temperature reactors, not necessarily with the actual production of large amounts of heat energy. Presumably the reactor would be used as the "boiler" of an otherwise conventional steam plant, ultimately producing electric power. Like all ordinary heat energies a high temperature is necessary for efficient operation. As yet there are no new kinds of engines producing electrical or mechanical energy directly from nuclear fuels. The manifold metallurgical and mechanical problems of the ordinary heat engine are multiplied by the presence of enormous densities of neutrons and radioactive radiations.

29.10 Nuclear Fusion

The loss in mass when two protons and two neutrons are packed together into a helium nucleus was discussed in §27.3, where it was shown that the mass loss was 0.0303 mu or 28 Mev. This suggests the possibility of liberating mass energy by the fusion of elementary particles to form a more complex nucleus. This process of the release of energy in building up nuclei is called *nuclear fusion* and is the reverse of nuclear fission. Whereas fission is possible for only the heaviest nuclei, fusion is energy-profitable for only the lightest nuclei. The difficulty lies in finding a mechanism in the laboratory by which one can "cook up" helium from a mixture of protons and neutrons. No such terrestrial mechanism has yet been developed, but it would be unwise to declare it impossible. In fact, a mechanism does exist—in the interior of the sun!

29.11 The Carbon Nitrogen Cycle of the Sun

The theory, now accepted, that the sun's heat energy is being produced by nuclear fusion was advanced by Bethe in 1939. He proposed that hydrogen was being used up in the production of helium with a consequent release of mass energy; this process is catalyzed by carbon, nitrogen, and oxygen, which themselves are unaltered in abundance. The nuclear reactions postulated are the following:

(1) $_6C^{12} + _1H^1 \rightarrow _7N^{13}$

(2) $\longrightarrow _6C^{13} + _{+1}e^0$

(3) $_6C^{13} + _1H^1 \rightarrow _7N^{14}$

(4) $_7N^{14} + _1H^1 \rightarrow _8O^{15}$

(5) $\longrightarrow _7N^{15} + _{+1}e^0$

(6) $_7N^{15} + _1H^1 \rightarrow _6C^{12} + _2He^4$

The total energy released is approximately 30 Mev for each helium atom formed. Note that though four protons are used, two of them indirectly lose their charges to positrons and hence are effectively neutrons. This "burning" of hydrogen to produce helium is activated by the very high kinetic energy of the particles and the very high density of matter. (In the solar interior the temperature is of the order of 20 million degrees, the density some hundreds of grams per cubic centimeter.) The 30 Mev released is shared by all the particles involved, thus maintaining the temperature and sustaining the reaction, as long as there is hydrogen.

The nuclear fusion cycle in the sun employs high temperatures as the means of inducing the mass-energy release. We have seen that fission fragments have kinetic energies corresponding to such temperatures. It might be possible, therefore, to use a furnace preheated by fission and use fusion as the combustion mechanism.

29.12   The Nuclear Reactor as a Research Tool

There are three roles which the nuclear reactor plays with consummate success: (1) in the manufacture of fissionable plutonium, (2) as a generator of vast amounts of heat (at present at relatively low temperature), and (3) in supplying neutrons, both fast and slow. The staggering implication of the first role as a weapon of war puts the reactor in a class by itself. That science has created the means by which itself and society can be destroyed is not a new phenomenon. The discovery of fire, of chemical explosives, of the methods of controlling disease, and many other instances could also have led to mass destruction. Instead man saw fit to give up a little of his personal rights to gain protection from and for his fellow men. The "atomic bomb" presents the same problem of control exaggerated greatly in intensity; the

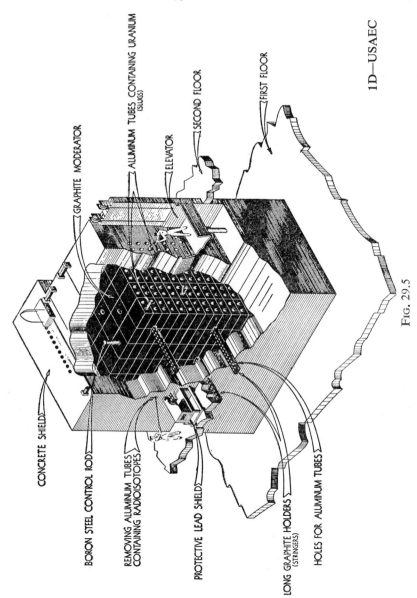

GRAPHITE MODERATOR

ALUMINUM TUBES CONTAINING URANIUM
(SLUGS)

ELEVATOR

SECOND FLOOR

FIRST FLOOR

1D—USAEC

CONCRETE SHIELD

BORON STEEL CONTROL ROD

REMOVING ALUMINUM TUBES
CONTAINING RADIOISOTOPES

PROTECTIVE LEAD SHIELD

LONG GRAPHITE HOLDERS
(STRINGERS)

HOLES FOR ALUMINUM TUBES

FIG. 29.5

sacrifice of sovereignty is no longer on an individual scale, but becomes a necessity for nations. The conceding of national sovereignty is a painful thing, but appears to be the only solution in the present case.

The use of the reactor as a source of power has been briefly discussed.

Power reactor development is limited at the present time only by the technical details of engineering (which are not trivial, to be sure).

As a generator of large numbers of neutrons the reactor becomes an effective research tool (Fig. 29.5). A target placed inside the moderator undergoes intense bombardment by slow and near-slow neutrons and is transmuted into a radioactive source of far greater intensity than can be produced by any kind of particle accelerator. If fast neutrons (a few Mev) are desired, a channel cut into the moderator will permit large numbers of them to escape for bombardment purposes. Though there is still a great deal to be learned in neutron physics, thus far the most productive research use of the reactor has been as a producer of transmuted nuclei, both stable and unstable. These have been employed in many fields of science as stable or radioactive *tracers*.

A brief example will explain this tracer technique. Analysis of our blood reveals the presence of salt (NaCl), which of course is absorbed from the food we eat. How long a time is needed for this absorption process? How quickly will a fresh supply of salt permeate all our blood? Analysis of blood taken from a finger tip will show the presence of salt, but not the time at which the salt was introduced. The question can be answered quickly and accurately with the use of radioactive NaCl, for though it is chemically identical with normal NaCl it is physically different. If one drinks a small quantity of radioactive NaCl, within a matter of three to five minutes a Geiger counter placed at the finger tips or toes will begin to record the presence of the NaCl tracer. A similar experiment reveals to what extent the thyroid gland concentrates iodine taken into the system. An analogous technique employing an element whose normal isotopic abundance ratio has been changed uses a mass spectrograph to reveal the presence of the "tagged" atoms (§19.8).

The extensive use of isotopic and radioactive tracers in medicine, biology, chemistry, metallurgy, physics, and many other sciences has been given tremendous incentive by the large quantities of such tracers which are now available from nuclear reactors. These studies are yet in their infancy, but the rewards are already great.

PROBLEMS

1. A fission fragment has kinetic energy of 100 Mev. What is its equivalent temperature?   *Ans.*   770 billion °K.

2. What is the mean energy of neutrons at 4.3 °K (the temperature at which helium liquefies)?   *Ans.* 8.9×10^{-16} ergs or 0.00056 ev.

3. What is the de Broglie wave length of the neutron of Problem 2?

Ans. 12.1 Å.

4. What is the temperature of a neutron gas of 1 ev average neutron energy?

Ans. 7700 °K.

5. Compute the energy release in the slow neutron reaction N^{14} (n, p) C^{14}.

Ans. 0.56 Mev.

6. Compute the mass of U^{235} in 1 mole of natural uranium.   *Ans.* 1.7 gm.

7. An ideal nuclear reactor using U^{235} fission to produce Pu^{239} with *no* loss of neutrons produces 10 gm of Pu^{239} per day. What heat energy is evolved per day? (Assume 2 neutrons released per U^{235} fission.)

Ans. 6.5 × 10^{11} joules or 1.8 × 10^5 kw-hr.

Suggested Reading

CAMPBELL, J. W., "The Atomic Story," New York, Henry Holt & Co., 1947.
A journalist's description of the atomic bomb project. Clear, readable.

GAMOW, GEORGE, "Atomic Energy in Cosmic and Human Life," New York, The Macmillan Co., 1946.
Gamow has a flare for making physics read like a best-seller. A clear discussion of the solar fusion cycle is included in this small book.

HECHT, SELIG, "Explaining the Atom," New York, Viking Press, 1947.
Chapters V through VIII form a good description of fission and the bomb.

SMYTH, H., "Atomic Energy for Military Purposes," Princeton University Press, 1945.
The famous Smyth Report is still the best account of the development of nuclear fission applications during World War II.

Appendix

Table A

Approximate Values of Physical Constants*

Gravitational constant (G)	$= 6.67 \times 10^{-8}$ cm^3/gm-sec^2
Standard acceleration due to gravity (g)	$= 981$ cm/sec^2
Standard atmosphere pressure (P_a)	$= 1.01 \times 10^6$ dynes/cm^2
Absolute zero (0°K)	$= -273$ °C
Avogadro's number (N)	$= 6.02 \times 10^{23}$
Molar volume at N.T.P.	$= 22{,}400$ cm^3
Molar gas constant (R)	$= 8.31 \times 10^7$ ergs/°K
Velocity of light in vacuo (c)	$= 3.00 \times 10^{10}$ cm/sec
Charge-mass ratio for electron (e/m)	$= 17.6 \times 10^7$ coulomb/gm
	$= 5.27 \times 10^{17}$ esu/gm
Electron charge (e)	$= -4.80 \times 10^{-10}$ esu
	$= -16.0 \times 10^{-20}$ coulombs
Electron rest mass (m_0)	$= 9.11 \times 10^{-28}$ gm
Energy of 1 electron volt (ev)	$= 16.0 \times 10^{-13}$ ergs
Unit atomic mass (mu)	$= 1.66 \times 10^{-24}$ gm
Mass ratio of $_1$H^1 atom to electron	$= 1837$
Energy equivalent of 1 atomic mass unit	$= 931$ Mev
Planck's constant (h)	$= 6.62 \times 10^{-27}$ erg-sec
Compton wave length (h/mc)	$= 0.0243 \times 10^{-8}$ cm

Table B

Units and Conversion Factors

DYNAMICAL UNITS

1 inch is 2.54 cm
1 mile is 1.61 km
1 quart is 0.946 liters $= 946$ cm^3
1 pound is 454 gm
1 mile/hour is 44.7 cm/sec
1 joule is 10^7 erg
1 watt is 10^7 erg/sec
1 angstrom is 10^{-8} cm

ELECTRICAL UNITS

1 coulomb is 3×10^9 esu of charge
1 ampere is 3×10^9 esu of current
1 volt is 1/300 esu of potential
1 ohm is $\frac{1}{9} \times 10^{-11}$ esu of resistance
1 oersted is $\frac{1}{3} \times 10^{-10}$ esu of magnetic field strength

---

* Adapted from a table by R. T. Birge, *Reviews of Modern Physics*, October 1941.

Table C

Chemical Masses of the Elements

ELEMENT	SYMBOL	ATOMIC NO.	MASS
Actinium	Ac	89	227.
Aluminum	Al	13	27.0
Americium	Am	95	
Antimony	Sb	51	121.8
Argon	A	18	39.9
Arsenic	As	33	74.9
Astatine	At	85	
Barium	Ba	56	137.4
Beryllium	Be	4	9.0
Bismuth	Bi	83	209.0
Boron	B	5	10.8
Bromine	Br	35	79.9
Cadmium	Cd	48	112.4
Calcium	Ca	20	40.1
Carbon	C	6	12.0
Cerium	Ce	58	140.1
Cesium	Cs	55	132.9
Chlorine	Cl	17	35.5
Chromium	Cr	24	52.0
Cobalt	Co	27	58.9
Columbium	Cb	41	92.9
Copper	Cu	29	63.5
Curium	Cm	96	
Dysprosium	Dy	66	162.5
Erbium	Er	68	167.2
Europium	Eu	63	152.0
Fluorine	F	9	19.0
Francium	Fr	87	227.
Gadolinium	Gd	64	156.9
Gallium	Ga	31	69.7
Germanium	Ge	32	72.6
Gold	Au	79	197.2
Hafnium	Hf	72	178.6
Helium	He	2	4.0
Holmium	Ho	67	164.9
Hydrogen	H	1	1.0
Indium	In	49	114.7
Iodine	I	53	126.9
Iridium	Ir	77	193.1
Iron	Fe	26	55.9
Krypton	Kr	36	83.7
Lanthanum	La	57	138.9

Table C—*Chemical Masses of the Elements*—Continued

ELEMENT	SYMBOL	ATOMIC NO.	MASS
Lead	Pb	82	207.2
Lithium	Li	3	6.9
Lutecium	Lu	71	175.0
Magnesium	Mg	12	24.3
Manganese	Mn	25	53.9
Mercury	Hg	80	200.6
Molybdenum	Mo	42	96.0
Neodymium	Nd	60	144.3
Neon	Ne	10	20.2
Neptunium	Np	93	
Nickel	Ni	28	58.7
Nitrogen	N	7	14.0
Osmium	Os	76	190.2
Oxygen	O	8	16.0
Palladium	Pd	46	106.7
Phosphorus	P	15	31.0
Platinum	Pt	78	195.2
Plutonium	Pu	94	
Polonium	Po	84	
Potassium	K	19	39.1
Praseodymium	Pr	59	140.9
Promethium	Pm	61	
Protoactinium	Pa	91	231.
Radium	Ra	88	226.1
Radon	Rn	86	222.
Rhenium	Re	75	186.3
Rhodium	Rh	45	102.9
Rubidium	Rb	37	85.5
Ruthenium	Ru	44	101.7
Samarium	Sm	62	150.4
Scandium	Sc	21	45.1
Selenium	Se	34	79.0
Silicon	Si	14	28.1
Silver	Ag	47	107.9
Sodium	Na	11	23.0
Strontium	Sr	38	87.6
Sulfur	S	16	32.1
Tantalum	Ta	73	180.9
Technetium	Tc	43	
Tellurium	Te	52	127.6
Terbium	Tb	65	159.2
Thallium	Tl	81	204.4
Thorium	Th	90	232.1

Table C—*Chemical Masses of the Elements*—Continued

ELEMENT	SYMBOL	ATOMIC NO.	MASS
Thulium	Tm	69	169.4
Tin	Sn	50	118.7
Titanium	Ti	22	47.9
Tungsten	W	74	183.9
Uranium	U	92	238.1
Vanadium	V	23	51.0
Xenon	Xe	54	131.3
Ytterbium	Yb	70	173.0
Yttrium	Y	39	88.9
Zinc	Zn	30	65.4
Zirconium	Zr	40	91.2

Table D

*Isotopes of the Light Elements**

Z	ELEMENT	A	ISOTOPIC† MASS (mu)††	ABUNDANCE (%)	HALF LIFE
0	*e*	0	0.000548		
0	*n*	*1*	*1.00894*		0.5 hr
1	H	1	1.00813	99.984	
		2	2.01472	0.016	
		3	*3.01700*		12 yr
2	He	3	3.01699	10^{-4}	
		4	4.00386	100	
		6	*6.0209*		0.8 sec
3	Li	6	6.01692	7.39	
		7	7.01816	92.61	
		8	*8.02497*		0.88 sec
4	Be	*7*	*7.01909*		50 days
		8	*8.00781*		10^{-15} sec
		9	9.01496	100	
		10	*10.01662*		2×10^6 yr
5	B	10	10.01617	18.83	
		11	11.01290	81.17	
		12	*12.0168*		0.02 sec
6	C	*10*	*10.0209*		20 sec
		11	*11.01502*		20 min
		12	12.00388	98.9	
		13	13.00756	1.1	
		14	*14.00774*		6000 yr
7	N	*13*	*13.00990*		10 min
		14	14.00753	99.62	
		15	15.00487	0.38	
		16	*16.011*		7.4 sec
		17	*17.012*		4 sec
8	O	*14*	*14.01*		76 sec
		15	*15.0078*		126 sec
		16	16.00000	99.757	
		17	17.00450	0.039	
		18	18.00485	0.204	
		19	*19.00937*		29 sec
9	F	*17*	*17.00758*		70 sec
		18	*18.00670*		112 min
		19	19.00454	100	

* Adapted from J. Mattauch, *Nuclear Physics Tables*, Interscience Publishers, N. Y.. 1946, and G. T. Seaborg and I. Perlman, *Reviews of Modern Physics*, October 1948.

† Mass of neutral atom.

†† Mass of *unstable* nuclei in italics.

Table D—*Isotopes of the Light Elements*—Continued

Z	ELEMENT	A	ISOTOPIC† MASS (mu)††	ABUNDANCE (%)	HALF LIFE
		20	20.0065		12 sec
10	Ne	19	19.00798		20 sec
		20	19.99889	90.51	
		21	21.00002	0.28	
		22	21.99858	9.21	
		23	23.00084		40 sec
11	Na	21	21.0035		23 sec
		22	22.00032		3 yr
		23	22.99644	100	
		24	23.99774		14.8 hr
		25	24.99771		60 sec
12	Mg	23	23.0006		11.6 sec
		24	23.9930	78.60	
		25	24.9946	10.11	
		26	25.9901	11.29	
		27	26.9926		10 min
13	Al	25	24.998		8 sec
		26	25.9944		6 sec
		27	26.9907	100	
		28	27.9908		2.3 min
		29	28.9892		6.7 min
14	Si	27	26.9961		4.9 sec
		28	27.9872	92.28	
		29	28.9865	4.67	
		30	29.9840	3.05	
		31	30.9866		3 hr
15	P	29	28.9915		4.6 sec
		30	29.9885		2.5 min
		31	30.9844	100	
		32	31.9844		14 days
		34	33.9843		12 sec
16	S	31	30.9896		3 sec
		32	31.9825	95.06	
		33	32.9819	0.74	
		34	33.9798	4.18	
		35	34.9790		87 days
		36	35.9780	0.016	
		37	36.9823		5 min
17	Cl	33	32.9857		2.5 sec
		34	33.9837		33 min
		35	34.9788	75.4	
		36	35 9780		10^6 yr

Table D—*Isotopes of the Light Elements*—Continued

Z	ELEMENT	A	ISOTOPIC† MASS (*mu*)††	ABUNDANCE (%)	HALF LIFE
		37	36.9777	24.6	
		38	37.9800		38 min
		39	38.98		1 hr
18	A	35	34.9847		1.9 sec
		36	35.9773	0.307	
		37	36.978		34 days
		38	37.9746	0.060	
		39	38.98		4 min
		40	39.9755	99.633	
		41	40.9774		110 min

Table E PERIODIC TABLE (ONLY NATURALLY FOUND ISOTOPES LISTED EXCEPT FOR TRANSURANIC ELEMENTS)

	I	II	III	IV	V
I	$_1$**H** HYDROGEN 1, 2				
II	^{3}**Li** LITHIUM 6, 7	^{4}**Be** BERYLLIUM 9	^{5}**B** BORON 10, 11	^{6}**C** CARBON 12, 13	^{7}**N** NITROGEN 14, 15
III	^{11}**Na** SODIUM 23	^{12}**Mg** MAGNESIUM 24, 25, 26	^{13}**Al** ALUMINUM 27	^{14}**Si** SILICON 28, 29, 30	^{15}**P** PHOSPHORUS 31
IV	^{19}**K** POTASSIUM 39, 40, 41	^{20}**Ca** CALCIUM 40, 42, 43 44, 46, 48	^{21}**Sc** SCANDIUM 45	^{22}**Ti** TITANIUM 46, 47 48, 49, 50	^{23}**V** VANADIUM 51
	^{29}**Cu** COPPER 63, 65	^{30}**Zn** ZINC 64, 66 67, 68, 70	^{31}**Ga** GALLIUM 69, 71	^{32}**Ge** GERMANIUM 70, 72 73, 74, 76	^{33}**As** ARSENIC 75
V	^{37}**Rb** RUBIDIUM 85, 87	^{38}**Sr** STRONTIUM 84, 86, 87, 88	^{39}**Y** YTTRIUM 89	^{40}**Zr** ZIRCONIUM 90, 91, 92 94, 96	^{41}**Cb** COLUMBIUM 93
	^{47}**Ag** SILVER 107, 109	^{48}**Cd** CADMIUM 106, 108, 110 111, 112, 113 114, 116	^{49}**In** INDIUM 113, 115	^{50}**Sn** TIN 112, 114, 115 116, 117, 118 119, 120, 122 124	^{51}**Sb** ANTIMONY 121, 123
VI	^{55}**Cs** CESIUM 133	^{56}**Ba** BARIUM 130, 132, 134 135, 136, 137 138	57—71 RARE EARTHS	^{72}**Hf** HAFNIUM 174, 176, 177 178, 179, 180	^{73}**Ta** TANTALUM 181
	^{79}**Au** GOLD 197	^{80}**Hg** MERCURY 196, 198, 199 200, 201, 202 204	^{81}**Tl** THALLIUM 203, 205, 207 208, 210	^{82}**Pb** LEAD 204, 206, 207 208, 210, 211 212, 214	^{83}**Bi** BISMUTH 209, 210, 211 212, 214
VII	^{87}**Fr** FRANCIUM 223	^{88}**Ra** RADIUM 223, 224, 226 228	^{89}**Ac** ACTINIUM 227, 228	^{90}**Th** THORIUM 227, 228, 230 231, 232	^{91}**Pa** PROTACTINIUM 231, 234

ITALICIZED ISOTOPIC MASS NUMBERS ARE RADIOACTIVE

Table E   PERIODIC TABLE (ONLY NATURALLY FOUND ISOTOPES LISTED EXCEPT FOR TRANSURANIC ELEMENTS—Continued)

VI	VII	VIII			O
					$_2$**He** HELIUM 3, 4
^{8}**O** OXYGEN 16, 17, 18	^{9}**F** FLUORINE 19				^{10}**Ne** NEON 20, 21, 22
^{16}**S** SULFUR 32, 33, 34, 36	^{17}**Cl** CHLORINE 35, 37				^{18}**A** ARGON 36, 38, 40
^{24}**Cr** CHROMIUM 50, 52, 53, 54	^{25}**Mn** MANGANESE 55	^{26}**Fe** IRON 54, 56, 57, 58	^{27}**Co** COBALT 59	^{28}**Ni** NICKEL 58, 60, 61 62, 64	
^{34}**Se** SELENIUM 74, 76, 77 78, 80, 82	^{35}**Br** BROMINE 79, 81				^{36}**Kr** KRYPTON 78, 80, 82 83, 84, 86
^{42}**Mo** MOLYBDENUM 92, 94, 95, 96 97, 98, 100	^{43}**Tc** TECHNETIUM ———	^{44}**Ru** RUTHENIUM 96, 98, 99, 100 101, 102, 104	^{45}**Rh** RHODIUM 103	^{46}**Pd** PALLADIUM 102, 104, 105 106, 108, 110	
^{52}**Te** TELLURIUM 120, 122, 123 124, 125, 126 128, 130	^{53}**I** IODINE 127				^{54}**Xe** XENON 124, 126 128, 129 130, 131 134, 136
^{74}**W** TUNGSTEN 180, 182, 183 184, 186	^{75}**Re** RHENIUM 185, 187	^{76}**Os** OSMIUM 184, 186, 187 188, 189, 190 192	^{77}**Ir** IRIDIUM 191, 193	^{78}**Pt** PLATINUM 192, 194, 195 196, 198	
^{84}**Po** POLONIUM 210, 211, 212 214, 215, 216 218	^{85}**At** ASTATINE 215, 216, 218				^{86}**Rn** RADON 219, 220 222
^{92}**U** URANIUM 234, 235, 238	^{93}**Np** NEPTUNIUM 237, 238, 239	^{94}**Pu** PLUTONIUM 232, 234, 236 237, 238, 239 240, 241	^{95}**Am** AMERICIUM 238, 239, 240 241, 242	^{96}**Cm** CURIUM 238, 240 241, 242	

ITALICIZED ISOTOPIC MASS NUMBERS ARE RADIOACTIVE

Table F

Greek Alphabet

Alpha	α, A		Nu	ν, N
Beta	β, B		Xi	ξ, Ξ
Gamma	γ, Γ		Omicron	o, O
Delta	δ, Δ		Pi	π, Π
Epsilon	ϵ, E		Rho	ρ, P
Zeta	ζ, Z		Sigma	σ, Σ
Eta	η, H		Tau	τ, T
Theta	θ, Θ		Upsilon	υ, Υ
Iota	ι, I		Phi	ϕ, Φ
Kappa	κ, K		Chi	χ, X
Lambda	λ, Λ		Psi	ψ, Ψ
Mu	μ, M		Omega	ω, Ω

Index

383